SCIENCE, OBJECTIVITY, AND CONSCIOUSNESS

By Emilios Bouratinos

Edited by Richard Grant
Foreword by Vasileios Basios, Ph.D.

ICRL Press
Princeton, New Jersey

Science, Objectivity, and Consciousness

ISBN: 978-1-936033-29-4

Cover images: Spiral image by Emilios Bouratinos;
sky image iStock.com/baona
Design: Smythtype Design

 For information address:
ICRL Press
468 N. Harrison Street
Princeton, NJ 08540-3530

TABLE OF CONTENTS

Dedicated to the memory of Robert G. Jahn
and to Vishnunarayanan Namboothin,
both of whose friendship and council remain invaluable influences

FOREWORD

Some thirty years ago, several friends and co-workers shared with me some extraordinary essays written by a "Mr. Bouratinos, a real Greek philosopher of our times," as they described him. Some of these had been published in esteemed journals, but most were just circulating among us. When I was introduced to him, via a common cherished friend, I understood at once that he indeed deserved the title. Talking with Emilios Bouratinos then has had the same effect ever since: an expansion of consciousness! Reading his texts has had a similar effect. It is not only his great command of language, the hidden inter-connections that are revealed or his erudite style, but there is something more. It is that his thought places the reader in direct contact with Logos. I will return to this a little later.

Through the long years of our friendship, I learned that although Emilios is not very well known in the modern intellectual scene, he is very well known to the people who are well known. Time and time again, I was surprised to learn that he has had personal correspondence with top scientists, leading academics and spiritual leaders. Their exchanges are profound and address key issues of our times. For Emilios, this comes naturally, as the motivation behind his thinking is deep compassion. He never boasts of all his highly influential friends and acquaintances, but I learned from others in the family that in his house in Ekali, in the outskirts of the city of Athens, he has hosted an array of impressive guests. When he was a youngster he met Krishnamurti there, and later he held discussions with the XIVth Dalai Lama in his garden. Many prominent scientists, esteemed academics, Catholic Trappists, Greek-Orthodox monks from the Holy Mountain, Sufi Sheiks, Hebrew Rabbis, and many other remarkable personalities and seekers would drop by to have a chat with Emilios. One day I asked him "how come all these people arrive here?" "I think that this garden has something magical, dear friend" he replied. I wanted to reply "No, I think that you have something magical, my dear friend," but I shied away.

Soon after I met Emilios, I felt and continue to feel the beneficial influence not only of his writings, which I am sure, dear reader, you will also feel through this book, but also of his personality and his unique approach to understanding and dealing with the pressing issues of our times. Reading this book will offer you a rare opportunity for a stimulating philosophical journey, but also a harvest of very practical guidelines as you think along with Emilios about the big questions, such as the fast-approaching bifurcation point of our global crisis, or perhaps I should say crises. I am almost sure that you will discover and eventually share his optimism, which is not only based on compassion, but also on the realization that this crisis and its eventual desired breakthrough—and avoidable total breakdown—rest on Consciousness, as Emilios articulates so wisely in this book. Our individual and collective consciousnesses, as reflections of Consciousness Itself, are the foundation of being and becoming.

As early as the late 1980s or early 1990s, Emilios asked me to help him organize a series of international symposia in Greece on the theme of a "Science and Consciousness." At that time, we had been witnessing a growing interest on the relation of science with the state of the world. The ozone hole, the Amazon deforestation, climate change, pollution, etc.—all these subjects had started to concern scientists and public alike. Would I help him organize such a conference? He didn't have to ask twice!

One conference led to another, and in the course of these Emilios generously shared his knowledge and insights. The conferences were a great success, attracting a host of brilliant speakers from all over the world. But that was not all that Emilios wanted. While the subject of "Science and Consciousness" does bear fruit, it does not address the root of the issue: namely the transformation of our minds. This could only be addressed by creating a "Science of Consciousness." Subsequently, Emilios inspired many key players to focus on the need for a science of consciousness that has to be interdisciplinary and able to reflect on itself: a "Self-Reflecting Science of Consciousness." I was honored when he asked me if I would help him and his friends to start organizing conferences and symposia towards this goal.

A few years after the symposia in Greece, the idea of a science of consciousness started taking roots. Conferences, meetings, private communications, even journals with related titles, started to appear. In all of this, Emilios played a key role in raising the awareness of the subject, and advising and inspiring thinkers all over the globe. The phenomenon of him being well known only within a circle of well-known people repeated itself!

My encounter with Emilios and learning this new way of thinking from him, affected my life in the most beneficial way possible. When I first met him, I was on the verge of a burnout with physics and was thinking about dropping out of graduate studies and just working for a probably decent salary somewhere. This nihilistic attitude, due at least in part to the mechanistic worldview instilled by the prevailing scientism in academia, had taken its toll and had poisoned any pleasure that I still managed to take in modern physics. Emilios kindly and mindfully reacted to my state of depression. By talking, thinking and meditating with him, I saw that another way of "doing science" was possible. The importance of being interdisciplinary renewed my love for biology and philosophy and made me see clearly where I could possibly pursue such studies.

Perhaps most important, life became worth living, as it would never be an unexamined life anymore. We talked and talked for hours at a time, and among the many things he taught me was the most crucial lesson: self-reflection is not only a conceptual tool of phenomenology that carries a great epistemological value, but most importantly requires living, lifelong practice. (Emilios has practiced meditation for a very long time and is also a respected teacher of the particular form of meditation called Vipassana.)

The dream of being able to work one day for this "new kind of science," as Emilios puts it, has kept me, and still keeps me active and happy, while at the same time instilling a sense of purpose. Being interdisciplinary is praised but not rewarded in the academic world, where specialization, and even extreme specialization, is still considered the right thing to do. Creative thinking has its own inertia, and institutions aggregate such inertia, confusing it with desired stability and failing to understand that in order to act efficiently within a specialized topic one has to relate it and communicate it with other topics. I was happy that, with the aid of Emilios and the expansion of my horizons that his friendship had brought me, I was finally able to find people and institutions where "a specialist in complexity" does not appear to be a contradiction of terms.

Let's return to the discussion of the "science of consciousness" that Emilios has proposed and encouraged ever since, to consider a few points that are central to this book. For Socrates, the science of consciousness was nothing more nor less than philosophy, and Emilios returns to the original aim and scope of philosophy as the pursuit of wisdom. But he does this in a very eloquent manner. First, he liberates philosophy from Her analytical straitjacket; then he allows the pursuit of wisdom to be informed by the spirit of science; and finally, he highlights the foundational role of consciousness in establishing objectivity and subjectivity. In the course of doing this, he offers his readers a rough outline of the evolution of consciousness. By listening to his narration of the history of consciousness, in the sixth chapter of this book, the processes and workings of consciousness become clearer.

When Emilios talked to me about the science of consciousness for the first time, my mind, constrained by analytical philosophy's straightjacket, conditioned and trained in analytical reasoning and the scientific method, immediately jumped to the question "How do you define consciousness?"

I still recall the smile accompanying his response: "The trouble is that there are as many definitions of consciousness as conscious beings." Then he added: "Seriously, definition doesn't catalyze meaning. Meaning catalyzes definition." I had a flash of understanding but needed quite a long time to fully digest this.

His take on the meaning of consciousness can be seen when he discusses the ancient Greek root, etymology, and usage of the word "syneidisis" in the third chapter. According to Emilios, this is the "fifth force." Not in the same sense as the four physical forces, of course. As he succinctly puts it ". . . consciousness originally implied 'the bringing together of objects known to be as they are.' Consciousness was not the end-product of evolution. It was that which triggered the unifying and complexifying principle of the physical world —in addition to the four forces of the standard model."

It is not easy to free our minds from object-oriented thinking, yet Emilios' text does just that. It uses language to set the mind free of its conditioning due to language. In his formative years, Emilios studied philosophy and the classics at the University of Innsbruck. A bastion of classical philosophy after the war, the University offered rare and farsighted courses. One of the leading modern universities in Europe, its curriculum in philosophy was far reaching and pioneering even by today's standards. There he read Aristotelean and Buddhist logic, and followed the nearby seminars of Martin Heidegger.

I can picture Emlios as a student, listening to the original, daring and controversial Heidegger advocating the importance of the Presocratic origins of Western thought, stressing the importance of "repeating the early Greek experience of being, so that the West could turn away from the dead end of nihilism and begin anew." This imperative of the return of Logos still stays with Emilios and is one of the driving motifs of the book you have at hand. In this work, however, Emilios goes beyond the origins of Western thinking by bringing in a well-informed and new kind of understanding that draws from an array of primary sources like Hua-Yen Buddhism, Advaita Vedanta, and of course the non-dualistic insights afforded by modern science, especially modern physics.

Emilios strides the Cartesian divide that has constrained and befuddled our thinking for the last four hundred years or so. Science, Objectivity, and Consciousness is a powerful double axe, a Minoan Labrys. On the one side, outwardly, it clears the path for the new *self-reflective interdisciplinary science of consciousness*. It gives us the tools and skills to navigate through a yet uncharted territory and prepares us to partake of the adventure. Our boon is an expansion and deepening of awareness of what is going on on the other side, the other side being inward. It clears the paths for our working consciousness. We learn about the self-locking and self-releasing modes of objectification and how we can harmoniously balance them, acquiring a free spirit that avoids their respective tyrannies. This Labrys is liberating and empowering, in both senses, in both ways.

In one of his essays "Science Toward the Limits," (a more elaborated form can be found in Part III of this book), Emilios points to five distinct broad areas—society, the environment, the economy, politics, and education—as the main targets and the apparent culprits in contemporary complaints. Analysts tend to treat them as separate and prioritize according to their agendas, but, as he points out, it is the "culturally-induced attitude" of avoiding in-depth questioning that makes them appear as distinct. "What prompts our choices?" he asks in a truly Socratic dialectic fashion. And thus, we are led to acknowledge, along with the author, the need of re-examining our intentions and our unexamined assumptions.

Indeed, the origin of science is the ceaseless investigation of reality, unconstrained by dogma, authority or popular belief. This special form of informed ignorance permits us to look into the abyss of the unknown and the unknowable without fear. From James Clerk Maxwell's dictum "thoroughly conscious ignorance that is the prelude to every real advance in science," or Max Plank's observation that "I regard consciousness as fundamental. I regard matter as derivative from consciousness. We cannot get behind consciousness. Everything that we talk about, everything that we regard as existing, postulates consciousness," and the investigations by the renowned physicist Wolfgang Pauli and the polymath Carl Jung of the nature of the psyche's archetypes, which led Pauli to write to his friend Markus Fierz that "When one analyzes the pre-conscious step to concepts, one always finds ideas which consist of symbolic images!" Most of the pioneers of modern physics understood well what Max Plank, again, encapsulated so famously: "Science cannot solve the ultimate mystery of nature. And that is because, in the last analysis, we ourselves are a part of the mystery that we are trying to solve."

From that brilliant stance to the excruciatingly domineering "shut up and calculate" zeitgeist of mainstream scientific practice ever since, what happened to the observer and consciousness? How did we come to confuse science with scientism? Moreover, this perversion of the scientific method helped establish another zeitgeist—a societal one this time: "shut up and work, buy and die." This cynical attitude is greatly aided by the idea of matter as a machine, a prevailing worldview of meaningless atoms in the void, mechanically and haphazardly evolving to become brains excreting consciousness as a by-product, an epiphenomenon of a blind evolution. Why have we gone down this path?

Kurt Gödel, when he conferred with Hao Wang about the state of the world, made this powerful, yet rarely quoted, comment: "The rulers find it hard to manipulate the population: so they use materialism to manipulate the intellectuals and use religion to manipulate the workers... The founders of science were not atheists or materialists. Materialists began to appear only in the second half of the eighteenth century." Maybe the great Kurt Gödel had it right after all. The denial of metaphysics is itself a metaphysical position, and one of the worst kind. It is this prevailing wrong and inhumane philosophy that is the root of our contemporary malaise.

As Emilios puts it, "each of us creates his own prison—including the key to unlock it." This book helps us to find this key. Thinking with Emilios throughout his book, you will discover for yourself how the imperative of a science critical of itself can play out its liberating role. To this end, Emilios introduces the term of "self-locking objectification," which plays a key role in the philosophy of *Science, Objectivity, and Consciousness.*

When we stick to our objectifications—and the more successful they are the more difficult it is to avoid their grip—we tend to replace reality with its representations. Once we realize this key issue, then we can see clearly his point that "all human difficulties start from a failure to see things as they are—or at least to be aware of the fact that we don't."

Emilios is a great lecturer, story teller (especially when it comes to ancient Greek myths), a reliable and trusted consultant, and, of course, a marvelous essayist and writer. He is equally a great listener. Throughout the development of this book he has been sharing material, testing ideas, pondering key points, and trying different passages with a wide array of friends and collaborators. Either locally or via distant communications, several groups of individuals have offered assistance, references, and arguments. It is impossible for me to enumerate them all even if I knew the whole extent of his influence and influences.

Being close to him all these years I can recall, though, certain pivotal venues and people. After the Athenean Society symposia mentioned above, most of Emilios' activities were hosted and encouraged by the Scientific & Medical Network of the UK. His good friends David Lorimer, Peter Fenwick, and Martin Redfern, first among others, planned and organized a series of conferences that culminated in the Millennium Conference on Integration at Cambridge University in 2000, co-hosted by the Study Society.

Professor Max Velmans, the prolific writer on consciousness studies, also encouraged and discussed with Emilios in depth from early on, as did the renowned Jungian analyst Anne Barring, and the author and speaker on physics, philosophy, complexity and management Dr. Dana Zohar and her late husband, psychiatrist Ian Marshal. Many other academics independently of "camp" and "rank" took part in the development of ideas that Emilios stimulated around the science of consciousness, along with countless other "non-scientist" people.

But the person who stands out in relation to the successful completion of this book, along of course with his caring, totally supportive and lovely wife Ruth, is undoubtedly Richard Grant. Richard has served as his chief editor, amassing, re-organizing and commenting throughout the preparation of this book, and has spent many hours discussing and consulting with Emilios, with just a little help from the rest of us. Together they produced the final form of the text that you are holding in your hands. But it was Richard's amazing editorial skills, his ability to tame every new and old word-processors' caprice, his far-sighted sense of composition, and his in-depth communion with the mind of Emilios, along with his broad knowledge of bibliography, that drove this project to completion.

It goes without saying that Emilios has a great command of language, both in content, context and meaning. But there is something more that comes through in his writing. He produces self-initiating texts! You will discover that this book not only greatly assists to the contemplation of the issues it treats, it also prompts a kind of expansion of awareness by revealing hidden connections within the words. Certain passages, admittedly difficult at first sight, are set to raise sudden "aha" realizations, and after a certain period of gestation cross-fertilizations spontaneously emerge. The reading experience is enriched, for sure, but at the same time you feel as if the text itself is enriched in your mind.

While editing this book "What does he mean?" questions would jump out of the reading. When Richard was editing the book and found a difficult word, he duly noted in the margin the need for more explanation, or a proposal for a different word that might serve better. After a while, when discussing and comparing notes, we both realized that the text was actually absolutely clear! "What does he mean?" would become evident, and on re-reading all the noted changes and charges to be dropped! Our minds had somehow expanded and the meaning shone through clearly, as if our consciousness was different and had become wider now than before studying it. Richard calls this experience "self-induction to a higher consciousness via jumps." I would dare to call it a great specimen in the tradition of self-initiating texts. Most probably you will share the same feeling as you read!

At a very successful conference almost a decade ago that I helped to organize, at ZiF (German initials for the "Center for Interdisciplinary Research" at the Institute for Advanced Study of Bielefeld University), Emilios was an invited speaker and met Robert Jahn and Brenda Dunne, who were also invited speakers. There was an immediate recognition of kindred spirits, and Bob and Brenda invited him to Princeton soon after, resulting in a deep friendship and mutual understanding and appreciation. An extremely fruitful and beneficial meeting of minds indeed, since somewhere in that connection the idea of producing this book was seeded.

I can recall the happy voice of my friend Emilios calling me from Princeton. "I am with Bob and Brenda, having a jolly good time, my dear friend," he announced filling my home in Brussels with all good feelings, "and you know what, remember our project of launching someday a Self-Reflecting Interdisciplinary Science of Consciousness? Well, they have already had started it without calling it such! They refer to it as a "science of the subjective" and are up to the challenge! We should meet them again and again. I am so happy." His optimism has been justified once more.

In order for such a project to thrive we do not need centralized headquarters or to establish any kind of ideology. What we need is rather a lively, organic, mycelium-like infrastructure that can realize a network of networks, acentric, multi-aspected and active on many fronts and levels. Each node, like in a mycelium, cooperating and sharing resources and ideas, providing nourishment for each other, and when the conditions are ripe the future fruits will surely sprout. Once upon a time, one of the starting points of science was, the famous "Invisible College" (transformed later to the Royal Society). This time, a science of consciousness must have a Visible College, with no further need for hidden agendas or institutionalized thinking.

Science, Objectivity, and Consciousness heralds a turning point for the development of a Self-Reflecting Science of Consciousness. Even as I write these lines, the main flagships of modern science, "Nature" and "Science," run editorials, articles and special focus issues about the devastating scandals that science experiences today: publishing false research results to gain fame, money and grants; the inadequacy of the peer review system to confront self-promoting individuals and groups; the menaces of no-rules self-publishing; the proliferation of journals and papers of irrelevant scientific value, serving only too well the careerists' need to publish; and even the covering up of "conflicts of interest." The scientific spirit of free inquiry strives to survive in niches deprived of grants and support. The art of the most profitable and productive "curiosity-based research" is perceived as not being "serious" or "professional" enough to be worthy of any endorsement. As this crisis among all the other crises continues and intensifies, a science able to reflect on itself will be more and more in need. So, the publication of this book is quite timely, helping to shred the straitjacket that science put herself into by denying the study of consciousness.

In this book, Emilios Bouratinos, "a real Greek philosopher of our times," describes and advocates an interdisciplinary and self-reflective science of consciousness. By providing us with a detailed, empowering, navigation guide that can liberate us from the shackles of an outdated materialistic world view, he opens the door to a new vision of reality that includes ourselves, and invites his readers to join him in this noble enterprise.

Vasileios Basios, PhD
Physics of Complex Systems
University of Brussels
October 2017

INTRODUCTION

Science, Objectivity, and Consciousness discusses the need for a less reductionist and mechanistic approach to the study of physical reality and of human nature. This notion is developed without arguing for a total break with the established scientific approach, as happens frequently with people aspiring to such an ambitious goal. Instead, a middle course is here advocated. Science and society are facing huge problems today because they have unwisely ignored the middle course. To redress this imbalance there is need for encouraging a more inclusive understanding. It must be open to both reductionist analysis and to holistic synthesis; both to what language transmits and to what slips in between the words[1] used for the transmission.

At the very least, there is a need for reconsidering the assumptions behind some fundamental theoretical considerations. They include the requirement for rational solutions, self-referencing loops, the validity of unique events, or the many insights derived from the influence of wholeness on fragments and of fragments on wholeness. Our epistemology, our mental health and our future depend on introducing such a middle course into our thinking and acting. It will secure an improved understanding—and handling—of reality.

However, this sensitive exercise needs to be carried out in full awareness of a major danger—that of projecting the qualities of fragmentation onto wholeness and the qualities of wholeness onto fragmentation. Blind reaction to what appears as detrimental or faulty has a price. It can cause as much damage as the detrimental or faulty state it rejects. All one needs to remember is how the Enlightenment reacted blindly to the excesses of Christianity when it pushed science and society into belief-laden experiments and reason-based proofs.

Understanding better how facts condition our view of reality plays a crucial role here. It doesn't mean that what we normally describe as facts should now be ignored. It means that we should keep in mind that the emphasis placed on facts arose from a need of science, philosophy, religion and society to repudiate the unwarranted theoretical assumptions of the immediately preceding centuries. Proposing a non-doctrinal adoption of the middle course will invite fragmentation

[1] The Latin word "intellectus" originally meant "that which articulates itself through the words—not by them." The same holds for the Greek terms signifying mind (dianoia) and dialogue (dialogos). They too meant what slips *through* the words and what asserts itself *beyond* them. The practice of using language to point to more than it says has extremely ancient roots. It reflects the reality of a world that contains far more than can be objectified and defined, however many words are used for that purpose.

and wholeness not to express themselves in the future separately. Fragmentation will thus articulate itself through wholeness, and wholeness through fragmentation. In this way the exaggeration of adhering to extreme views will hopefully be replaced by a more measured and qualitative theoretical stand—truer to how nature itself usually operates.

Evolution does this all the time. It happens through "self-organization" on the one hand and through "strange attractors" on the other. Wholeness becomes the unseen force underlying the movements and actions of fragments. It brings about their constructive interaction. Scientists enamored of doctrinal reductionism and mechanism mostly fail to take that component into consideration.

Tyranny of the objectifiable

In attempting to remedy the above failure, we must start focusing on two questions. First, what has caused civilization to adopt objectifiability as a criterion for reality. That question shouldn't be examined merely in terms of scholarly analysis. It should be examined as much as in terms of experience; not just through what has become perceptible, but also through what is being intuited; not only by dint of what has been discovered by our researches, but also by what we ourselves have become as a result of these researches.

The second question is about understanding the objectifiers of reality. In arriving to know ourselves as objectifiers, we will get to know others better, while in getting to know others, we will arrive at knowing ourselves as we actually are in our deepest structures. What we objectify depends on what we are biologically, psychologically, and culturally prepared to pick out from the seamlessly interconnected units, structures, levels, tendencies and aspects of nature.

It is in the light of investigating the above two interdependent questions that the importance of the middle course suggested in the previous paragraphs becomes clear. A truly equidistant path from extreme positions doesn't run automatically between two opposite stands. It manifests only as the conscious attempt to continuously *re-discover* the shifty middle ground. Much more important than the exact direction of the middle course, is the ability to develop a feel for the equidistance from opposite positions.

The middle course not a doctrine

The inquirer first realises that the middle course is not something that automatically occupies an equidistant position between two extremes. He needs to struggle in order to discover what the middle course actually is in every case he comes across. It could mean that on occasion the inquirer has to adopt a near-extreme position for some time. Or it could mean that he has to constantly adjust his actual course to the twists and turns of the two opposite stands.

The only way the inquirer can succeed in this delicate balancing act is to be in a position to sense when a choice for moving or not moving in a particular direction begins to fossilise. The inquirer must then be completely prepared to abandon it. Indeed, he must do that before the stand he has adopted becomes a permanent fixture in his mind.

Avoiding extremes and maintaining the middle course always requires a delicate balancing act. One can espouse holism without rejecting reductionism; one can embrace dynamics without throwing out mechanism; one can serve clarity without sticking to explicitness.

Readjusting[2] one's understanding to establish a proper middle course isn't something one achieves only by adopting absolute concepts. One achieves it also through specific states, trends, situations, fields, waves, systems, transformations and others. Bertrand Russell describes this practice of readjustment vis-à-vis generalities and specifics in the following words: "Everything is vague to a degree you do not realise until you have actually tried to make it precise."[3]

The one positive thing that can be said with a degree of certainty about the usefulness of reductionism and mechanism is that there are many areas of reality (especially those connected with the senses) which cannot be studied without them. One can handle more efficiently the non-local substrate of reality and in that way understand better its local manifestations; one can appreciate more fully causal chains for perceiving more clearly nature's need for differentiation; one can appreciate better the importance of details for having developed a clearer vision of the whole informing them.

A true middle course constantly demands self-adjustment. To begin with, there is need for a multi-aspected examination of nature itself. This must be carried out in the light of two fundamental concerns. The first expresses how nature has been studied and interpreted since the 18th century Enlightenment. The second expresses how nature appears in the light not just of 20th century

---

[2] Readjustment isn't something that applies only to human understanding. It happens also to all entities that understanding is about. The entities elbow their way around in order to find their niche in the scheme of wholeness. They need to be vague in order to fit ontologically into a framework that houses many diverse entities and forces.

[3] Bertrand Russell, "Vagueness," *Australian Journal of Philosophy 1*, 1923.

physics, but also of more recent developments in biology. These breakthroughs[4] are too important to ignore. They have implications for the very way we feel, think and act.

Underlying all this is the reality of and the concern with the role played by consciousness. Understandably, the first thing we must then do is to develop an overview of the physical background of consciousness. It will help us familiarise ourselves with how consciousness moulds the brain and directs its operations. Toward the end of this book some ideas will be presented on what can be done with insights that have developed as a result of people becoming aware of the fundamental role played by consciousness in both nature and our own selves.

From epistemology to pre-epistemology

When we get to learn a little more about all this, an additional area of investigation will appear on the horizon. It is that which precedes epistemology, or more simply put, "pre-epistemology." Consciousness and pre-epistemology will be studied for both their connection with brain physiology and their impact on thought. Attention will be given to cognitive flexibility, neuronal plasticity, and above all, the brain's creative response to stimulation from the mind. Here will also be studied the brain's ability to recover from functional injuries, regardless of what is today described as "brain localization." Functions can be transferred from one brain "center" to the next, which had earlier dealt with completely different "subjects."[5]

This will go very much against the grain of current scientific belief. As presently conceived, neurophysiology and cognitive science conceive consciousness as an expression of mainly mechanistic operations in the brain. Scientists believe that the latter is the seat and instigator of all we feel, conceptualize and apprehend. Whatever we experience occurs there. When we witness an automobile collision we see it in our skulls. Nobody really gets hurt! What appears as a collision in fact amounts to something that can be denoted only as a virtual reality!

What we objectify depends on what we are prepared to select from nature's seamlessly interconnected structures, levels, tendencies and aspects. Thus, if we try to define virtual reality, we end up in trouble.[6] The seamless interconnections

---

[4] The most impressive of these breakthroughs are non-locality, non-temporality, reverse causation, plus plasticity in biology and the brain.

[5] Jesper Mogensen, "Almost Unlimited Potentials of a limited Neural Plasticity," *Journal of Consciousness Studies*, Vol. 18 No 7-8, 2011, pp13-37.

[6] The virtual reality paradox is a modern version of the ancient Cretan Liar paradox, which had caused quite a few headaches to Bertrand Russell.

of things and states break up into separate entities. Then the thing researched can be virtual only in comparison with another that isn't.

This means that if we take the approach of mainstream neurophysiology and cognitive science seriously, we unwittingly end up with a totally relativistic belief that in essence there is nothing real in the universe at all. This represents a highly challenging conclusion. The notion of an exclusively virtual universe ends up as a contradiction in terms. If it is true then it must be false and if it is false then it must be true—in which case it is false anyway!

Bart Kosko observes on this: "You get no more out of an argument than you put into it. You assume premises and derive conclusions. If you assume an ought in a premise, you derive an ought in the conclusion. But that begs the question and just moves the debate to the level of premises."[7] It is here that we set the foundation for a new field of study: a *self-reflective interdisciplinary science of consciousness.*

A science critical of itself

For now, suffice it to make two points. The first is that proposed courses for a *self-reflective interdisciplinary science of consciousness* will cover both the physical aspects of consciousness and their epistemological after-effects. The second point is that new courses proposed will be in addition to the formal curriculum provided by universities for each discipline. At the same time, suggestions will be offered on how interested scientists and theorists may best reduce the many distortions of reality incurred by the one-sided Enlightenment approach, which had no concern for either consciousness nor its implications.

Some of the aspects of consciousness aired during *self-reflective interdisciplinary science of consciousness* courses could touch on the physiology, taxonomy, culture, education, and the psychological factors that have been influencing human perception and conception since the beginning of civilization around 10,000 BC.[8] There is ample research concerning these influences,[9] including their origins, char-

[7] Bart Kosko, *Fuzzy Thinking*, Harper Collins Publishers, London, 1944, p 254.

[8] In the author's reckoning, the beginning of our type of civilisation is tied to the discovery of agriculture in the Middle East around 10,000 BC. Before that there were only what the author calls "ways of living." People operating under such conditions had no goals other than securing their daily existence. Taoist philosophy, with its emphasis on merely dealing with daily needs and avoiding more general preoccupations, are a distant expression of this pre-agrarian attitude. Happiness then meant merely to exist—and to enjoy so doing.

[9] For a thorough overview of these influences and their widely ranging impacts on not just science and philosophy, but on society, business, politics and education, see Iain McGilchrist, *The Master and His Emissary: The Divided Brain and the Making of the Western World,* Yale University Press, New Haven and London, 2009. The volume is packed with information on such research.

acter and impact. Becoming aware of them and the way they condition their understanding of it, will then help everybody to improve the quality, objectivity, validity and usefulness of their work.

Of course, in the end there can be no science without reductionism or computation. But the history of science shows that its problem has never been what the scientist actually reduces to. The problem has always been what the scientist in effect reduces from. It starts from the use he makes of what kind of information his physiology, culture, education, psychology, experience and personal beliefs allows through—and how the recipient of that information interprets and handles it once it has elbowed its way to the foreground of his consciousness.

In so many words, the problem lies in the openness and depth of the scientist's mind and his willingness (plus ability) to confront his conditioning. The proposed middle course will initiate a systematic self-questioning program, which will make both students and researchers aware of how deeply conditioned their perception and conception have become. Attending individuals will be helped to develop a more accurate view of the various dynamics, structures, complexities and interconnections that go into the making of nature and man. The most important of these is wholeness. Awareness of its role will allow the scientist and the theorist to make much more sense of fragmented reality than is presently possible.

Once people have thoroughly familiarized themselves with the distorting effects of biological, cultural and other influences, they can (and should) go back to using reductionist and computational practices whenever circumstances in physical reality call for it. Abstraction, reductionism and computation prove extremely useful in helping scientists and philosophers to study specific processes in nature. Thus, the problems created by abstraction, reductionism and computation are not due to some innate flaw in their practical application. They are due to the way the structure and operation of the human brain have evolved since the institutionalization of civilization.

It follows that the issue here is not that scientists and theorists increasingly rely on analysis to advance their studies of mind-related subjects. The issue is that scientists and theorists consider analysis to provide faithful accounts of what nature is about and how it functions. Once people have become fully aware of the role played by consciousness in the appearance of nature and they have learnt to free themselves from the blind belief in abstraction and the practices of reductionism and computation, they will be in a position to use the two practices a lot more effectively than other people who have not yet gone down that path.

The important condition for this to happen is to establish a holistic mindset.

That is certainly possible, though it requires some mental preparation and training. Once scientists and philosophers have gone through that training, they can analyze and compute as much as their work calls for. The results they obtain will be holistic even when the scientists and theorists are involved only in studying the makeup and function of parts. The whole is not the addition of its parts. The parts are the local manifestations of the whole.

We today face increasing conceptual and practical problems because for too long we have stopped taking into account the indirect manifestations of wholeness. Society has turned specifically applicable rules into sweeping generalizations. Our post-Enlightenment tendency to think of research in solid-object-mediated terms[10] has strengthened this tendency.

To redress the above imbalance, we must develop a subtler inclusive outlook. We need to heed not just what language transmits; we need to heed what eludes the transmission. We must embrace not just what learning elucidates; we must embrace also what the elucidation obscures—and why.

At the very minimum, we need to reconsider our assumptions about what constitutes a fact and what doesn't. Our epistemology, our mental health,[11] our material well-being, and our future depend on us being able to pursue such a middle course. But the exercise must be undertaken in a way that avoids excursions into the irrational. Whereas absolute faith in factuality prevents a complete view of nature, limited factuality reveals its intrinsic oneness. When non-factuality articulates itself through factuality, it takes the form of self-organization.

If a more intuitive and subtle attitude is to have an effect on science and philosophy, we must first familiarize ourselves with the attitude that has deified factuality and turned it into absolute belief. The quest for increased understanding should be pursued not merely by dint of what has been discovered, but by dint of what we ourselves have developed into as a result of what has been discovered.

---

[10] By "objects" most people mean something hard and solid—like a stone, a piece of wood, a book, a machine etc. "Solidity," in our unconscious, has become synonymous with "object." It thereby colours our conception of reality. Indeed, it colours our very conception of nouns.

[11] The World Health Organisation predicts that by 2030 60% of the world population, particularly in the West, will be suffering from one kind of mental disease or other.

Progress is not a question of moving ahead. It is a question of increasingly penetrating the surface of reality. The deeper we sink into it, the less are we liable to get stuck in what we have arrived at knowing. This explains why: the deeper people penetrate into themselves, the more common ground they discover. Democritus hints at this when he points out that "truth lies in the deep."[12]

Abraham Maslow has come up with a famous metaphor that reveals not merely what has happened here, but why it has happened. "If the only tool you employ is a hammer," he writes, "you tend to mistake everything for a nail!"[13]

Maslow shows what has happened to science and society as a result of its tendency to approach reality only from one angle. People conceive the world in terms of a computational and reductionist model, leaving out that part of nature that lies beyond the reach of abstraction, computation and reduction to smaller sub-units. To the extent that the world is objectifiable[14] it may be conceived in such terms. But to the extent that it isn't, it cannot. Indeed, a lot of the world is not objectifiable—at least not in the sense that we today conceive objects.

This doesn't mean that the non-objectifiable part of nature is a figment of imagination. It is as real as its objectifiable counterpart. However, non-objectifiability looms not only beyond what can be described. It looms beyond what can be symbolized. According to William Poundstone, Henri Poincaré believed that in this world there are many realities, depending on how we ourselves are able to grasp them. Some of these realities are easier to work with than others, Poincaré points out. But Poundstone also attributes to Poincaré the following sentence: "A reality completely independent of the spirit that perceives it or conceives it is an impossibility."[15]

All conceptions of nature depend on a prior, or at least on a parallel, understanding of the conceiver by the conceiving mind itself. In getting to know ourselves we know others, just as in getting to know others we get to know ourselves a little better than we did before. As already hinted at earlier, what

---

[12] Democritus, fragment *589*.

[13] Abraham Maslow, *Maslow on Management,* Kindle Edition, 1998, p29. (In its entry on Maslow, Wikipedia mentions that Maslow used this quotation in more than 20 of his books.)

[14] In principal, objectifiable nature is that part of nature which can be concretised and measured. Inversely, non-objectifiable nature is that part which cannot be measured—at least not directly. In the latter case partial measurability occurs because non-objectifiable nature exercises a certain influence on its objectifiable counterpart. Electromagnetic fields, non-local relationships, mind-first situations or retrocausality are some examples of non-objectifiable nature. There are obviously other examples too. But they are so far removed from our established ways of thinking, that nothing about them can be said—or intimated.

[15] William Poundstone, *Labyrinths of Reason: Paradox, Puzzles and the Frailty of Knowledge,* Penguin Books, London, 1988, p 78.

we objectify depends on what we are physiologically, psychologically and experientially prepared to pick out from the seamlessly interconnected structures, levels, tendencies and aspects of nature.

Chris Tomson states the above in a nutshell when he asserts: "The understanding of the knower actually creates the thing known."[16] Does it mean that if there are many realities we also need many sciences to study them? Not necessarily. Western science can pride itself as the only intellectual practice capable of using its tools for pointing to the reality of other realities than its own. It can be objective about its own subjectivity!

The point that this book argues is that discussing creation in both factual and non-factual terms is not as such unscientific or self-contradictory just because some hard-nosed logician considers factuality and non-factuality as mutually exclusive. Though himself a master abstractor, Einstein warned his fellow physicists against getting too deeply enmeshed in such exclusive thinking and its mathematical formulations.

He writes: "Not everything that counts can be counted; not everything that can be counted counts."[17] Elsewhere he becomes even more explicit. He observes: "As far as the laws of mathematics refer to reality, they are not certain. As far as they are certain, they do not refer to reality."[18]

Coming from the greatest mind that modern science has produced, Einstein's warning against overdoing the mathematical elaborations of either factuality or non-factuality, can (and must) act as a guide for us all. Abstraction fails when blindly pursued. So it is a great irony that Einstein himself didn't remain faithful to his initial resistance to the over-mathematization of nature. He spent the last thirty years of his life chasing after the chimaera of a "Theory of Everything."

Like many others since, Einstein failed in his attempt to play mathematical God for a very simple reason: lack of proper epistemological and pre-epistemological grounding. The universe is not a gigantic clockwork orange. It is a living self-organizing system that changes even its mechanism of changing from one level of complexification to the next.

All abstractions are versions of generalization. A generalization that is too successful in doing its job, as a theory of everything aspires to be, undermines itself conceptually and logically. It eliminates the differentiation that would make it meaningful.

---

[16] Chris Thomson, in email communication, December 9, 2011.

[17] Sign hanging over Einstein's desk at his Princeton office.

[18] Included in "On Truth and Reality, Famous Quotes on Mathematics." Google as of December 9, 2011.

In other words, generalizations eliminate the differentiations about which they could theorize. In this way they render generalizations less meaningful. They are based not on knowledge but on information, which always leaves out those chunks of reality that it cannot objectify or conceive. That is why a theory of everything will never yield any real knowledge, even if physicists manage to put it together. It doesn't provide knowledge. It provides only increasingly abstract—and therefore meaningless—generalizations. "Everything" turns out to be as good as "nothing."

Jason Brown presents some interesting thoughts on the question. He observes that "the interpenetrating motion of the totality is missed when interest settles on one object only or its features." A few lines down the same page he adds: "Elements condition theory. . .thereby reinforcing the notion that a field is an aggregate or that the world manifold is a composite held together by external relations . . . The real questions are how the mind/brain unit perceives succession in the first place, the nature of implicit and explicit change and how the past relates to the present." If one perceives things in the light of "events," as indeed they are, these pre-epistemological problems pointed out by Brown, do not arise.[19]

Evolution is not a mechanistic process. It doesn't depend on pre-existing rules. It depends on rules expressing the potential that lies buried in chance developments. This potential can then blossom into a new expression of existence with stable and repeatable conditions.

Science and the concern for consciousness

Science, Objectivity, and Consciousness is the product of a self-organizing effort to find out what can be done to allow all this to express itself in a carefully thought out manner. The proposal put forward here is to tackle the problem systematically, but gradually. New ideas must be tested through means capable of handling them on their level of abstraction, without getting stuck in it. This, for the moment, means a three-stage project.

The first stage entails investigating the arguments, reasons, and uses of the new approach to consciousness studies, referred to here as a Self-Reflective Interdisciplinary Science of Consciousness or SRISOC. The second stage calls for the actual realization of the first. To the extent that the proposed discipline becomes a functioning reality, it will then help to undo the mental blockages that

[19] Jason Brown, "Simultaneity and Serial Order," *Journal of Consciousness Studies,* Volume 17, No 5–6, 2010, pp 8–9.

have prevented us so far from experiencing nature as a dynamic, self-adjustable and self-transcending whole. The road will thus be opened to bring about the third stage—*a science toward the limits.*[20] It will be informed by the conclusions drawn from the operation of the *self-reflective interdisciplinary science of consciousness.*

A legitimate question now comes to the foreground. A science of consciousness has been in place already for at least the last twenty years in a number of universities, especially in the USA. Shouldn't there be some cooperation with that discipline—particularly in the areas of neurophysiology and cognitive science? Wouldn't both the old approach to consciousness and its *now*-proposed new counterpart gain from mutual interaction?

Surely the stock of information accumulated by the *self-reflective interdisciplinary science of consciousness*, and the accumulation of insights into that information secured by the second stage, would be mutually enriched if they were to merge into a single large store. However, this cannot happen in practice. Object-mediated thinking and rationalized objectification do not in themselves constitute a scientific theory. They represent an article of faith. It is therefore unlikely that scientists adhering to object-mediated thinking and rationalized objectification would even consider examining the premises, arguments or empirical evidence for either a *self-reflective interdisciplinary science of consciousness*, or *a science toward the limits.*

If they responded at all to such a proposal, they would claim that there already exists a well-established science of consciousness, capable of dealing with epistemological issues in general. There is therefore no need for a *self-reflective interdisciplinary science of consciousness*, leave alone *a science toward the limits.* If somebody requires something additional after all, two roads are open to him. First comes inviting scientists involved in the existing science of consciousness to extend their research in the areas where information seems to be lacking. Second comes increasing dependence on the rational assumptions and premises of science in general.

Why then introduce self-reflection into consciousness research? What will self-reflection contribute to the existing research and its conclusions? The answer is that self-reflection will contribute a return to what the ancient Greeks called "first principles."

---

[20] The expression "a science toward the limits" is one inspired by the interest of William James for a more integral view of science, which he believed ought to include deep structural concerns for consciousness.

For us today such a return means re-introducing an important function into scientific activity—self-criticism. Science must be submitted to the same critical examination as that which it uses when researching physical reality. The objectivity of science's "first principles" is neither a given, nor self-evident. It reflects an effort to disentangle our understanding from our understanding. So long as our finds are not projected back onto the premises of research, there cannot be true science. It will depend on unquestioned assumptions and arbitrary interpretations.

For example, Michael Polanyi emphasizes that knowledge in science is personal, "committing us passionately and far beyond our comprehension, to a [particular] vision of reality. Of this responsibility we cannot divest ourselves by setting up objective criteria of verifiability—or falsifiability, or testability, or what you will."[21] Also, Israel Scheffler epitomizes the thinking of E. H. Gombrich when he writes: "We can never separate data from construction, never observe in the sense of simply registering unconceptualized content."[22]

Another important testimony against the existing infrastructure of science of consciousness research is one of the most interesting breakthroughs in recent neuro-physiological and cognitive research: the brain doesn't work like a computer, as had been assumed until recently by proponents of reductionist and mechanistic science. This pulls the carpet from under most of the existing science of consciousness research. In reviewing two books on this important finding, Carol Lee Flinders writes the following:

> Dr. Paul Bach y Rita, a pioneer neuroplastician has demonstrated that the brain is not machine-like after all and that specific mental functions are not hardwired into particular locations. The mechanistic model of the brain made sense only at a time when our only insights into the brain's workings derived from accidents that damaged a specific location and resulted in predictable disabilities.
>
> Now, though it is clear that regions of the brain which have been dedicated to one sense can be—and have been—re-trained to serve another. The auditory cortex can reorganize itself to have the structure of the visual cortex. Our sense receptors translate different kinds of energy from the external world into electrical patterns sent

[21] Michael Polanyi, *Personal Knowledge,* The University of Chicago Press, Chicago, 1962, p 16.
[22] Israel Scheffler, Science *and Subjectivity,* The Bobbs-Merrill Company, Inc, Indianapolis, New York, 1967, p 25.

> down the nerves. These patterns are the universal language "spoken" inside the brain.

"We see with our brains," Bach y Rita explains, "not with our eyes." Francis Crick made a similar discovery when he studied vision at the end of his life, in collaboration with Fr. Koch.

Flinders continues with a quotation from one of the two books reviewed by her that was written by Norman Doidge. "Nature has given us a brain," she remarks, "that survives in a changing world by changing itself." A little further down her review, Flinders quotes the other author (Sharon Begley) whose book she reviews. Referring to the work by Jeffrey Schwartz, she quotes him as saying that there is no doubt "the mind can change the brain."[23] It looks as though the brain serves a similar purpose to a football stadium. It is at the disposal of the teams that wish to play in it.

The very fact that it will now be possible to envision a new science of consciousness (in comparison with the mechanistic/reductionist model still prevailing among neurophysiologists and cognitive scientists) gives rise to two further realizations. One is that the foundations of a deeper and broader approach to consciousness were already laid out 150 years ago by a succession of impressive breakthroughs in physics, biology, mathematics, psychology, abstract reasoning and neurophysiology.

These breakthroughs outline a non-dimensional and non-linear form of physical existence. Being mostly conceptual in character, they impinge qualitatively on how the mind works and what it concludes by so doing. They refer more to how we look at things and less to what we see when we are actually looking.

The other important realization is that pushing ahead with a *self-reflective interdisciplinary science of consciousness* needn't wait for the full working out of its theoretical tenets, justifications and specific implications. Establishing the here proposed new kind of consciousness studies can (and must) begin while people are still struggling with a fuller overview of the issue. We are bound to feel uncertain about the emerging picture of reality. This is preferable to an illusory certainty. We can only arrive at knowing things by not expecting them to be knowable through abstractions alone. We will then be in a position to invite objects to use us in order to collapse themselves not just into accessible existence, but beyond accessible existence—beyond even that beyond.

---

[23] Carol Lee Flinders, "Does the Brain Have a Mind of its Own? Ask a Neuroplastician," *Network Review,'* Summer 2008, pp 41–42.

Grounding high flights

The idea of establishing a *self-reflective interdisciplinary science of consciousness* will grow, adapt and transform itself to the extent that people develop some capacity to know themselves better than they do today. Not only the new discipline but establishing the project's two stages will open the road to establishing its third stage. This will consist of creating *a science toward the limits*. The clearer people perceive consciousness and their own selves, the clearer will they become about the other natural processes they are attempting to understand, and the reasons why these have taken the particular form they have.

To secure clarity, this three-stage project will have to deal with some tough conceptual issues. Of course, the old ways of conceiving, practicing and validating science need to be partly retained—depending on the particular level of abstraction inhabited by the particular subject being researched. These ways will be seen as existing in complementarity with the new ways just outlined, however, when the level of abstraction is deeper, shallower or looser, reality, in terms of distinct states and their either/or logic, will be viewed in terms of dynamic wholes and their fuzzy logic.

This seemingly contradictory state will also extend to what Leibniz and Wittgenstein call "the principle of sufficient rationality." It stipulates that the universe embodies the necessary and sufficient conditions for anything to be as it is, including its logic. Isabelle Stengers puts this in a nutshell when she claims that "for finite knowledge there will always be a gap between what comes into existence and what can be defined."[24]

The important point here is that going beyond objecthood also entails going beyond language (without however abandoning it!) The new discipline will enable people to realize that in each object or process something always goes missing when it is put into words or symbols. Gödelian incompleteness reigns supreme, not only in abstract mathematics, but in nature and in every investigation of it. Creativity is intimately tied with this intrinsic tendency of manifest existence. That everything in nature can be put into a formula is not only mentally restrictive. It is entirely untrue.[25]

Knowledge, information and the dynamics of reality

Obviously, the continuity of the old approach with the new one just outlined depends on how epistemologists view knowledge. Knowledge, in the sense of

---

[24] Isabelle Stengers, "Whitehead's Account of the Sixth Day," *Configurations*, Volume 13, Number 1, Winter 2005, pp. 35-55.

[25] So much for a Theory of Everything!

information, is necessary. But it is also insufficient. It neither covers what happens to the mind when information hits it, nor what the mind does to information when it absorbs the hit. Still less does information enlighten scientists about what happens on the deeper levels of organization of physical existence, where the objects of knowledge congeal into recognizable form and their mutual inter-penetration settles into discernible patterns.

Knowledge as information leaves us in the dark about the importance of the subtle dynamics pervading both reality and how we comprehend it. Indeed, the difference between knowledge and information explains why we can learn everything about something without getting to know it, as we can know it without getting to learn everything about it.

Stengers sums up Alfred North Whitehead's thoughts on this topic when she writes: "We need to understand how the unity of the universe presupposes its multiplicity. We need to understand how infinitude requires the finite. We need to understand how each immediately present entity or state requires its past and its future as essential features of its body... The discussion of present fact, apart from past or future, is to rob the universe of Its importance... We no longer know [in the sense of information]. But we demand to know." [26]

Information is only about self-proclaiming facts. We need self-revealing facts—data—that reveal as much about themselves as they reveal about the ever complexifying universe.

From self-awareness to pre-epistemology

Let us examine another pre-supposition for the proposed *self-reflective interdisciplinary science of consciousness*. It is what in other sections of this book is called *pre-epistemology*. This is an area of interest that has not been investigated before as a distinct issue. The term takes its cue from what was meant in earlier paragraphs when it was claimed that not enough self-reflection is invested in contemporary consciousness studies.

Pre-epistemology, as here conceived, is concerned with how we isolate, objectify and lock into our fundamental perceptions and conceptions. It rejects the classical notion that truth consists of a mere correspondence between mind and reality. Instead, it adopts Kant's notion that truth corresponds to what mind

[26] That is probably the reason why one of the words used by the ancient Greeks to denote "science" was "historein," from which the English term "history" is derived. The past is woven into the present as well as the future. Things, literally, are their history. Only the continuity and influence of time can throw light on to why it is as it is and why it is changing into what it is becoming.

can (and is willing to) perceive. Pre-epistemology thus becomes the starting point for both the proposed *self-reflective interdisciplinary science of consciousness* and the new type of science this will be asked to inform: *a science toward the limits.*

Each observable or computable entity or event merely represents the local expression of a network of interacting entities or events that is relevant to the present predicament. By the same token, each identifiable piece of information merely manifests the outward expression of a network of interactions among other pieces and qualities of information. These are overshadowed by their conceptual *objectification.*

No true understanding of reality is possible without developing a feeling for what goes beyond the definable, or at least without some awareness of it. The things illumined don't reflect categories in nature. It is we who are able, or unable, to focus on specifics without limiting them. And it is we who, by so doing, are able or unable to get locked into these specifics.

Without sensing the whole behind things no outline of reality can be made; without an outline of things no whole can be sensed. We are the makers (and the destroyers) of our conceptions. We alone can both see a fence and peep over it, or look through a hole in it. In the words of Stengers (writing about A. N. Whitehead's process philosophy): "The mode of excitement Whitehead's [thinking] is designed to induce us to think. It is not designed to make us become . . . a soul in general, but to make us feel how to become a soul[27] which *demands* to understand."[28] (Emphasis added.)

[27] The term "soul," which Stengers refers to here, is a word Whitehead frequently uses when he wants to present a key point in his process-philosophy. However, "soul" for Whitehead means something quite different from what people with religious sensibilities imply when using it.
[28] Please re-read the first footnote in this chapter.

Part I

THE ARGUMENT FROM QUALITY THINKING

Chapter 1

NOT BY FACTS ALONE: Unblocking the flow of self-organisation

There must exist authentic persons
before there can exist authentic knowledge.
Chuang Chu

To grasp the invisible delve into the visible as deeply as you can.
Johannes W. Rohen

The study of music needs to include the inner development
of the musicians, as well as the acquisition of skills and theories.
Clement Jewit

In the Introduction the reader was provided with some glimpses into what has motivated the writing of this book. Attention was drawn to the mental attitude currently prevailing in the world, the problems this causes and the way it might be possible to tackle them.

This chapter presents a deeper and more extensive discussion on these themes. It gives the reader an opportunity to become familiar with the specific subjects, practices, qualities, insights and particularities encountered in the next chapters.

What the new consciousness studies will attempt

We will start with some general observations about the novel approach to the study of consciousness hinted at in the Introduction. We will then proceed to discuss some ideas about *a science toward the limits*. This second discipline (one can call it an umbrella-science) is informed by a major line of thinking. It is none other than the *self-reflective interdisciplinary science of consciousness* mentioned in the Introduction. This science embodies a number of new ideas on the study of consciousness.

The *self-reflective interdisciplinary science of consciousness* will have four distinct functions.

The first is to penetrate behind the most basic assumptions about the way we perceive, objectify, conceive and handle reality. The second function is to work out how we might change those of the above assumptions we find inadequate. The third is to use some of the conceptual findings of recent neurophysiology for formulating a set of new assumptions that will be truer to what happens in both nature and the brain. Finally, the fourth function is to eventually employ such new assumptions for underpinning a far richer, relevant and rewarding social existence than is currently possible or conceivable.

Experience has shown that reliable experimental results are due not so much to how we employ in the lab the abstract principles and methodologies in the ways prescribed by the old science. The principles and methodologies of the old science become useful only when they assist the new science to develop two particular sensibilities.

The first concerns the living relationships and workings of nature itself. The second concerns the outlook prevailing at the time of carrying out the experiments. Both sensibilities strengthen the experimenter's potential to know what his culture and he himself project onto his experiments. This applies to both how he sets them up and how he interprets their findings. The two sensibilities assist the experimenter to find out how best he can establish a less conditioned outlook. His perceptual approach shouldn't dictate what kind of understanding he applies. His understanding should dictate what perceptual approach he should adopt.

Things can change radically when the experimenter becomes aware of his filters. They become transparent, so that they point both to what they let through and to what they don't. Since things extend well beyond their visible boundaries and the level of organization on which they manifest, unreflecting objectification will always leave some elements or aspects of physical reality out of the picture—if not out of the field of observation altogether.

This reflects the great philosophical lesson imbedded in Kurt Gödel's two famous theorems on incompleteness. We must apply their conclusions to science as a whole if we want to properly prepare the ground for both *a self-reflective interdisciplinary science of consciousness* and a science toward the limits informed by it.

Here we cannot but recall a famous insight by Werner Heisenberg. It says that physics doesn't really study nature itself. It studies the means whereby nature is studied. This doesn't apply just to our research tools or computational skills. It applies to the way of thinking that informs our approach (a) to physical reality, (b) to science as such, and (c) to the creation of research tools and computational skills whereby we can deepen our investigation.

As Jeff Dunne explains: "The distinction of calling something physical or non-physical is a consequence of a choice about how to order/structure/interpret ourselves and our sensations. It isn't because there is something inherently real or fundamental about a 'physical' or a 'non-physical' world."

Dunne continues: "To draw an analogy, it is like us debating about the inter-relationships of the energy and momentum of an electron, forgetting that electrons have neither energy nor momentum. These traits arise only from the process of enforcing a particular framework/expectation on the poor, apathetic electron through the process of measurement. I am not saying that it can't be done—we certainly relate momentum and energy all the time. But in so doing, what we are "exploring" is the nature of our model, the nature of our artificial (albeit convenient) framework of interpretation . . . and then pretending that it has something to do with the electron."[29]

A philosophy through science

Some readers may take what has been written so far to mean that by attempting to tackle this book they are letting themselves in for a strong dose of philosophy of science. They aren't. Readers are letting themselves in only for a philosophy[30] *through* science. This book has little in common with what philosophers of science normally do. There is little systematic exposition of theoretical models, rational arguments or conceptual refinements.

On the contrary, there is lots of uncertainty and ambiguity about these issues. Whatever rationality comes through has not been taken from the existing literature. The subjects discussed dictate their own logic. The logic doesn't dictate what the subjects should be, or indeed how they should be handled.

Neither does this book mark a return to older metaphysics. It marks a step toward an awareness of what transpires in the heart of things when the mind is able to refrain (a) from fragmenting physical existence unwittingly and (b) from locking into its objectification of the fragments. Mind then understands because it is able to *stand under* the things it is preoccupied with, while actually observing them from above. The non-local components of reality illumine their local manifestations.

---

[29] Jeff Dunne, email to Princeton Engineering Anomalies Research group, November 5, 2010.

[30] Philosophy here is not conceived in the contemporary sense. It is not seen as a mere exercise in logic, applied to technical questions. Philosophy is conceived in the sense in which the ancient Greeks had used it: an attempt to look behind the appearance of things.

Science, Objectivity, and Consciousness will articulate itself on two levels. On the first, there will be a discussion of insights into some of the greatest scientific breakthroughs of the last 150 years. On the second level there will be an indirect invitation to the scientific community to draw useful lessons from these breakthroughs. Rigor without intuition distorts as much as intuition without rigor derails; science and scholarship without philosophy are as handicapped as philosophy without science and scholarship becomes irrelevant.

This explains why we need to isolate and correct the shortcomings in the way consciousness is studied. If organized with care and discretion, the proposed exchanges on consciousness could produce far reaching benefits for both science in the broad sense and society. [31]

The root problem of civilization

Most problems faced by science and society today are due to the way we objectify and handle nature. Unthinking objectification, and its theoretical extensions into how we conceive, lie at the root of all our troubles in science and society. We may have advanced to the point that we no longer need to rely on the senses as an exclusive source of information. But one thing is certain: we have stuck to a logic informed by the senses. Not only have we been locked into our objectifying minds. We have alienated ourselves from nature and distorted our understanding of it.

The new type of consciousness studies here advocated will thus mediate changes in two key areas. The first covers a more rewarding existence for the individual and a more sanguine orientation for society. The second change covers a more rewarding operation of science and scholarship in general. Once these changes have been achieved, *a science toward the limits* will surface seamlessly and effortlessly.

Almost by definition, consciousness cannot become an object of scientific enquiry without the seeker asking himself in the same breath what sensibilities he brings to his investigation, and for what particular purpose. Self-questioning in the context of this project will be of paramount importance. It will aim at how older studies of these subjects have been pursued so far and where they need to go in the future.

---

[31] One way to go about this could be Bohmian Dialogue, which has proven itself very successful for many years.

Breakthroughs as teachers

Consciousness has been researched so far mainly as a distinct area of interest which can be conceptually isolated like any other. Depending on the scientist's particular psychology, training, attitude, interpretive skills and philosophy, consciousness has been viewed as a by-product of either brain complexification, of DNA instructions, of biochemical accident or of mechanistic causation.

The approach here adopted is inspired by some of the unexpected conclusions reached in consciousness research, as presently conceived.

Doesn't the discovery of non-locality in neuronal firing indicate the existence of a brain that reflects mind-activity rather than generating it? Don't the differences between the two brain hemispheres show that nature underwrites our objectification practices (left hemisphere) with a sense of wholeness (right hemisphere)? Isn't wholeness that which allows the objectification practices to be conceptualized, understood and applied in an effective manner? Is anything as it is irrespective of context? Can it even exist without context to begin with?

If we have learnt one thing from neurophysiological and cognitive research, it is that consciousness can be investigated both as factual reality and moving force; both as quantity and quality; both as cause and effect. The major problems facing society are as much due to objective causes (like the exponential population increase or atmospheric pollution) as to subjective reasons (like the perception of nature as a mere tool).[32]

It follows that going systematically into how we focus, think, conceive or even perceive is essential for handling such issues. Essential too is that in so doing we avoid blindly reacting to the old ways of pursuing science. We must not reject such tools as analysis, fragmentation or reductionism. They should be used by researchers accepting the new approach all the way down to that level of physical reality where there is nothing further to objectify, compare or classify.

Reductionism to wholeness

What then will be the difference between the old approach to the use of such research tools and the new approach here suggested?

---

[32] The Taoist tradition of ancient China sees nature is an example worth imitating. So long as people and rulers were inspired and informed by nature, all would go well. But all hell would break loose as soon as people and rulers started using nature as a tool—in the Heideggerian sense. Tools were seen as being truly useful only in the hands of those who didn't care to exploit their usefulness.

A descent into the world of smaller units needs to be undertaken in full awareness of the limitations imposed on it by the way our intellectual faculties have been trained to function and how we use them to carry out scientific projects. Researchers are misled when they believe that mastery of the conceptualized particulars of nature elucidates them. Only awareness of the whole informing the particulars leads to such elucidation.

Reductionism becomes a truly useful tool of analysis only when it is not viewed as the royal road to scientific knowledge. J. Panksepp makes this clear when he observes: "Although language is the only way we can scientifically bridge the chasm between mind and brain, we should always remember that we humans are creatures that can be deceived as easily by logical rigor as by blind faith."[33]

Sinking into a level of understanding which cannot be broken into smaller analyzable units has two effects. First, we become aware of the qualitative wholeness holding the parts together. Second, we come face to face with the quantum vacuum informing the parts from below their manifestation. Consciousness informs both processes. It acts as the originator and as the end-product of physical and neuronal structural hierarchies.

So pronounced is the involvement of consciousness on this deep level of objectifiable reality that even a hard-nosed physicist like Steven Weinberg admits "consciousness not to be derivable from physical laws."[34] If Weinberg is right, one is justified to also reverse his saying and claim that physical laws are derivable from consciousness.

Weinberg's admission goes hand in hand with evidence showing that, though strong correlation between brain and mind does exist, brain takes its cues from something outside its domain. We *react* to events external or internal in unique, or at least in highly idiosyncratic, ways. It wouldn't happen if all action *started* from a mechanistic brain that functions in computer-like regularity.

---

[33] J. Panksepp, *Affective Neuroscience: The foundations of human and animal emotions,* Oxford University Press, Oxford, 1998, as quoted by Iain McGilchrist in *The Master and his Emissary,* Yale University Press, New Haven and London, 2009, p 287.

[34] This passage was quoted by David Chalmers in his "The Puzzle of Consciousness Experience," *Scientific American*, 1995, 273(6), p 80–86. Chalmers goes on to inform the reader that Weinberg—well known for his belief that a theory of everything is possible (and necessary)—defends physics by arguing that it "might eventually explain...the neural correlates of consciousness itself." But here Chalmers enters the perceptive observation that "if the existence of consciousness cannot be derived from physical laws," a theory of physics cannot become "a true theory of everything." Thus such a theory must take consciousness into account, *if* it is to remain true to its claim of informing everything.

Mind first

The thought-initiator isn't "outside" the brain in the geographical sense. He is "outside" in the functional sense. There is no X group of neurons triggering an X function. There is only a non-local X component that makes the group of neurons function locally in a particular way. Brain research offers several indications for this. Some of the hitherto inexplicable features in structured reality thus find an explanation.

For example, Werner Heisenberg wrote repeatedly about how the observer "disturbs" the quantum event he observes or measures. Robert Jahn and Brenda Dunne amassed experimental data for 28 years on how the individual influences electronic equipment without physical contact, across space and time.[35] Helmut Schmidt showed that quantum interactions can be influenced by the observer even *after* they have already taken place (i.e. against the "normal" flow of time).[36] Daryl J. Bem has acquired evidence of retrocausal and anticipatory action.[37] Both psychology and the subconscious have been found to play important roles in combating sickness.[38]

The list continues. Dean Radin and Roger Nelson have demonstrated that people are able to influence random processes with the odds against this happening by chance being a trillion to one.[39] Informed intuition has been recognized by Albert Einstein, Paul Dirac, A. Kekkule, Niels Bohr and many others to have played a more crucial role in their discoveries than either experiment or calculation could (or has) explained. Indeed, the conception and carrying out of experiments is more often the outcome of powerful intuition than of rational decision.

The most telling example of the non-brain instigator's role as an actor-perceiver, however, is written language. The lines the reader is ploughing through at this very moment derive their meaning from words. But words don't create meaning. Meaning creates words. Iain McGilchrist explains that "we do not need

---

[35] R.G. Jahn and B.J. Dunne, *Consciousness and the Source of Reality: The PEAR Odyssey*. ICRL Press, Princeton, NJ, 2011.

[36] H. Schmidt and H. Stapp, "PK With Pre-Recorded Random Events and the Effects of Pre-Observation," *Journal of Parapsychology*, 1993, 57, pp 331–349.

[37] Daryl J. Bem, *The Journal of Personality and Social Psychology*, as reported in the science section of the *New York Times*, January 5, 2011.

[38] Medical literature recounts thousands of such instances. One very famous case of a 15-year-old boy who suffered from a severe skin complaint called Brock's disease and who was cured through deep hypnosis in 1951, has been reported by H. Gordon and K. Cohen, "Case of congenital linear naevus treated by hypnosis," International Dermatology Congress 10, 1952, p 376.

[39] Dean Radin and Roger Nelson, "Evidence for Consciousness Related Anomalies in Random Physical Systems," *Foundations of Physics* 19, 1989, pp 1499–1514. (As quoted by Brian Olshansky and Larry Dossey, "Retroactive Prayer: An Outrageous Hypothesis?," *Network Review* 84, 2004, pp 3–11.)

language to think, even to conceptualize . . . Tribes not using numbers above three, can calculate perfectly well to much larger numbers. They develop concepts they cannot even put into words."[40]

This obviously happens only when the non-brain instigator becomes aware that the words he has chosen fail to express the meaning he really intends. He then seeks other words capable of doing so. Through a strenuous exercise in trial and error, he eventually pushes his meaning into the realm of satisfactory clarity. At long last, his implicit concepts have become explicit.

So powerful is the urge of the speaker to communicate what he really means, that the listener gets the message even if the actual words he uses are wrong, or poorly put together. Meaning definitely dictates expression only if (and when) meaning is there to begin with.

The proposed *self-reflective interdisciplinary science of consciousness* will act in a similar way. It will reflect continuously on its most fundamental assumptions, principles, practices and insights. It will also recognize intuition as an important component in its overall operations.

The new discipline will articulate this awareness in non-binding terms, so that it can exercise its self-reflectivity unimpeded by older crystallized objectifications. Development along pre-determined lines will not be an option. The option will be to make certain that the new discipline continues to unfold without getting stuck on what it discovers in the act of so doing, however significant or profound such discoveries may be.

Current consciousness studies avoid such commitments. Most researchers believe that consciousness can be observed and investigated like any other phenomenon. However, as Willis Harman put it in a personal communication to the author in 1993: "The study of consciousness is qualitatively different from the study of any other subject."

A *self-reflective interdisciplinary science of consciousness* will try to make up for the current failure of researchers to see this, or to act on it when they do. *Science, Objectivity, and Consciousness* has been written in the light of the fundamental insight that consciousness spans the eternal-ephemeral divide. There can be no examination of consciousness without a consciousness informing that examination. If the observer in quantum physics influences the inorganic particles he is handling simply by observing them or measuring them, as Heisenberg believes, how much more will he influence the organic material he is investigating?

[40] Iain McGilchrist, "The Master and his Emissary," *Network Review,* Spring 2009, pp 4–6.

We need to cultivate full awareness of the physics involved in how we perceive and conceive. Weinberg and other scientists have been frustrated over their inability to find a purely scientific solution to the problem of consciousness; some attribute their failure to the inscrutable nature of the subject. *Science, Objectivity, and Consciousness* attributes it to the kind of thinking that has so far dominated its investigation.

Need for a qualitative science

It follows that John Searle may have been right when he pointed out that "consciousness is one of the rare philosophical problems that has a scientific solution."[41] Science will surely play a role in illuminating it. But the question is not what kind of phenomena we are investigating as we probe consciousness. The question rather is what kind of science undertakes the investigation—to what extent it is willing (and able) to learn from its own findings and how the latter qualitatively alter its ways of thinking.

If Searle *is* right and science can indeed throw light on the question of consciousness, the least to be said about it is that this science will have to be substantially different from the kind we are currently practicing. The medium has to be adequate to the subject mediated, as both Plato and Goethe have warned. We cannot look at the stars through a microscope.

The approach necessary for dealing with the proposed new discipline requires a different conceptual base. In order to advance effective consciousness studies, there needs to be increased sensitivity toward interactive processes; and in order to develop such increased sensitivity there needs to be effective consciousness studies. The subtlety of understanding depends on the understanding of subtlety.

But we must not forget that locking into our objectifications is the mental habit that prevents us from remembering that physical reality is the handiwork of consciousness. This doesn't imply adopting some new form of idealism. We don't create things through our consciousness. We merely choose them—from among many. In being what we are, we pick those blocks we can best use for building the house of our choice.

That includes indeterminate and pliable blocks; or even no blocks at all, but energetic events, as Einstein once called them. The very fact that quantum

[41] This happened on June 27, 2005, at the conference of the Association for the Scientific Study of Consciousness in California.

mechanics works through indeterminate micro-excitations of the one field, as Einstein called them on another occasion, shows one thing: we cannot use the macroscopic view of an object to understand what happens on its microscopic counterpart, where all physical processes begin to unfold.

Peter Ryser draws attention to this. "[T]he laws of quantum theory," he writes, are not strictly determined. "[This] means that the future of a physical system is not necessarily determined by its past . . . Indeterministic quantum events give rise to indeterminate thermal and chemical fluctuations which lead to indeterminate neural noise and thereby to indeterministic processes within the neural network [itself.] . . . At any moment the brain [can] take on many different states, [but of course] only one of these possibilities is [ever] observed or experienced."[42]

The occurrence of quantum mechanical superposition is a product of the simultaneous co-presence of everything that has, is, and will happen. Quantum superposition represents the universe as viewed from the angle of no-space and no-time, as happens when one treats physical existence as a total phenomenon. Things then exist on all levels of self-organization throughout the system.

In this sense everything, including opposites, is intertwined through quantum mechanical super-position in the one universe we know. There is no need for endless bifurcating universes. On one level we exist in space-time. On another we exist outside of it. And on a third we partake of both. We make our way through the labyrinth of existing possibilities. Creativity expresses itself in and through such choices.

Some tasks for the new consciousness studies

To become more aware of the pliable state of phenomenal reality will force scientists preoccupied with pre-epistemology in the *self-reflective interdisciplinary science of consciousness* to undertake a number of investigative projects. Some are:

First, exploring the notion and reality of objectivity. The reason is that the one thing science hasn't yet been able to be objective about is objectivity itself. Researchers have considered adherence to objectivity so self-evident that they have not questioned what goes on in their minds when they perceive, concretize, and eventually lock into what goes on. No consciousness-based tool for examining the validity of knowledge (including its relationship to intuition and

[42] Peter Ryser, "Creative Choice: How the Mind Could Causally Affect the Brain," *Journal of Consciousness Studies*, Vol 16, No2–3, 2009, pp 7–29.

factuality) is available. People totally ignore the need for a pre-epistemology. The very term for it sounds strange to them.

Second, developing a special "translation" technique from one discipline to the other, from all disciplines to self-aware consciousness studies, and from self-aware consciousness studies to all disciplines. This will be indispensable in view of the specialization tendency, which makes communication among workers in particular fields difficult, if not impossible.

Third, inquiring into the particular tasks and experiences that increase meaningfulness. Meaningfulness represents the very bent of mind which allows individuals to acknowledge the existence of something additional in objects than their mere "objecthood." The more meaning we see in such individual systems, the more we care for them; the more we care for them the better we understand them; and the better we understand them, the better we handle both the objects and ourselves.[43]

Penetrating behind the scenes

These types of investigation are but a few that show why self-reflection needs to be institutionalized in consciousness studies. Becoming an integral part of the investigation and the philosophy of consciousness, self-reflectivity can contribute substantially to formulating a more open, effective, relevant and self-correcting science that is better able to reflect on what actually happens to physical reality when we observe it.

Relativity, quantum mechanics, Bohr's complementarity, Heisenberg's uncertainty, incompleteness, chaos and complexity theory, gene expression research, brain scanning techniques and fuzzy logic all cry out for a more holistic understanding of the physical world—as well as of the mind investigating it. It has become evident that a rationality mediated by the notion and the behavior of objects can no longer describe how nature works.

It isn't as if from an understanding of things as given, separate and structured, we now move to an understanding of them as more flexible, interdependent and process orientated. It is rather as if we have now come to realize that several modes of thinking are often indispensable for describing reality both in its local, its non-local and its trans-temporal manifestations.

[43] This idea was first expressed by Petros Lezos in a personal communication with the author in October 1986.

We simply cannot continue to treat numbers, fields, tendencies, dimensions, relationships or indirect influences in the light of our understanding of how hard objects behave and how they interact in linear-time or container-space. Vision-mediated comprehension and object-informed rationality are misleading guides. Today we believe that we no longer think in terms of solid objects. The fact remains that we still perceive objects in the light of what we think about them—rather than *what* they are in themselves.

The dis-objectification and re-wholification of nature

Awareness of the limitations of factual knowledge is only natural in the light of what has been discussed. It explains why the twentieth century has dis-objectified and re-wholified both the "smaller" structural levels of matter (quantum mechanics) and the larger ones (special relativity.) But awareness of the limitations of factual knowledge is not enough itself to complete and safeguard the task of restoring wholeness to the understanding of reality. The damage done by the ancient practice of self-locking objectification[44] is extensive, pervasive and—above all—entrenched.

That is why our society needs a *self-reflective interdisciplinary science of consciousness*. It will help us to understand what causes self-locking objectification. In addition, it will help us to establish a realistic overview of theoretical physics, theoretical biology, social and physical anthropology, epistemology, history of civilization, philosophy, psychology, mathematics and other disciplines.

This overview will allow us to establish which particular aspects of the above can best contribute to an understanding of the two most important issues facing us right now. The first is what causes objectification both in us and in nature. The second is how we can re-wholify our outlook, without denying the need to objectify (and thereby to fragment) reality.

The quantum vacuum reflects our inability to objectify reality beneath a certain level of physical organization. What lies below that level *is* genuine enough. But it is not objectifiable. What lies above it is objectifiable, but not

[44] "Self-locking objectification" is a term that plays a key role in the philosophy of *Science, Objectivity, and Consciousness*. It implies the following process. We don't just objectify those aspects or components of reality we require for dealing with it practically or emotionally, as animals do. We get stuck in these objectified aspects or components. More importantly, we substitute the now objectified aspects or components for their actual counterparts. In this way we both distort reality and diminish our ability to handle it adequately. All human difficulties start from a failure to see things as they are—or at least to be aware of the fact that we don't.

genuine. It can be authenticated only by the objectifying mind itself—in accordance with the forms, qualities, states, principles, inclinations, categories or relationships it is able to work with.

A meta-rational world?

So, should solid, objectively definable entities and unchanging patterns be replaced as a criterion for objectification? Yes, it should. What then must be the new criterion be? Incomplete, but self-organizing, plasticity.

Information from different sources is as significant for the proposed *self-reflective interdisciplinary science of consciousness* as new ways for conceptualizing reality. The different sources could include fields, successive levels of abstraction, informed intuition, plus data from non-temporal and non-local conduits. We must become more sensitive to this multi-layered, trans-informational, poly-functional, meta-rational and cross-definitional world.

Researchers in the areas of science and the humanities cannot continue to be unaware of the way their perceptions are formed, their conclusions arrived at, their theories put together and their insights validated. Too much work has gone into the investigation of these issues in too many disciplines to allow scientists to ignore it any longer.

But won't this approach undermine the various certainties that have been established in the last 150 years through much toil and ingenuity? Yes, it will. Even so, we won't be any the worse for it. If anything, we will be better.

Institutionalized non-factuality and uncertainty

In the introduction there was some talk about non-factuality playing a bigger role in our understanding of nature. The same must now be said about uncertainty. It too will be called upon to play a bigger role in the understanding of nature. The reason why non-factuality and uncertainty can play such a significant role has little to do with the structure and processes of physical reality. It has everything to do with the apprehending mind. The more non-factuality and uncertainty are accepted as valid forces in the world, the more of physical existence we will be able to explore than would be possible if the neo-cortex was allowed to objectify reality too soon.

The longer the mind remains in feeling communion with things, states and forces, the better is it able to assess their specific role and potential. Three things happen then. First, the mind discourages the neocortex from wrenching out a specific reality prematurely from its embeddedness in implicate nature. Second, the mind develops a more accurate and dynamic view of this specific reality. Third, isolating the particular reality and objectifying it happens before that becomes fossilized into unchanging form—i.e. before it becomes a separate brush stroke in the painting of the world image.

However, for this to have a long-term effect, non-factuality and uncertainty will have to be institutionalized. Students will have to be told what these two forces are, how they interact with physical reality and why they will improve the practice of science and deepen the understanding of physical reality.

Institutionalization will allow people to come closer to how things are than is presently possible. The more factuality and certainty is engineered, the more will the world image be fossilized. And the more factuality is crystallized, the more will it prevent the articulation of those aspects that resist either mathematical formulation or ontological explanation.

It goes without saying that reality can be "nudged" into material expression. But that depends on the potential imbedded in both the actual world and our own insightfulness. Of course, by sticking to questions rather than answers, we will never get the unified picture of the universe that Einstein so much hankered for. However, we will come closer to this picture than is presently possible through the doctrine of mechanistic factuality.

Absolute certainty presupposes objectifiability and fixity. Institutionalized non-factuality and uncertainty presuppose incompleteness, striving and change. To the extent a scientist is 100% certain that he's got the right approach for obtaining the best answers, he undermines his opportunity to move a little closer to what actually happens. His certainty undermines his hope of being able to delve a little deeper into nature. It makes him blind to what he sees—though his sight remains unimpaired.

Learning from what is not

That is why researching consciousness represents a pre-condition for researching nature. If we are not sufficiently aware of what we invest in our consciousness research, we are simply not doing with it what we aspire to achieve: research how consciousness operates. We are merely researching an *abstraction* in our mind, as molded by the established use of language, the conceptual inquiries of philosophy and the experimental trials of neurophysiology, cognitive science and psychology.

Lacking an overview of what informs his thinking and why, he cannot develop an understanding of what informs his consciousness and how. This embodies the main argument for the new type of consciousness research envisioned here. Without a willingness to enter into institutionalized self-reflection, non-factuality and uncertainty, we may soon prove ourselves unable to preserve a civilization which has pushed our curiosity so far that it is now attempting to *investigate* the very mindset which has engineered it in the first place.

In the words of Vasileios Basios: "If we want to establish a true science of nature, we must first inquire into the nature of science."[45]

[45] V. Basios and E. Bouratinos, "Gödel's Imperative for a Self-reflective Science," the Kurt Gödel Society, Collegium Logicum Vol. IX, pg.1–5, (2006.) Special Issue for the conference "Horizons of Truth," Gödel Centenary Conference, University of Vienna, April 27–291, 2006.

Chapter 2

CONTEXTUAL WHOLENESS: The Qualitative Potential in Science

Man, in an invisible act of creation, put the stamp of perfection on the world by giving it objective existence. This act we usually ascribe to the Creator alone, without considering that in so doing, we view life as a machine calculated down to the last detail, which, along with the human psyche, runs on senselessly, obeying foreknown and predetermined rules. In such a cheerless clockwork factory there is no drama of man and God; there is no "new day" leading to "new shores," but only the dreariness of calculated processes. What we need is a myth of our own.
Carl Gustav Jung

It becomes increasingly apparent that physical reality can be objectively affected by subjective factors that are usually disregarded in the prevailing scientific paradigm.
Robert Jahn and Brenda Dunne

A mathematical proof always reflects a proof in and with reference to a given formal system. On the other hand, truth is absolute, by definition . . . Syntax cannot replace meaning.
Kurt Gödel (as summarised by Palle Yourgrau)

In his *The Passion of the Western Mind*, Richard Tarnas suggests the need for society to develop a new attitude. He argues that the old one has diminished the ability of humans to be receptive. We have reduced our potential for understanding the world and have undermined our knack for handling it. No longer can we truly commune with the objects, events and situations surrounding us—even those encountered in daily life. We can commune only with our mental images of them. And of course, we are oblivious of the fact that the latter are *just* what these words mean: mental images.

Applied to science, Tarnas' insight that society needs to develop a new attitude means that he perceives the old one as detrimental. This is why the desired new attitude must differ from the old not only in content, but in approach and quality. Its goal must be nothing less than to question what the author calls "[t]he basic a priori categories and premises of modern science, with its assumptions of an independent external world that must be investigated by an autonomous human reason, with its insistence on impersonal mechanistic explanations and its literal interpretation of a world of hard facts."[46]

It stands to reason that, because they will have regained at least part of their lost receptivity, scientists embracing the new attitude will come up with much better solutions, more relevant interpretations and above all, much broader applications than their colleagues who stick to the old ways. This will happen for two reasons.

First, the scientists adopting the new attitude will be much more aware of what the old attitude screens from their view. Second, they will be much more open to the increased opportunities offered by the new attitude, compared to those of the old. Einstein probably had this in mind when he remarked that "in the eyes of a systematic epistemologist, scientists must look like [a bunch of] irresponsible opportunists."[47]

Choosing the information that suits us

Obviously, what the researcher arrives at illuminating doesn't depend just on his experience and skillfulness as a scientist. It depends as much on the kind of information he is open to; on the parts of this information he decides to use; on what he reads into the parts making it up; and finally, on how he evaluates the latter in relation to other pieces of information.

The need to reflect seriously on incoming information and outflowing bias is privately acknowledged by many researchers. It can be summarized by saying that the reality we humans experience is mostly the one we have chosen for our own reasons. Every species selects itself into its particular form, potentiality and degree of openness. We therefore need to know why and how we have selected ourselves to be as we are at the present moment before we can hope to understand the world.

Other components are important here as well. One of them is conceptual and has been described in a nutshell by James Hillman. He writes: "The evidence we gather in support of a hypothesis and the rhetoric we use to argue for it are already part of the archetypal constellation we are in . . . The 'objective' idea we find in the pattern of data is also the 'subjective' idea by means of which we see the data."[48]

---

[46] Richard Tarnas, *The Passion of the Western Mind,* Balantine Books, New York, 1991, p 431.

[47] Albert Einstein, "On the movement of particles floating in unperturbed fluid substances, in accordance with the molecular theory of heat," *Annalen der Physik,* 17, pp 549–560, 1950b.

[48] James Hillman, *Re-Visioning Psychology,* Harper and Row, New York, p 126, as quoted by Richard Tarnas in *The Passion of the Western Mind,* Balantine Books, New York, 1991, p 431.

Another component is attitudinal. It refers to how consciousness itself works. The basic issue here is described by Elizabeth Lloyd Mayer in the context of her work on CIA research into anomalous cognition in the 1970s and 1980s. Mayer quotes physicist Harold Puthoff, who had been involved in these CIA experiments. In describing the very impressive data collected on anomalous cognition—in violation of the basic assumptions of contemporary science—Puthoff remarks:

> The impressive data . . . got me reading people like Physicist David Bohm with new and passionate interest. Bohm helped me because he turned the essential question upside down. Since everything in the world looks so separate, I had been asking how can the connections that would seem to be required by this evidence be possible? On the other hand, Bohm was asking, since everything in the world is interconnected, how come everything looks so separate?[49]

Mayer goes on to explore the related issue of human bias, which prevails even among scientists paying lip service to "objectivity," "fairness" and "openness." She recounts a story about the editor of a prestigious technical journal—*Proceedings of the Institute of Electrical and Electronic Engineers.* In the introduction to an article which this editor published in spite of its rejection by one peer reviewer, he writes: "[The reviewer] had assessed the [submitted] article as methodologically impeccable and could find no substantive basis for rejection. However he recommended rejecting it with the following declaration: 'This is the kind of thing I would not believe in even if it existed.'"[50]

Evidently, the question of what influences the scientist's work goes much deeper than proof, choice, structure and methodology, leave alone interpretation. It extends to the very quality of awareness the mind brings to bear on what it is fixing its attention on. Not being in a position to perceive reality away from philosophical or scientific prejudices, our mind is unable to develop properly. In the words of Max Payne: "The world view of orthodox science has not kept pace with the actual advance in scientific knowledge."[51]

---

[49] Elizabeth Lloyd Mayer, *Extraordinary Knowing: Science, Skepticism and the Inexplicable Powers of the Human Mind,* Bantam Books, New York, London, Sydney, Auckland, 2008, p 113. Mayer here refers to insights developed by David Bohm in his *Wholeness and the Implicate Order,* Ark Paperbacks, London and Boston, 1983.

[50] Op. cit. p 133.

[51] Max Payne, "A Seismic Shift," *Network Review,* Winter 2005, pp 55–56.

The scientist as part of the problem he is trying to solve

By this sentence Payne doesn't mean the quantitative or computational aspect of scientific investigation. He means its qualitative aspects. Modern physics started from strictly quantitative preoccupations, only to end up with profoundly qualitative insights. It transformed itself in and through this process. We seem to have forgotten that. Science today is as stuck in its ways of investigating and interpreting reality as it had been before Maxwell brought electromagnetism into the picture.

For this unscientific attitude to change, the scientist must develop a willingness, and some ability. to ask if his specific way of apprehending physical existence is adequate to the task. Colin Hales discusses this. "If a particular scientific problem remains intractable indefinitely, defying all approaches, at what point do we inherit the latitude to question ourselves as scientists? What level of failure justifies some doubt that we scientists are [really] equipped for solving such a stubborn problem? How would we tell if we [are] actually part of the problem?"[52]

This question is directed at the scientist as a unique person. At the same time, it is directed at the prevailing assumptions in the scientific community. Drawing attention to how our consciousness gets ensnared by the major breakthroughs in science poses a complex problem. It involves the spirit of critical inquiry the scientist is supposed to be imbued with. It equally involves the extent to which the scientist is willing to diversify the ways he observes reality—so that he can make the best use of whatever information he is exposed to.

There are many aspects to this issue. Four will be examined here below.

Not by one logic alone

The first involves the entrenched belief that one type of logic only (and hence one type of science only) can be applied to the investigation of *all* quantities, qualities and levels of physical organization in the universe.[53] This logic can be anything from Cartesian, quantum mechanical, positivist, language-based (as in the case of Aristotle,) idealistic, or sense-orientated (as in the case of Ernst Mach).

But experience has shown that one cannot conceive nature in such a simplistic way. In reviewing the ideas presented by Matte Blanco and Rodney

[52] Colin Hales, "Dual Aspect Science," *Journal of Consciousness Studies,* Volume 16, No 2–3 (2009), pp 30–73.

[53] Such a person was Gottlob Frege, who believed that there exists only one genuine logical system—his own—and that it was impossible for one to break out of it.

Bomford in Chris Clarke's *Ways of Knowing*, David Lorimer epitomizes their thinking as follows: "The challenge here is to let go the conviction that there is only one valid form of logic."[54]

It is clear that the investigative rationale should adjust to the character of the special object under scrutiny. The object investigated should not adjust to the special character of the investigative rationale. For example, not all objectifications occur on the same level of abstraction. It is impossible to project the rationale of one such level on objects inhabiting another.

This realization became particularly pertinent when sub-nuclear physics began to be investigated experimentally in the early 20th century. Werner Heisenberg points this out repeatedly. After describing the confusion created by the different values reached in early 20th century experiments on sub-atomic particles with criteria borrowed from the operation of elements or molecules, he asks: "Can nature possibly be so absurd as it seemed to us in these . . . experiments?"[55]

Quantum theory was born when physicists realized that the results they were obtaining couldn't be classified as "experimental" in the old sense of the word. They were *probabilities* of experimental results. But what actually are probabilities? Can one claim that recording their occurrence constitutes an "object"? If so, does that object belong to the same general category as a stone, a mathematical abstraction or a flying bird?

The suggestion put forward here is that what a physicist conceives as probabilities on the quantum level is no more than *non-objectifiable reality breaking through to a reality dominated by self-locking objectifications.*[56] The problem with such objectifications is that they are not viewed as tentative focal points. They are viewed as permanent ubiquitous features. Nature exists as a structured compilation of them. This approach is only natural, considering that Enlightenment

---

[54] David Lorimer, "Beyond Epistemological Imperialism," *Network Review* 89, Winter 2005, pp 41–42.

[55] Werner Heisenberg, *Physics and Philosophy*, Harper and Row, New York, 1962, p 114.

[56] As already hinted at in Chapter 1, the expression "self-locking objectification" reflects an autistic-like practice employed by people and cultures to make sense of and handle their internal and external environment. Self-locking objectification unfolds in five stages. In the first people and cultures pick out those elements from their perceptions that serve the idea they have of themselves. In the second stage they concretise these elements. In the third they abstract the elements from their natural embeddedness in reality. In the fourth they lock mentally not just into their abstractions of the elements, but into their most obvious conceptual implications. Finally, in the fifth stage people and cultures project these abstractions both on to all they perceive subsequently and on how they make sense of it. They don't see the world as it is, or even only as their senses dictate. They construct it out of what their self-locking points of view dictate. The opposite of "self-locking objectification" is 'self-releasing objectification.

science grew out of alchemy,[57] a basic tenet of which was expressed in the famous Hermetic adage "as below so above"—and vice versa. Alchemy, like mainstream science today, believed that what applies to one level of physical organization equally applies to all. It doesn't.

Translating what we discover into how we think

The second aspect of the science-consciousness interaction concerns the translation of scientific findings into how we actually perceive and conceive.

In the past, scientific findings have had powerful impacts on the way we think. Displacing the Earth from the center of the universe, Copernicus removed us from our (seeming) oneness with it. Introducing physical determinism as the principle by which the universe operates, Newton and Descartes introduced a mechanistic conception of reality—including God. Discovering the powerful role of the unconscious in shaping our feelings, behavior and thinking, Freud forced us to see that ultimately we are driven by forces hidden deep in our psyche—"which don't readily submit to either rational analysis, or to conscious manipulation," as Richard Tarnas comments.[58]

The great breakthroughs of 20th century physics, however, have not yet had a commensurate impact on how we think or act. For example, wholeness has surfaced powerfully in areas researched by physics and biology. But this hasn't spilt over into the way we perceive reality, or the mental qualities by which we do this. It hasn't even helped us to apprehend reality, or to think in more holistic terms as such. On the contrary, we think about wholes as mere collections of parts.

Again, non-linear connections crop up more and more in the complex systems we study. But this hasn't made us adopt non-linear thinking as a matter of course. On the contrary, we have learnt to think about non-linear connections in linear terms. The implications of 20th-century physics are so radical that we still see determinisms where only general contexts are at work; we still conceive of "things" where only forces come together; we still attribute insights to the senses or the brain where mostly inner reflections and non-local inputs are involved.

Some people believe that Heisenberg's uncertainty principle restricts our ability to know reality. They misunderstand what he was about. Heisenberg's uncertainty (and other conceptual dead-ends in particle physics) merely "measures the extent to which the scientist influences the

[57] Isaac Newton was passionately interested in alchemy.

[58] Richard Tarnas, *The Passion of the Western Mind,* Ballantine Books, New York, 1991, p 328.

properties of the observed objects," as Heisenberg himself clarifies in an interview to Fritjof Capra. Capra points out the following in relation to this:

> In atomic physics scientists can no longer play the role of detached objective observers; they are involved in the world they observe and Heisenberg's principle is a measure of the unity and the interrelatedness of the universe. In the 1920s physicists . . . came to realize that the world is not a collection of separate objects. Rather . . . it is a web of relations between the various parts of a unified whole.
>
> Our classical notions, derived from ordinary experience, are not fully adequate to describe this world. Werner Heisenberg, like no one else, has explored the limits to which human imagination must be *stretched* and the extent to which we must become involved in the world we observe . . . [59]

If we truly wish to comprehend reality on its terms rather than our own.

A significant conclusion now emerges. From focusing on the behavior of things, we must turn to focusing on a behavior *through* things. Particles act as particles so that atoms can act as atoms; elements act as elements so that molecules can act as molecules, etc.

Again, from thinking in terms of structures, we must switch to thinking in terms of processes. Molecules form cells and cells form smaller living units so that life may grow in complexity, and thereby increase in potentiality. Action invites direction, structure of things invites process. A person who chooses permanent states to fix his gaze on conceives the world differently from a person who fixes it on self-transforming states.

An interweaving logic

The third aspect of the science-consciousness interaction is that science can help us to better understand consciousness, but only to the extent that consciousness helps us first to better understand science. This echoes the bootstrap physics of Geoffrey Chew. As he explains to Fritzof Capra, "the existence of consciousness, along with the other aspects of nature, is necessary for the self-consistency of the

[59] Fritjof Capra, *Uncommon Wisdom: Conversations with Remarkable People,* Flamingo (published by Fontana Paperbacks), Glasgow, 1989, p 18.

whole."[60] The interweaving of aspects into one another is unending.

In one sense, Aristotle's *Metaphysics* supports Chew's insight. Aristotle insists that no one can attain to the full truth—ever. Gödel's incompleteness theorems do the same. They undermine the dream of arriving at a complete mathematical description of either reality, or of the perceiving mind.

For thousands of years people have believed that object-mediated understanding (plus the type of absolutist reasoning it encourages) leads to improved understanding. But it has turned out that this was true only for the objects of daily experience, as apprehended by the senses. It is not true of the forms, forces, tendencies and patterns informing these objects.

We need to pay more attention to those voices that have become aware of the problems caused by object-mediated thinking through the ages. One of them is Leibniz's. Each of his famous "monads" represents the whole, as in a hologram.[61] The latter symbolizes equally the qualitative presence of the whole in the fragment; the organizing influence of it; and the existential interpenetration of all fragments, however far apart they may appear from one another physically.

Strangely, another dissenting voice is again Aristotle's. He warned against the belief that true knowledge can be obtained through a mechanistic, non-involved attitude. As W. D. Ross explains in commenting on the subject, Aristotelian induction (epagoge) should not be considered merely as an automatic passage from the particular to the general.

Neither does Aristotle equate the term "epagoge" with abstract reasoning. Ross clarifies that "epagoge" expresses, in addition to induction, two further notions. The first is a "psychologically mediated overview of particular instances."[62] The second is "the flash of insight through which we pass from an overview of particulars to a direct knowledge of the underlying general principle [informing them]."[63]

Knowing how we re-create the world

We come now to the fourth aspect of the science-consciousness interaction. Experience, culture, education and personal psychology influence the choice of material

---

[60] Ibid, p 62.

[61] G. W. Leibniz develops this thesis in his famous *The Monadology and Other Philosophical Writings,* originally published in 1714 and republished by Oxford University Press, London, 1951.

[62] W. D. Ross, *Aristotle,* London, 1974, p 55.

[63] Ibid, p 41.

that will be observed, interpreted and self-transformed. The question is all about how formulated knowledge influences what the researcher chooses to study; and in so doing, to objectify.

The question is equally about how the researcher's particular sensibilities[64] and assumptions influence the nature of his objectifications.

The world appears quite different, depending on how we conceive its ultimate building blocks—if such there be. Do we base our understanding on a belief that the world is made up of poor copies of perfect forms (as Plato thought); of cogs and wheels (as Descartes believed); of energetic events (as Einstein called what we currently refer to as "particles"); of strange attractors (as chaos theory stipulates); of mutual relationships (as Pythagoras and Gregory Bateson proffered); of fundamental equations (as mathematicians hold); or of a cosmic web of relations beyond the manifest, as David Bohm's implicate order suggests?

Could there also be another possibility—one that combines some of those mentioned above, depending on the level of organization on which an entity exists? Furthermore, if such an additional possibility is realistic, don't we have a situation similar to the well-known controversy between those who believe that space and time are ultimately granular and those who believe that they are wave-like?[65]

The interesting point about this controversy is that Niels Bohr (who bridges it by introducing the principle of complementarity) is very much inspired in his choice of the term by two things. The first is that his father, whom Bohr greatly admired, was a biologist and he himself toyed with the idea of studying biology as a teenager.

The second thing is that Bohr was much swayed in his thinking by William James' description of the "complementary" modes through which consciousness manifests in schizophrenics. Discussing this, Stanislav Grof emphasizes the very important issue of *inclusive thinking*, which he considers essential for understanding reality—and which schizophrenics lack.

Of course, Grof is not speaking specifically of physical dichotomies. He is touching on how seemingly opposite ways of thinking can be integrated. He says: "To perceive reality exclusively in the transpersonal mode is incompatible with our normal functioning in the everyday world, and to experience the conflict . . . of the two modes without being able to integrate them, is psychotic."[66]

---

[64] There are numerous such sensibilities, depending on the degrees of self-awareness achieved by the researchers and the particular purpose of their objectifications.

[65] The particle-like choice would be an analogy to the building blocks approach. The wave-like choice would be an analogy for both the energetic events approach and the relationships approach.

[66] Fritjof Capra, *Uncommon Wisdom: Conversations with Remarkable People,* Flamingo (Fontana Peperbacks), London, 1989, p 127.

With its strong emphasis on objectification and the type of reasoning it presupposes, Grof's formulation has serious implications for the way we think. Psychotic reasoning doesn't merely reflect an inability to integrate seeming opposites—such as the notion of cogs and wheels with the notion of energetic events. It extends to all seemingly opposite, or just apposite, poles of thinking that people fail to integrate.

Carl Jung was therefore more than justified when he claimed that *our entire civilization has turned psychotic*. Its exclusive preoccupation with object-mediated thinking both shows it and accounts for it. Jung had accumulated lots of evidence showing that about 30% of mental diseases have their origins in the fact that there is no meaning in or to people's lives.

Beyond dichotomies

Not all is lost, however. Karl Pribram suggests a way forward when he advances the epistemological claim that "mentalism and materialism imply one another." He makes the point that "if the mind-brain problem arises from a distinction between the mental and the material and we find that on a particular level of analysis we can make no such distinction, then the very assumptions upon which the issue rests may be found wanting."[67]

A person capable of releasing his objectifications, after their immediate usefulness has been exhausted, should have no problem with Pribram's insight. For him matter would represent the static element of existence, while mind would represent the dynamic. Matter would embody the quantity, mind the quality. The person would do nothing more than to allow the activity of his limbic brain to inform his neo-cortex.[68]

Pribram further clarifies this issue by asking in the same text: "Is information contained in a [computer] program or a 'mental' state? If it is either, what of the information in a book? Dana Zohar provides an answer in summing up Einstein's Special Relativity. "Space and time," she writes, "are integral functions of each other."[69] Were Pribram writing this, he might have added that mentalism and materialism are equally integral functions of each other.

---

[67] Karl H, Pribram, "Quantum Information Processing in Brain Systems and the Spiritual Nature of Mankind," *Frontier Perspectives,* Vol 6 No 1, Fall/Winter 1996, p 7–15.

[68] The limbic brain is that which governs our ability to feel and associate with things. The neo-cortex is that which governs our ability to abstract and reason.

[69] Dana Zohar, *Through the Time Barrier,* Heineman, London, 1982, pp 116 and 118.

Perhaps Eugene Marais' understanding of "a termitary as both a collection of individuals and a complex organism"[70] offers a way out of the above conundrum. As does J.G. Bennett's attempt to hold seeming opposites together at the same time, and G.W.F. Hegel's claim that Jacob "Boehme is the true founder of modern philosophy" because he believed that "all things consist of a 'yes' and a 'no'—simultaneously."[71]

A critique of reason

By using the accepted scientific method, it is possible to measure some of the conditions making up nature, like solid states, radiation, or complex systems. The fact that many other conditions (energy, dark matter, gravity or the nature of health) have still not been measured, is attributed by most to the fact that science has not yet advanced sufficiently to fathom ways of doing so. These people believe that to secure progress in the above area all they really must do is to extend their research methods, improve their measuring devices and perfect their computational skills and techniques.

The possibility that there may be conditions in nature for which the familiar criteria of acquiring scientific knowledge are inadequate doesn't enter their thinking even as a remote chance; all the more reason to raise the question about criteria. Scientists will have to deal with it eventually, as the old criteria increasingly fail to explain the new findings like non-locality, retro-causality, man-machine interactions, out-of-the-body experiences and others.

Immanuel Kant expresses in his *Critique of Pure Reason* the opinion that reason requires a critique from within its own domain. If he is right, we are justified to also invite a critique of that critique. For example, we today analyze our understanding in terms of unconscious forces, memories and conceptual projections. Should we not attempt to do the same for our scientific understanding? Should we not look into what Carl Jung calls "rationalist neuroses" and "rationalist superstitions of our age?"

There is only one point we must be careful about in going down such a path. The critique of a critique of reason must be formulated from a level of abstraction deeper than that which was conceived by Kant. To understand something well enough to pass judgement on it, requires an ability to stand

[70] Eugene Marais, *The Soul of the White Ant,* Capetown and London, 1971, p 12.
[71] Henri Bortoft, "The Transformative Potential of Paradox," *Holistic Science Journal,* July 2010, p 32–35.

under it—to see where its roots are and where they draw their nourishment from. Richard Tarnas made this the cornerstone of his *The Passion of the Western Mind* when he wrote: "[O]nly by recalling the deeper sources of our world and world view can we hope to gain the self-understanding necessary for dealing with our current dilemmas."[72]

Seeing beyond objects through objects

Ultimately, reason cannot sit in judgement of reason. Reason can be judged only by a mindset that has become aware of what informs the above objectifications on the strength of which reason has come into being. The careful weighing of how these objectifications have been arrived at, is what gives reason its particular character and direction. Equally it points to its limitations.

Another conclusion emerges as well. That which invites us to develop a structured view of things matters more than that which the view itself reveals; that which allows us to form a judgment matters more than that which the judgment refers to.

Through their dynamic interplay, the four aspects of the science-consciousness interaction here discussed establish a kind of feedback process. What we know and think influences what we perceive and conceive; how we perceive and conceive influences how we know and think.

Consciousness thus can be used to influence science as much as science can be used to influence consciousness. A model proving useful here may be that of the mind-brain interaction. Firing brain cells trigger emotions, sensations and thoughts. By the same token, emotions, sensations and thoughts trigger brain cells into firing.

Which comes first (the neuronal arousal or the thought) determines for many whether consciousness is ultimately physical or non-physical. The notion put forward here is that the dichotomy between physical and non-physical reality stems from object-mediated thinking, which restricts understanding. Consciousness, like nature itself, is what it does and does what it is. Important is not which comes first—the neuronal arousal or the thought. A neuronal arousal may result from *retrocausal action*.[73] It may also be the outcome of some particular

[72] Richard Tarnas, *The Passion of the Western Mind,* Ballantine Books, New York, 1991, p XIII.

[73] Retrocausality represents the ability of physicists to effect some changes in the past interactions of particles and sub-particles. For information on this, plus its profound implications for the way we conceive physical reality, consult Daniel P. Sheehan *Frontiers of Time,* AIP Conference Proceedings No 863, San Diego, California, July 2006.

non-observable initial conditions, of the type that chaos theory sees happening on all levels of self-organizing objectification.

The mental event (thought, feeling, belief, interest, information, etc.) doesn't only mobilize the neurons; it affects them physically. There is growing evidence for this. Scientists became aware of it during the "Mind and Life" experiments conducted at Harvard on meditating Tibetan monks in 2004. These experiments show that meditational practices have a significant bearing both on how the individual thinks or acts and on the very neuronal *structures* where the thinking manifests and the action begins.[74]

Unsatisfactory understanding

At this point, yet another conclusion becomes obvious. We need to establish a new discipline, such as the *self-reflective interdisciplinary science of consciousness* we hinted at in the introduction. Such a discipline will empower science to become more useful in investigating reality. It will also empower society to shed light on the root causes of some of its major problems, including suggestions on how best to handle them.

The fact that brain-wiring is now known not to be determined before birth, the realization that brain structure can be changed even through plain measuring, shows that a *self-reflective interdisciplinary science of consciousness* can play a decisive role in showing not merely what needs to change in science and why, but where the change should start from and how.[75] The new non-paradigmatic

---

[74] Antoine Lutz, Lawrence L. Greishar, Nancy B. Rawlings, Matthieu Ricard and Richard J. Davidson, "Long-term meditators self-induce high amplitude gamma synchrony during mental practice," *PNAS*, Vol. 101 No 46 (Nov. 16, 2004), pp 16369–16373. Also Sharon Begley, "Scans of Monks' Brains Show Meditation Alters Structure, Functioning," *Science Journal, The Wall Street Journal,* Nov 5, 2004. In a different series of experiments, Andrew Newberg and Eugene d' Aquili, working with Fransiscan Nuns and a group of different Tibetan monks, found that a section called the "orientation association area" in the parietal lobes, which provides a sense of distinction between the self and the world, was virtually inactive during their brain scans. The two researchers concluded that the diminished activity in this area might account for the characteristic mystical descriptions of limitlessness by the nuns and monks. (Reported in Scott D. Phelps "Grappling with Uncertainty: On the Relationship between Science and Religion," *Network Review,* 82, Summer 2003.) Also, in his article "A New Intellectual Framework for Psychiatry," published by the *American Journal of Psychiatry* in 1998.

[75] There should be no fears that some individuals or groups could in the future manipulate techniques such as meditation in order to brainwash people into submission. Tests show that people can be influenced only up to a certain (harmless) point. The minute the would-be manipulators pass this threshold, the techniques become counterproductive. The reason is that meditation can be successful only to the extent that it is used for purposes beyond those conceivable or worked out by the neo-cortex. Once this tendency is reversed and the neo-cortex dictates what meditation should be used for or how, the exercise no longer works.

science here envisioned will need a *self-reflective interdisciplinary* component to find its way, and thereby point to a more satisfactory understanding of reality than is presently possible.

The unsatisfactory nature of our current understanding of reality doesn't arise from what we conceive as its content. It arises from the unsatisfactory way our understanding has come to operate. To such an extent have we allowed ourselves to conceive the world in the guise of a collection of objects, that we approach even the need for corrective action in object-mediated terms? We don't ask ourselves what has caused the damage to begin with, or what can be done to rectify it.

A *self-reflective interdisciplinary science of consciousness* represents one way of doing exactly that. To succeed, however, we need to start from examining two things. First, how did it happen that for us in the West consciousness lost sight of itself. In Asia, through meditation and in pre-classical Greece, through introspection, we used to be able to check on ourselves. We didn't allow our minds to run away with us.

Today the sense of just-being has been replaced with the sense of just-objectifying. From experience we have moved to description of experience and from self-awareness to self-consciousness. Psychology has taken over from ontology, information from knowledge, crystallizing from focusing.

Chinese fuzziness

The second thing we need to examine is why we developed the tendency to clearly delineate the objects we perceive and then to get gradually absorbed into their outlines to the exclusion of others.

Some may claim that dealing with clearly delineated objects represents an all-human trait. It doesn't. In old China nothing was considered purely one thing or another, subject or object. Chinese logic was fuzzy par excellence. People didn't focus on unchanging states. They focused on changing patterns and the regularities these manifest.

Neither did people believe in crystallized relationships. Synchronistic occurrences and the deeper existential patterns they reveal, were what attracted the Chinese. In the Chinese worldview, creation is the outcome of a natural fluctuation. A physical unit develops this or that characteristic, or moves in this or that direction, because of the particular circumstances and pressures enveloping it. But the circumstances and pressures are not local, appearances to the contrary. *The entire universe determines what happens to each of its trillion units.* And it does so by means of the local and non-local links bonding it to that one particular physical unit.[76]

The crucial question is whether scientists allow the "what" of their personal beliefs to spill over into the "how" of nature, or, on the contrary, they invite the "how" of nature to spill over into the "what" of their personal beliefs. Since the Middle Ages the former has been the case. Scientists have felt that they had to be truer to what the reigning doctrine spells out than to what nature reveals. There were rebels of course—there always are. Copernicus, Galileo, Paracelsus, and in our times Einstein, Gödel, and Jung are telling examples. But at the end of the day, the "what" of human understanding prevailed over the "how" of nature. The rebels of yesterday became the models for today.

It will hopefully become the purpose of a *self-reflective interdisciplinary science of consciousness* to reverse this trend. A new qualitative science will thus emerge. Nature itself, not some mental construct of it, will become the arbiter of what can be safely considered a "what."

It doesn't mean that humans must revert to instinctual behavior. It means only that humans must stop dictating what nature's phenomenal order is like. They must invite instead "the spirit of nature to bring forth its own order through the human mind when that mind is employing the full complement of [its] faculties—intellectual, volitional, emotional, sensory, imaginative, aesthetic, epiphanic," as Richard Tarnas puts it. In such conditions, Tarnas explains, "the human mind lives itself into the creative activity of nature . . . and the world speaks its meaning through human consciousness."[77]

Science, objectification and consciousness

So far it has been argued that to successfully meet the growing challenges facing science and society today we must abandon the object-mediated approach from which we investigate physical reality. But some thought needs to be given to how science and society may be reformed so that more of their inherent potentialities surface. Can shining the torchlight of consciousness on science and society help in such an enterprise? If so, shouldn't this torchlight first be directed on its own self? Is it feasible for a person, intent on knowledge beyond information, to avoid Socrates' imperative for self-knowledge?

---

[76] This is the way that Joseph Needham perceives the main traits of the Chinese worldview in his *Science and Civilisation in China,* Vol 2, Cambridge University Press, Cambridge, 1962.

[77] Richard Tarnas, *The Passion of the Western Mind,* Ballantine Books, New York, 1991, p 435.

Becoming familiar with why we carve up the world in the way we do will be the first step in such a direction. Other steps will follow. How does consciousness sense that which cannot be objectified? How (and why) does it lock into the objectifications it concocts? How does it handle (and relate) the objectifications to one another? Most of all, to what extent does consciousness bring wholeness, experience and memory to bear on what attracts its attention?

In spite of having dealt extensively with consciousness and its neurophysiological base, neither contemporary science, nor epistemology, have asked such basic ontological questions. They haven't even suspected that they should be asking them—that without so doing the answers they obtain by way of usual research are only partially true and often quite misleading.

Having said that, however, it would be a mistake to consider that the problem of science today is that it apprehends reality in terms of object-mediated determinism. The problem is that object-mediated determinism has become a paradigm. We lock into what we grasp and a little later we lock into how we interpret that which we have locked into. Things, ideas, feelings become permanent fixtures. They lose their dynamic aspect. The left hemisphere of the brain, as Iain McGilchrist suggests, has taken over.[78]

Detrimental paradigms

Here a different path is followed on the question of paradigms. It applies particularly to new paradigms formulated by some in blind reaction to the old. To brand things "right" or "wrong" means that the world is conceived in terms of unexamined clichés—not in multilayered, trans-conceptual and interpenetrating wholeness.[79]

The roots and effects of object-mediated thinking (not to mention the broad implications of this thinking) will not be discussed here. Attention will be drawn instead to the following two questions: (1) What is the good of replacing fragmentation with wholeness if we objectify the conception of wholeness and thereby lock into it? (2) What is the use of replacing "wrong" with "right" so long as we believe that "rightness" is decidable?

---

[78] Iain McGilchrist has written a huge book on the subject under the title *The Master and his Emissary: The Divided Brain and the Making of the Western World,* Yale University Press, New Haven and London, 2009.

[79] Adjectives like "right" and "wrong" mean that we are not fully in touch with what is. We are in touch only with what *we* perceive it as being in the light of our experience.

To think of an answer to these questions we must start from realizing that wholeness is not the totality of things. It represents their qualitative and ontological interpenetration. This being the case, science and society should be concerned less with being "right" and more with being responsive to nature—without projecting paradigmatic conceptions onto it. Nature equally uses wholeness and fragmentation, structure and process, linearity and non-linearity, consistency and spontaneity. But it never does so exclusively. There is always a little of the one in its seeming opposite. Furthermore, there is always a lesson to be learnt from the ancient Chinese practice of considering the opposite of a true sentence as also being true.

New ways of thinking, not just new thoughts

Each time we lock into our objectifications we ignore nature's ways. We treat things as though they occur on the same level of description, or are informed by the same rationale. Differences among units of existence are ironed out. They are not viewed from the specific observational outpost appropriate to them. They are not apprehended with reference to what prompted the observer to isolate them in the first place, to compare them and to study them.

We need to be preoccupied less over *what* to conceive and more over *how* to conceive. We need to care less for the nature of physical reality and more for the quality of knowing. We need to be concerned less with what to accept as appropriate and more with what not to discard because the reigning theory considers it inappropriate. New observations (leave alone new findings) demand new ways of thinking. They don't demand just new thoughts. We cannot practice holistic science with a fragmented, and a fragmenting, mindset.

Paradigms, even seemingly desirable ones, are detrimental because once established, they make us apprehend reality on their terms. They assign arbitrary significance to certain features, relationships and patterns at the expense of others.[80] They edit out all the gradations, subtleties, dynamics, spontaneity and multi-levelness of physical existence. Paradigms thus undermine the ultimate search for what obtains beyond the perceptible.

From the minute we lock *into* an entity, state or relationship we lock out the variability of the whole it is a part of. We exclude the most fundamental

---

[80] Xenophanes puts this strikingly in fragment 15, where he says: "If cattle and horses... had hands...horses would draw the forms of gods like horses and cattle like cattle and they would make their bodies such as they had themselves."

quality of the world itself—not to mention the way this quality influences the particular entity, state or relationship we are momentarily involved in. Aristotle's criticism of the Pythagoreans becomes pertinent here. He writes: "All the properties of numbers and scales which they could show to agree with [their conception] . . . of the heavens, they collected and fitted into their scheme. And if there was a gap anywhere, they readily made additions so as to render their whole theory coherent."[81]

Not merely contemporary science, but contemporary philosophers and theorists could learn from the above astute Aristotelian observation. However, they would first have to become aware of how Aristotle conceives objectivity. So far this hasn't happened. Existing definitions are mostly circular. You define in terms of what you think you know and you know in terms of what you think you can define.

A holistic approach to wholeness

To re-educate people in such ways, we need to look more seriously at the holistic nature of reality. This entails endorsing at least three significant epistemological premises, which impinge directly on how perception is affected.

The first premise is that we can never acquire an objective overview of all the entities, states, forces and relationships in the universe. There are four reasons for this:

(a) As Werner Heisenberg has pointed out, we ourselves are part of the whole.[82] Consequently we can never truly observe all of it, leave alone abstract it.

(b) Even if we did manage to get outside our skin and observe the whole universe; too much of it is around for us to be able to take it all in by way of abstraction. It would require at least as long as the universe has been around to do the job!

(c) The constituent parts of the universe interpenetrate one another in such a complex fashion across space, time, form, levels of organization, electrical charges, structural varieties and ontological strange attractors that any attempt to fit them into one coherent objective picture would completely overwhelm us.

(d) Those who insist on concocting such a picture do so by leaving out what they consider as being of secondary importance.

[81] Aristotle, *Metaphysics*, A 5, 985b23.

[82] Werner Heisenberg, *Der Teil und das Ganze* (Of Part and Whole), Munich, 1969, p 28.

Thus, they undermine whatever claim to objective description of nature they may nurture. Being partial, all descriptions of nature suffer from this kind of discrimination. Gödel's incompleteness theorems merely substantiate the fact mathematically.

Plunging into experience

Let us move to the second epistemological premise. It is that we cannot tackle wholeness with a mindset schooled in bottom-up structuring. Indeed, we cannot investigate any subject through a methodology not informed by it. If we desire to really understand the whole on its terms, we need to stop seeing physical reality exclusively as a compilation of fragments.

Finally, the third epistemological premise, which must be taken into account when trying to add a qualitative to the quantitative understanding of wholeness, is that we view the whole as the organizing principle of the world in its entirety. I.e. we need to see it for what it actually achieves. We cannot film successfully an object racing along at a speed and in a trajectory for which our camera has not been built.

The same applies to the understanding of wholeness. The mindset required for apprehending it must be adequate to the task. It won't be sufficient for it just to conceive wholeness through a combination of quantitative components. Wholeness is the context, as well as the fiber, of being itself. It resides in the mind of the perceiver to the extent that it infuses the reality that the mind perceives.

While aspects of the whole may be studied both philosophically and scientifically, the normal everyday consciousness is not adequate to the task. The deeper understanding required for studying wholeness arises only when philosophers and scientists are prepared to allow themselves to be conceptually challenged by the material they are studying. A point must then come when philosophers and scientists are no longer studying qualitative wholeness. They are moving into qualitative wholeness themselves.

Chapter 3

THE FIFTH FORCE: An informed guess about consciousness as self-organizing wholeness

Only when the one is completely the many can it be called the one; and only when the many are completely the one can they be called the many.
Fa-Tsang

The man who does not use reason will never get to that boundary beyond which reason really fails.
St Thomas Aquinas

Mind exists independently of its individual properties. It is everywhere, as opposed to being localized in the brain.
Kurt Gödel (in conversation with Rudy Rucker)

In the last chapter some thoughts were aired on the unsatisfactory state in which science finds itself today. It was argued that the roots of this unsatisfactory state lie in the domination of the scientific enterprise by the left hemisphere of the brain. Reason, or logos, once shaped by the ability to experience reality both as a whole person and a whole reality, was taken over by rationality, shaped by the tendency to increasingly lock into the objectification of this experience.

Concepts thus became "more rigid, rarefied, mechanical and governed by explicit laws," as Iain McGilchrist puts it.[83] Reason or logos (originally derived from an understanding of the flexible relationship of things to one another) became "formal logic" and "scientific methodology." Formalism overtook intuition, prediction overshadowed openness.

In the light of these developments, Chapter 2 also argued that we shouldn't react to the present unsatisfactory state of science by adopting a seeming opposite

[83] Iain McGilchrist, *The Master and his Emissary: The Divided Brain and the Making of the Western World*, Yale University Press, New Haven and London, 2009, p 330.

choice, i.e., we shouldn't replace one conceptual paradigm with another. If science is to become once again sensitive to nature as it manifests, we should avoid adopting paradigms altogether.

The practice of objective subjectivity must be ushered in. This includes holism. We don't so much need new thoughts about how to comprehend nature. We need new ways of thinking about it. Direct personal experience must once again walk hand-in-hand with abstract theorizing. Logic must be dictated by nature, it cannot be imposed on it.

In this chapter we will pursue this line of thinking a little further. This chapter will be all about the primary function of consciousness in the heart of matter. Five components are here involved. The first is the creation and evolution of the world itself. The second is which of its parts the mental faculties of man are able to grasp. The third is what aspects of the world our intuition invites us to sense. The fourth is which of our hitherto unexpressed potentials the world invites us to develop.

Finally, the fifth (and most powerful) component is what to make of the joint action of the preceding four components. More threads go into the making of perceivable reality than our minds invite us to think. So we need to see not just where these threads originate from. We need to see how they interweave. This will enable us to comprehend reality more fully and to handle it more effectively. The present predicament of humanity mandates a fuller appreciation of reality. We will either get to know more about the world, or we will destroy both the world and ourselves through our ignorance.

Ignorance may not have harmed us too much in the past. Today it represents a luxury we can ill afford.

The physics and philosophy of the block-universe

We will commence with some thoughts on what some students of Albert Einstein and Kurt Gödel have called the "block universe."[84] The reason is that on this initial stage of creation, the opportunities, but also the malfunctions, of consciousness show their faces unveiled. We can see more clearly the fundamental

[84] It is impossible to really separate philosophy from science when dealing with such basic states of physical existence as the block universe. Each experiment, calculation or computation galvanises a mental attitude, a philosophy, while every mental attitude leads to a corresponding set of experiences. Just as space is inextricably woven into no-space and time into no-time, so philosophy is inextricably woven into physics and physics into philosophy. Of course, there are many scientists and philosophers, even major ones, who are too tied to a particular mindset to see this, or if they do, to handle it appropriately.

conceptual problem of man. We can also understand where the lesser problems and opportunities have their roots, and what we can gain by familiarizing ourselves with them.

The block universe is usually referred to as that state of organized physical existence where the spatial and temporal dimensions don't apply.[85] The presence of space and time depends on how we modern[86] humans conceive the two dimensions and experience them. The absence of space and time depends on the calculations and computations that Einstein and Gödel thought through. They refer to reality as a whole on a deeper level of organization than we humans are normally wont to grapple with.

Louis de Broglie describes this situation as follows:

> Space and time cease to possess an absolute nature . . . In space-time everything, which for each of us constitutes the past, the present and the future is given in just one piece. Thus the entire collection of events, successive for us, which form the existence of a material particle, is represented by a line, the world-line of the particle. In so many words, each observer, as his time passes, discovers new slices of space-time which appear to him as successive aspects of the material world, though in reality the ensemble of events constituting space-time exist prior to his knowledge of them."[87]

A first conclusion emerges: If the block universe describes a world *without* space and time, then its all-embracing "blockishness" must also include everything that is happening *in* time and space. Illusion becomes real by being completely illusory. We require the two dimensions not only to function at all as human beings. We require them in order to pursue the necessary mental exercises that show time and space to be mistaken perceptions!

A second, even more important, conclusion now emerges. Space and time are both present and absent in each event or entity. This may appear

---

[85] These ideas of Einstein and Göedel have been summarised and rendered accessible to the non-specialist (a) by Rebecca Goldstein in *Incompleteness* (Greek translation by Elena Pissia, published by Travlos Publishing under '*Aichmalotos ton Mathematikon*,' Athens, 2006) and (b) by Palle Yourgrau *A World Without Time* (Greek translation by Elena Pissia, published by Travlos Publishing under *Enas Cosmos Dichos Chrono*, Athens, 2005).

[86] The ancient and non-lettered peoples have a different concept of space and time—if they have one at all.

[87] Louis de Broglie, in *Albert-Einstein: Philosopher-Scientst,* ed. P.A. Schlipp, The Open Court Publishing Co, La Salle, Ill., 1949, p 113.

contradictory, or even mad. But it makes perfect sense when one allows oneself to be guided by chaos physics. There *different levels of organization and description can co-inhabit the one varied but continuous unfolding process of existence.* Time can become a tool in the hands of objective timelessness, locality can become an expression of non-locality. In itself, movement is so unstoppable that it eventually becomes no-movement; place is so localizable that it finally becomes no-place.

Many philosophers have suggested such a conception of the world, even in the distant past. Parmenides believed that time and space are sense-derived and therefore illusory; the universe is of one piece.[88] Heraclitus wrote: "Each thing both is and is not . . . Of all things the one is born and of the one all things are born."[89] Zeno of Elea praised Palamides of the Eleatic School for convincing his audiences that things are both "similar and dissimilar, both one and many, both at rest and in motion."[90]

Foreshadowing William Blake, Murray Gell Mann and John Wheeler, Fa Tsang wrote in the 7th century AD: "When contracted, all things reduce to one particle of dust; when expanded, one particle of dust unfolds into all things."[91]

Einstein partly worked out the notion of the block universe within the framework of special relativity. Gödel did the same when he contributed his deeper mathematics to general relativity. But the fact remains that both men had unquestionably embraced the conventional (object-mediated) thinking prevalent among Western scientists at the time. This thinking didn't allow Einstein and Gödel to work out the relationship of locality with non-locality and temporality with non-temporality. Neither did it allow the two men to build on the picture of reality suggested by their actual calculations and computations. Their insightfulness ran way ahead of their actual understanding, their thinking lagged way behind their deeper knowledge, especially in the case of Einstein.

The two men didn't quite grasp that the block universe they espoused has profound epistemological and ontological implications. Indeed, on its level of articulation, Einstein's and Gödel's block universe affects perception, conception,

---

[88] Parmenides, condensed and abstracted from *fragments* 5 and 8.

[89] Heraclitus, *fragment 10.*

[90] Zeno of Elea, as quoted by Plato in *Phaedros* Section 261d. Aristotle also praises Zeno for his unconventionality. In *Topics,* TH8,160b7 he quotes Zeno's famous pronouncement "that motion is impossible," so that one cannot really go from the one end of a measurable distance to the other. After Parmenides, Zeno is the second greatest exponent of the idea that all self-locking objectifications lead to paradoxes. The reason for this is that, in last analysis, all happens to be in a state of flux. Thus self-consistency represents an unrealisable goal.

[91] David Ray Griffin and Donald W. Sherburne, ed., *Religion in the Making,* New York, Macmillan Co., 1960, p 67.

reason and even expression. They failed to comprehend that the old invariant view of reality as objectively ascertainable throughout space and time, doesn't really hold.

A world where everything both is and isn't as it appears; where everything shows up as both evolving and remaining unchanged; where everything appears both accessible and inaccessible; and finally, where everything acts as both cause and effect, radically differs from the object-mediated deterministic world which the prevailing mode of thinking prescribes. You cannot think of self-releasing reality with a self-locking mindset any more than you can describe processes in structural terms.

Hsuan-Tsang (596–664 AD) offers an insight on this thorny epistemological problem for those who want to disregard the paradoxical nature of the conventional (or object-mediated) universe. "A seed produces something manifest," he writes. "In turn, what has been manifested affects the seed. The three components (seed, manifestation and affectability) mutually stimulate one another into existence."[92] Cause triggers effect which, in the same breath, triggers cause. The task of working out the full theoretical implications of this conundrum fell to two other famous 20th century mathematicians: John von Neumann and Alfred North Whitehead.

Von Neumann was among the first to link consciousness organically with physics. In his 1932 book, *The Mathematical Foundations of Quantum Mechanics*, he went so far as to claim that consciousness not only "chooses" the event experienced from within the quantum possibilities available but affects this event by observing it. It looks as though, without wishing to and without being aware of it, we create our own world. Starting from von Neumann's thinking, one can argue that quantum possibilities are not ghostly situations hanging around in existential suspension. They are block universe events perceived from a space-time perspective—a rich self-service buffet from which we pick tidbits according to our tastes, mood and hunger.

Let us now turn to Alfred North Whitehead. He is responsible for two relevant insights of ontological proportions. First, he came up with the notion that consciousness has been around and active right from the beginning. Indeed, consciousness has been responsible for the direction evolution has taken from the first sub-particles to the staggering complexity of the human brain. Second, Whitehead is responsible for bridging the notion of ontological wholeness with the notion of the block universe. He achieved this through elaborate theorizing.

[92] Stelmo Nauman Jr, *Dictionary of Asian Phlosophies,* Routledge & Kegan Paul, London, 1978, p 95.

He finally encapsulated his thinking, however, through the following six-word sentence: "Everything is everywhere at all times."[93]

This telegraphic definition reflects a conclusion Whitehead considers inescapable. But this conclusion doesn't prevent it from being laden with conceptual ambiguities. From our youngest days we have been conditioned to conceive what we come across on a day-to-day basis in terms of time, space and linear connections. Conceiving physical reality without such connections, or rather conceiving physical reality as consisting of temporality woven into non-temporality, conceiving locality woven into non-locality, and of these two woven into one another, inevitably leads to self-contradiction. It is as impossible to discuss multi-faceted reality in invariant terms as it is to discuss infinity in finite terms or vice versa.

From epistemology to pre-epistemology

One thing is now clear. We don't have here just an epistemological issue. We have a pre-epistemological one. Let us therefore delve into "pre-epistemology" and let us see what the new term means and where it points to.

Pre-epistemology represents a sub-discipline-in-waiting which one day may assist students of consciousness to approach their subject matter from a perspective that takes into account all the disciplines consciousness either affects, or is affected by. At stake is the very way we objectify our perceptions, and even more so, our conceptions.

Should it ever become actual, pre-epistemology will deal with the cult of the clearly definable object, which has bedeviled Western humanity at least for the last 2500 years. Here we will examine how the natural biological mechanism, originally used for filtering out superfluous environmental data, was reprogrammed to help us also retain a lot of wholeness-related information. That such retention occurs became evident when neuroscientists discovered that, in contrast with other primates, the human right hemisphere contains more myelin, which promotes more neuronal activity, than the left. This means that myelin speeds up the operations of this hemisphere, each time the latter attempts to work out the relationship of wholeness with those particulars that allow the individual to deal with his specific needs and circumstances.

Iain McGilchrist explains how (and why) this happens. "The defining features of the human condition," he writes, "can all be traced to our ability to stand back from the world, from ourselves and from the immediacy of experience.

[93] Alfred North Whitehead, *Science and the Modern World,* New York, Macmillan Co,1967, p 91

This proclivity to stand back enables us to plan, to think flexibly and inventively and in brief, to take control of the world around us rather than respond to it passively."[94] Standing back constitutes an integral operation of wholeness. It allows us to handle everyday problems more effectively than would have been possible if we handled them individually.

But today this unique asset for humans has been mostly undone by culture, and thus, on the whole, people have lost their ability to commune with a broader and deeper reality. Their potential to know has diminished, their group-intelligence has shrunk; their ability to draw satisfaction from just living has almost disappeared. Survival into a meaningful future depends on reversing the above trend. We need to become sensitive once again to how the whole makes us aware of other objectifiable entities, of semi-objectifiable configurations and of entirely non-objectifiable states or entities.

Such a renewed sensitivity to wholeness will reflect no more than how the brain actually works. Alva Noe summarizes this sensitivity in the area of vision: "Large-scale [non-local] interactions between widely separated areas of the brain are necessary for visual consciousness"[95] to operate effectively.

Non-locality of brain arousal also applies to a person's connection with what exists beyond the body. No particular activity can be successful without reference to and information from the framework within which it originated. Frameworks don't only render a particular manifestation possible. They make it effective. We see most clearly when (and because) we contemplate most deeply. Indeed, we grasp individual things most effectively when we perceive their connection to the whole.

The identity of wholeness and consciousness

It will be difficult to sense what these thoughts are driving at without first becoming clear about what consciousness actually means here. Clarifying the term is necessary because what is conceived as consciousness in this book differs from what most people understand by the term. They get their cues from neurophysiology, cognitive science and psychology. The notion of consciousness put forward here also gets its cues from different sources. Among them are physics, fuzzy logic, epistemology, anthropology, linguistics, philosophy proper, chaos theory, intuition and psychology.

---

[94] Iain McGilchrist, *The Master and his Emissary: The Divided Brain and the Making of the Western World,* Yale University Press, New Haven and London, p 183.

[95] Alva Noe, *Out of Our Heads: Why You Are Not Your Brains and Other Lessons From the Biology of Consciousness,* Hill and Wang, a division of Farrar and Giroux, New York, 2009, p 13.

The interpenetration of tangible with intangible components in the understanding of consciousness may appear strange to an individual raised in the belief that reason alone—and the sense-mediated view of reality informing it—allows one to figure out consciousness. But the history of civilization is packed with examples showing that reality, and therefore consciousness, indeed reflects a total interpenetration of the tangible with the intangible and the finite with the infinite.

Not only can factual observation, conceptual analysis and personal intuition co-exist. They thrive on one another when paradigmatic prejudices are dropped. There is no fact or computation where previous intuition has not shown us where to look. By the same token, there is no intuition where a known fact or instructive computation has not shown us what to make of what has been found—and where to look next.

Let us pursue our investigation of the meaning of consciousness a little further.

Consciousness is not a mere synonym for mind or awareness. Still less does it come into being only with the appearance of humans, the birth of the critical faculty, the "invention" of language, or even the appearance of life. Consciousness plays *the* key role in the creation of physical reality itself—a fifth force added to the other four making up nature according to the standard Copenhagen interpretation of quantum mechanics. It acts as the unifying agent pulling together the weak nuclear force, the strong, electromagnetism and gravity, thus giving them form, structure, cohesion and drive.

In the beginning consciousness attracted the units of matter in a purely mechanical way. Later the attraction gradually self-transformed, until it started to engineer life forms. The nervous system then began to assert itself as the main unifying agent. Living organisms grew ever more complex, and thereby increasingly aware. The *sense* of unity now increasingly replaced its structural need.

It follows that if active consciousness, or the fifth force, relates to any other concept at all, it is that of primordial wholeness. The further from wholeness one moves, the less conscious he becomes, so that one now feels a need to reverse this trend. Consciousness now becomes the power that heals the original breakup of the universe during (and because of) the big bang. The more active wholeness is sensed as informing the physical fragments of reality, the closer the individual physical units link up to one another. And the closer the individual physical units link up to one another, the more powerfully wholeness re-articulates itself in and through them.

That is how and why reality is being constantly knocked into self-transformation. As Robert Jahn and Brenda Dunne put it: Mind "is the ultimate [self-organizing force] of the universe, creating reality through its ongoing dialogue with the unstructured potentiality of the Source."[96] In coming out with this profound intuition, Jahn and Dunne are in line with the thinking of Sir Arthur Eddington. They quote him as saying: "Not once in the dim past, but continuously, by conscious mind is the miracle of Creation wrought."

Consciousness as wholeness in action on its parts

Let us now examine some of the implications of this conception of primordial consciousness and its role in the unfolding of physical reality, including civilization.

The long history of reactions and counter-reactions to the loss of communion with primordial wholeness (a state of affairs described in most cultures as "paradise") enables us to better understand evolution in both the physical and the cultural sense. It also helps us see more deeply into the interpenetration of tangible with intangible forces in all modes of organization and on all levels of abstraction.

We will start from Descartes. Ever since his time, consciousness has been viewed as a state separate from the material in which it manifests. This reflects an understanding engineered by the object-mediated mode of thinking that has become characteristic of the Western intellectual ethos since Aristotle.[97] Another more general, functional and feeling way yields a different picture, however: consciousness embodies the process whereby physical reality wraps itself into form. It doesn't represent a definable commodity. It represents what triggers form within the constant reconfiguration of reality in its various manifestations.[98] Without consciousness, ontogenesis is impossible. Being literally thinks itself into existence.[99]

---

[96] Robert Jahn and Brenda Dunne, "Sensors, Filters, and the Source of Reality," in Zachary Jones, Brenda Dunne, Elissa Hoeger and Robert Jahn (editors) *Filters and Reflections: Perspectives on Reality*, ICRL Press, Princeton, New Jersey, 2009, pp 1–29.

[97] Object-mediated thinking is not restricted to the tangible or rational. As the history of Christianity shows, it applies also to the religious and philosophical. God or Idea are viewed as huge all-powerful objects—and that includes the reaction to this conception in the form of atheism, scientism, or materialism.

[98] Form is what keeps matter together. But just as matter without form disintegrates into disjointed existence, so form without recurring reconfiguration ends up as a fossil. In the last analysis, change preserves—and re-enforces—structured matter. Since form is a no-thing, things are supported by no-things.

[99] In no way does this imply idealism. It implies only that our ways of perceiving and thinking make us choose particular instruments which deal just with particular elements and interactions from the many on offer by physical reality.

In this sense, consciousness has its roots in what J. Scott Jordan and Marcello Ghin call "proto-consciousness." There is a difference, however. Proto-consciousness doesn't come into existence with the unfolding of organic matter, as the two researchers believe. It comes into existence with the first combination of particles after the sudden generation of space-time following the big bang. Inactive primordial compactness transforms into active qualitative wholeness, or active consciousness. It rearranges particles into ever more complex patterns of interaction.

Consciousness thus becomes "a contextually emergent property"[100] of the great self-organizing system that keeps the universe evolving in and through time and space. In the beginning this self-organizing system just brings things together. It extracts quality from quantity and order from chaos. It reflects what the etymology of the ancient Greek word for intelligence (euphyia) suggests: "to grow well." The end product of the exercise is homo sapiens itself.

From compactness to complexification

Two notions follow. First, in this protean sense, consciousness resembles energy. Though pushing electrons in a specific direction, energy itself cannot be isolated as an observable force or entity. One can only detect it in (and because of) the fundamental particles it pushes around.

Something similar seems to be happening with consciousness. Whereas energy pushes particles in specific directions, consciousness binds them into sustainable wholes. The one type of action is impossible without the other. Consciousness and energy are the two mutually dependent intangibles underlying all tangibles. They violate the classical scientific principle according to which everything reduces to observable or computable initial causes. Chaos theory has established that such initial causes can never be actually perceived or conceived. The deeper one digs into the processes of nature, the more is revealed of it to dig into.

Second, active consciousness catalyzes a new order of existence in relation to what held sway before creation. Particles, which had earlier been literally inseparable from each other because of the absence of tangible time and space, suddenly become not just separate, but distinct. In the beginning they fly all over

[100] J. Scott Jordan and Marcello Ghin, "(Proto-) Consciousness as a Contextually Emergent Property of Self-Sustaining Systems," *Mind and Matter, An International Interdisciplinary Journal of Mind-Matter Research,* Vol. 4/1, 2006, pp 45-68.

the place in chaotic disarray.[101] Later, under the influence of such unifying forces as syntropy, gravity and what chaos theory calls "strange attractors," active consciousness gradually promotes coherent interaction among particles.

In this way compactness before the big bang transforms into ever tighter complexification after it. Consciousness counteracts the disorder initially sowed by the sudden appearance of space-time. It sees to it that differentiation replaces similarity and organization.

The ancient Greeks, who first coined a term for "consciousness" in the West, realized that it plays a unifying, and therefore form-sustaining role. Their word for it, "syneidesis," is composed of the prefix "syn" ("bringing together") and the noun "eidesis" ("thing, plus the information concerning it.") So the Greek word for consciousness originally implied "the bringing together of objects known to be as they are." Consciousness was not the end product of evolution. It was that which triggered the unifying and complexifying principle of the physical world, in addition to the four forces of the standard model.

In particular, the "con" in consciousness brings together two fundamental creative thrusts. The first is that of making available all the modalities necessary for physical existence. In their order of appearance, they are the quarks, particles, nuclei, atoms, elements, molecules etc. used for bringing about the ongoing process of complexification we call creation.

The second tendency is that of stimulating awareness of what can be created with all these raw units of material existence, how and when. The two tendencies are absolutely dependent on one another. Awareness creates composite entities so that it can become aware of them; composite entities create awareness so that they can come into being.

Duality of description

At this point a critical clarification becomes necessary. It concerns the relationship between consciousness and physical reality. The way consciousness has been discussed since it was rediscovered by modern science is predominantly dualistic. Consciousness is conceived as a product, a force, or a field ontologically different from the medium it acts on, appears in, or emerges out of.

---

[101] From a relativity point of view, one can claim that the particles actually created the "space" by flying into it. Space leads into time and time leads into space. They represent the two poles of the same continuum. When one objectifies action, one gets time. When one objectifies its effects, one gets space.

For some workers in the field, consciousness has what one can only describe as "purpose." Attention has already been drawn to the fact that in this particular book consciousness is seen as bringing together seemingly separate particles. This is done in such a way that increasingly composite units of physical existence come into being. Each successive "generation" of them ends up as fodder for even more complex units in the future, *ad infinitum*.

For such workers, the moment has arrived to realize that purpose-informed consciousness is not impermeable to influences from what it directs its attention on. Two particular sets of influences are worth mentioning. The first derives from the characteristics of concrete objects, as perceived by the senses. The second influence derives from the dictates of a logic conceived in the light of time, space, linearity and causality.

The link between consciousness and physical reality becomes obvious only when descent into an older order of organizational development is conceptually possible. Consciousness and physical reality are then seen as depending on what was called, in the beginning of this chapter, the block universe. In such a universe time, space, linearity and causality are both absent and present simultaneously, in the literal sense.

Thus, for such researchers living in this vast interconnected universe, it is profitable to become aware that *duality in expression doesn't necessarily imply duality of being*. To speak of consciousness and physical existence as separate but interacting (as Cartesian thinkers do) shows only that the modern mind has been dominated by space/time considerations. It conceives wholeness as a union of previously separate units. It does not conceive the units as local manifestations of a pre-existing whole.

After indulging in self-locking objectifications for thousands of years, mind today can no longer follow in the footsteps of our mythic ancestors. They believed that one and the same deity (as, for example, the Indian goddess Kali or the Greek god Zeus) can have both positive and negative attributes at the same time. We today would have great difficulty doing the same. We cannot accept the co-presence of conceptual opposites. Locality and non-locality, or temporality and non-temporality, manifest for us as separate modes of existence. We are incapable of grasping how these modes can also exist in one and the same place at the same time and for the same reason.

Oneness of consciousness and physical reality

This doesn't apply only to the duality of consciousness and physical reality. It applies to all dualities. We see the world steeped in dualistic objectifications because doing so helps us *become more aware of its fine print*. We are thus able to handle it more effectively. It is not that there exists something like a universal consciousness that organizes creation in particular ways. Neither is it that creation automatically accepts to be organized by such a universal consciousness.

Rather, it is that consciousness is *potentiality* manifesting concretely in things. It expresses the block universe in its persistent and consistent effort to re-establish inner coherence after losing it as a result of the big bang. All physical attraction, formal expression, organization, making good use of offered opportunities, energy exchanges, or adjustment to new situations, serve this purpose.

Consciousness cannot be found *in* nature, or *in* ourselves. It is not a separate entity or force added to, or parallel with, nature. Consciousness is physical existence "discovering" its innate potential. We humans have turned this activity on itself, thereby becoming self-aware. But active nature and consciousness remain one and the same. There is no being without an intelligence that protects and expands it.

Action in nature aims at bringing things together again in the new circumstances established by the big bang. Its specific purpose is to increase the potential of fragments through complexifying the relationship among them ever more and on ever more levels. The process doesn't take place only on the immediately observable plane of existence. Nature (consciousness) also engineers relationships on a plane that cannot be observed, fathomed or computed. Our linear ways of thinking preclude it.

What this means is that consciousness does not conceive creation. It embodies it. As human beings, we don't *have* it. We *are* it. More importantly, we *know* that we are. There is no reality in the absence of consciousness, as there is no consciousness in the absence of reality. The best that Cartesian thinking can do for us is to make us consider consciousness and reality as mirror images of one another. And the best we can do with our present mindset is to work out the ontological duality of dualism and monism itself.

Such a working out will take the heat, and the philosophical hair-splitting, out of the age-old debate between dualism and monism. As Robert Jahn and Brenda Dunne point out, we will then recognize the complementary nature of all divisions making up reality.[102]

[102] Robert Jahn and Brenda Dunne, "Sensors, Filters, and the Source of Reality" in Zachary Jones, Brenda Dunne, Elissa Hoeger and Robert Jahn, *Filters and Reflections: Perspectives on Reality*, ICRL Press, Princeton, 2009, pp 1-31.

This recognition of the function of complementarity will be possible, however, only so long as we are still obliged to work with self-locking objectifications in a world requiring the opposite. Once we learn to work again with self-releasing objectifications, we will be able to automatically transmogrify monism into dualism and dualism into monism. Not only that: we will manage to do so without causing paradoxes,[103] conceptual difficulties, or logical inconsistencies.

We will have come up with a different rationality altogether. Monism will reflect for us the non-local, non-temporal, non-linear and non-causal manifestations of the block universe; reality will be seen as static and highly isomorphic. On the other hand, dualism will reflect for us the dynamic, local, linear and causal manifestations of the block universe and reality will be seen as searching for its own way to the future. We will have arrived at a stage in which we are able to embrace both monism and dualism through informed intuition. The conditions will have been prepared for a science *toward the limits* to work properly, and profitably.

As this happens, we will perceive that the oneness of dualism and monism is why we today can know consciousness; why consciousness can know us; and why our reality and our consciousness are literally synonymous. Parmenides knew exactly what he was talking about when he famously claimed that "understanding and being are one and the same."[104] Consciousness determines not just our personal existence, but the universe as a whole. As we see so we are—and as we are, so we see.

Self-organizing wholeness

We now turn to more tangible issues. Specifically, we turn to the main events that shaped physical existence after the sudden appearance of space/time 13.7 billion years ago. During the initial phase of this long period, the interaction among physical units mutually attracting one another was relatively slow. But once the momentum toward reunification grew and a certain threshold of complexity was reached, patterns of interaction (and later patterns of such patterns) began to form more easily, and quickly.

At one stage organic matter emerged. Conscious physicality pushed for something more than merely ordered existence. The patterns of particle

[103] Paradoxes typically arise when an object-mediated language cannot accommodate a reality-mediated fact.
[104] Parmenides, *Fragment 2.*

interaction then began to change. Whereas during the initial inorganic phase conscious physicality brought physical units together through interactions applicable to *all* reality and quite slowly, during the later phase it brought them together only in particular units for particular activities and quite quickly.

That is when (and why) a proto-brain came into being. It enhanced the previous ability of physical units to commune with other local manifestations of wholeness.

Of course, communion had been possible earlier too, when physical units owed their very existence to the general state they participated in. But as evolution moved toward ever-increasing complexification, physical units began to redirect themselves toward wholeness through specificity. The specific would just reveal the whole of which it was a natural, and organic, part.

This was achieved by developing a third tendency toward ever-increasing potentialities. Existence began articulating itself *through* things rather than *in* them, as had been the case earlier. Non-temporal and non-local wholeness, which had been shattered by the introduction of space-time, began to re-articulate itself through inter-temporal and inter-spatial activity. From an initial undifferentiated expansion, nature moved to variability: from absolute determinism to considered build-up.

Humans represent the latest stage in this creative movement. They pursue a different class of choices altogether: composite long-term choices. Through them they develop not just a new sense of wholeness. They develop a vision of it in the form of gods, forces, and tendencies (or laws). The two extremes—the tendency toward uniqueness and the tendency toward generality —begin to interpenetrate. Zeus' name (like Deus in Latin) is derived from the name used for the number "two." It literally means "the spanner [of duality]."

Evolution toward re-wholification

The increased potential for choices became manifest through two uniquely human types of yearning. The first was for what exceeds our grasp. The second was for getting to know what knows, and what is there for the knowing to begin with. Mere awareness of reality no longer sufficed. It needed to turn on itself. Humans wanted to know if they could improve awareness, or free it from at least some of the object-mediated conceptions obstructing their communion with wholeness.

That is why, ever since the Greeks, two sets of questions have become important in Western religious and philosophical thinking. The first touches on how we apprehend the world to begin with. Do we focus on specifics exclusively or inclusively? Are we able to apprehend new entities, states or relationships independently of previous perceptions? In conceiving such entities, states or relationships do we inform our image of them, does the image inform us, or do we and the image *mutually* inform (and enhance) one another?

The second set of questions touches on how the human being conceives himself. Does he extend ontologically into the world, or is the world separate from him? To what degree do his immediate whims overshadow his long-term requirements?

In principal, ancient cultures realized that whereas events and entities appeared self-circumscribed on the local/temporal/causal level, they also interpenetrated with their environments and with other events or entities outside their immediate locus and time frame.

Today we have mostly lost the ability to develop a feel for such an interpenetration and for the sense of measure it gives rise to. Of course, the know-how for acting in measured ways still survives. But at the same time, we have developed an opposite habit. We use our biological filters for locking into those objectifications alone that are in tune with our ontological, cultural, informational and individual predilections.[105]

Unquestionably, we need some sort of ontological filters to pick out those events, forces, entities, fields, interactions or relationships that we require for enhancing and protecting our unique existence. But this doesn't mean we should use the filtering mechanism for purposes other than those for which it was intended. If properly handled, ontological filters can both isolate the objects we need to interpenetrate with and reveal their relationship to other objects and the whole. They needn't switch from an ontological function to a conceptual one. They can play both roles simultaneously.

Where did consciousness filters come from and why?

Two further questions become pertinent. The first touches on how the ontological filters connect with the brain. Two stages seem to be involved here. The

[105] Our body is bombarded by two million bits of information every minute. If we were unable to filter out the vast majority of these, we would go mad in one second. Indeed, remembering more than one needs is considered today a handicap.

first appears in conjunction with brain growth. As we acquire more and more neurons in the course of evolution, we abandon our earlier habit of sensing the whole behind everything. The result: nature, from the tight embrace of which we have now disengaged, starts to fascinate us. So we lock into our objectifications of it. In this way we filter and color our perceptions of it.

The second stage in the emergence of ontological filters appears in conjunction with a new notion. Starting from our mental habit of locking into our objectifications,[106] we think that communion with wholeness, which in earlier times had been purely intuitive and ineffable, can be abstracted as well. This marks a setback. We are unprepared for handling wholeness as an abstraction without losing its experiential component.

Wholeness cannot be conceived as an object, or an addition of things to other things. It can be conceived only as a continuous, profound, active and silent presence. When we apprehend wholeness as a quantity, our return path to it increasingly twists and turns until it becomes labyrinthine. We forget not just how to experience reality without locking into some objectification of it; we forget how it feels to accept a notion without identifying with it. Wholeness now represents for us a state to *describe* and *reach*. It doesn't represent a state in which to *be*, much less to *act from*, spontaneously.

It is this type of intellectualized approach that feeds belief-mediated religion and ideology-inspired philosophy. The wholeness in which we occasionally succeed to re-immerse ourselves no longer resembles the wholeness we were once at one with. It has become a construct, an idea. Only certain highly evolved mystical states and practices can insure immersion in it. If anyone happens to discover wholeness by accident, he fails to understand what has happened to him. More than that, he cannot sustain the experience.

From implicit information to representational description

Let us move to the second additional question. When did human communion with purposeful consciousness (or with the primordial whole) begin to slacken?

To answer, we need to come to the history of civilization itself. It looks as though the slackening of our communion with wholeness commenced after

[106] By this expression is meant the concept of an entity, idea or relationship that one has isolated from the rest of reality, believing it to have an identity all its own, and thereby being capable of retaining this identity throughout time and space.

we fully developed our inclination to make artefacts of one sort or another around 42,000 years ago.[107] By creating these artefacts as we were beginning to get estranged from wholeness, we probably hoped to achieve two things. The first was to remain in touch with what underwrites the entities, states, fields or relationships that were most meaningful to us. The second was to better understand the world we were now beginning to conceive objectively. We probably believed that in this way we could retain the advantages of both worlds.

Indeed, we discovered that we could. One indication was that we still retained the older ability for handling some of our particular requirements through interpenetration with the whole. On the other hand, we also started locking into at least some of our new objectifications. That is when ontological filters really started to extend themselves beyond their original biological function. Implicit information transmogrified into explicit "representational re-description," as consciousness researcher Karmiloff-Smith puts it.[108]

The implications of this shift didn't become apparent immediately. To the extent we still managed to release some of our objectifications, we were able to continue handling our affairs in a more or less satisfactory manner. But to the extent we locked into some others, we began having problems. Just local and provisional elements now claimed our attention. The sense of measure—so dependent on a feeling for and an experience of, wholeness—began to wane. The more we stuck to our objectifications, the more we lost our ability to handle the entities, ideas or relationships they referred to.

In this way, both the positive and the negative effects of objectification came to be attributed to semantic content. The logical and philosophical pitfalls in discussing this semantic content were not considered. When we experienced the effects from some particular object-mediated perspective, we either elevated them to the heights of absolute truth, or rejected them as the lowest expressions of deplorable falsehood.[109]

---

[107] There is here a misunderstanding among neurophysiologists. Brain uses don't depend on brain capabilities. They depend on the *wish* of an individual or group to engage in a particular new type of activity, or to obtain particular results. This wish, if persistent, will eventually develop the brain capability necessary for fulfilling it. If the individual or group are fully satisfied with the way their lives are going, there will develop no wish to change anything—and no brain capabilities to serve the change. Mind comes first; brain follows.

[108] Karmiloff-Smith, A. *Beyond Modularity: A Developmental Perspective on Cognitive Science,* MIT Press, Cambridge MA, 1992. (As quoted in John Stewart, "The Future Evolution of Consciousness," *Journal of Consciousness Studies,* 14/8, 2007, pp 58–92.)

[109] Such perceptions are, for example, that of the distortion of the notion of sacrifice after the invention of farming around 10,000 BC; that of the conceptual inconsistencies contained in Aristotelian logic; or more recently, that of the possible dangers inherent in genetically modified foods.

Culture and self-locking objectification

Since Aristotle, the Western mind has failed to consider the qualitative nature of wholeness. On the one hand we became aware of losing the ability to commune with wholeness naturally.[110] On the other, we unwittingly attributed this failure to the fragments we were now stuck in, rather than to the way we ourselves conceived the fragments to begin with.

As a result, wholeness became as concrete, permanent and definable as its semantic opposite: fragmentation. Its qualitative and experiential dimension was weeded out, or at best consigned to the unconscious. Thus object-mediated understanding spread to all schools of thinking and areas of understanding—spiritual, philosophical, artistic, scholarly and scientific.

We were encouraged to embark on such a path because many of our most cherished insights were considered to have been the product of a profound experience of wholeness under various masks (mostly gods, shamans, saints and ceremonies.) People didn't realize that unless they consciously protected and enhanced their ability to commune with the whole on a qualitative level, wholeness (or the block universe) would eventually be transformed into a solid objectification itself. If an instinct for qualitative wholeness was still alive in the individual engaging in such mental gymnastics, it would be informed by his personal beliefs and the words he used for expressing them. It would not be informed by what goes *beyond* the words *in* the words themselves, as used to happen when humanity still lived in the paradisiacal embrace of non-objectified primordial wholeness. Experience had at last been totally subsumed under conceptualization and comprehension under information.

This may explain why Western philosophy developed like a self-perpetuating succession in semantic misunderstandings of, or conceptual reactions to, earlier formulations. The latter may have originally been triggered by some profound insight in relation to older ideas and notions. But they were later systematically abstracted. Each successive generation of philosophers or religious innovators discovered different points of agreement or disagreement with them *on a purely semantic level*. Why such ideas were formulated to begin with seems not to have preoccupied either their upholders, or their detractors.[111]

---

[110] Richard Tarnas illustrates brilliantly the disaffection this caused in the depths of the Western psyche in his *The Passion of The Western Mind: Understanding the Ideas That Have Shaped Our World View* (Ballantine Books, New York, 1993). Tarnas shows how the fall from wholeness influenced most, if not all, subsequent expressions of the Western mind.

[111] Many current attitudes, such as fundamentalism, secularism, scientism, political correctness, meaningless art and reductionism are the product of such misunderstood experiences.

Identification with abstract ideas, religious or secular, became the dominant cultural practice.

Passion for unification theories

Be that as it may, the longing for qualitative primordial wholeness, or creative consciousness, is so all-pervading that it can manifest even in avowed proponents of object-mediated thinking. A striking example is the fascination of modern physicists with unification theories.

This fascination articulates itself in two ways. The first is to base all understanding on Hilbert-like mathematics and on Carnap-like logic. The second way is to search for a "theory of everything." The manner in which physicists go about these two enterprises differs but little from the way monotheism extends its purview to engulf all reality. The urge for unification is as powerfully ingrained in believers as it is among scientists.

A final conclusion emerges. It is that we need to promote both the intellectual comprehension and contemplative experience of wholeness. We can then start to make sense of things in terms of what sustains them. More importantly, we can use the ontological filters both for what they invite us to focus on and for making us aware of what this focus leaves to be desired.

Such an attitude will express the essence of our humanity in its rational, conceptual, and intuitive aspects. It will, furthermore, do so in a balanced way. Through awareness of the conceptual issue involved, we will no longer confuse what we *conceive* of wholeness with wholeness *itself*; through reason we will discover the best way to handle phenomena in the light of their rootedness in qualitative wholeness, and through intuition we will penetrate to the deep-lying level of reality that informs the phenomena from *within their ontological expression*.

The latter function will be achieved in a manner quite different from that employed by mathematicians when they define their premises. What they call "intuition" is no more than a conjunction of the biological and cultural biases playing on their object-mediated senses. What is meant by "intuition" here is something much more epistemologically relevant. It is the ability of an individual to penetrate feelingly and unconditioned to the underlying web of non-local interpenetrations that keep physical reality together.

An insight may be objectified for the purposes of science, philosophy or religion.[112] But its hallmark is that when the intuited state is objectified, the objectifying agent doesn't lock into it conceptually—or if he tends toward solidified objectification, he immediately becomes aware of it and corrects his steps. Feeling imprints itself on the object the agent expresses, however formalized his expression may look. The expressed object doesn't impress itself on feeling, however detailed its description may be. The purpose of penetrating behind the veil of phenomena is to sense the qualitative aspect of reality. It is not to *analyze* its mechanics.

Moving toward self-releasing objectification

A scientist or scholar who thinks unencumbered by his objectifications uses them as much as an encumbered scientist or scholar. But the former is aware of the limitations of the ontological filters he introduces as he objectifies reality. He doesn't allow these to write off such non-objects as long-term interactions, resonances, fields, or overarching links. Rather, he senses what can never be an object to begin with, just as he knows what falls in between solid objects on the one hand, and clearly definable categories of objects on the other.

Such a mental reversal by the unconditioned scientist will have a significant effect on him, on those around him and on science as a whole. The drive to objectify ever more different states, modes of being, intuitions, things, sensibilities, fields, interactions, relationships and levels of organization or abstraction, is fundamental to the unfolding of consciousness. However, we have so far failed to form such objectifications without solidifying them, or locking into them. The moment has come to reverse this habit. Once again, we must learn to focus our understanding without isolating its objects.

The less objectifications we lock into, the better equipped we are to use those we need without distorting reality; the less we distort reality, the more

---

[112] The early Wittgenstein, who maintained that profound experiences cannot be put in words, was too influenced by his object-mediated understanding of language to realise that the latter has a far greater potential than strict adherence to meaning or rationality allow. Words are both symbols for something specific and keys to one's subconscious familiarity with the roots of any specification in wholeness. Words, so to speak, integrate objectifiable with non-objectifiable knowledge. You know things to the extent you see them for what they are today and you see them for what they are today to the extent you have always known them. This doesn't depend only on the sensibilities of language. It depends on two additional requirements. The first is the individual's openness. The second is his ability to become aware of his conditioning—and to escape from it, even provisionally.

actual entities, ideas, states or relationships we become aware of; the more aware we become, the better can we handle things or situations; and the better can we handle things and situations, the more easily are we able to savor the primordial wholeness, or whole consciousness, sustaining them.

This reintegration of objectification with what underlies it, this re-linking of the specific to what it specificity grows out of, represents what science and society most need today. We can learn to objectify and not lock into the outcome. We can even learn to objectify many more entities and aspects than we do today. But we can achieve this only so long as we retain our sense (and our experience) of wholeness. We will then be in a position to objectify, but not that which cannot (or should not) be submitted to objectification.

In this way we will succeed in becoming a lot clearer about what our ontological filters to begin with, and what civilization later have actually done to our conception of the world. We will perceive first, why we have chosen to pick out from physical reality one particular characteristic. Second, we will perceive why, from all the rationalities implicit in this characteristic, we have picked out object-mediated rationality as the most representative. Third, we will perceive what other characteristics can be picked out from the same raw material. And fourth, we will perceive what different rationalities can be extracted from this raw material as a whole, so that together with a re-evaluation of already perceived characteristics, our conception of reality deepens, broadens, and becomes more relevant.

It is not that in making a choice of particular images and object-mediated rationalities civilized man somehow took the wrong turn. Rather, it is that in pursuing his choice, civilized man consigned to oblivion all that these images and rationalities left out. Properly handled, objectifications affect us both for what they carve out and for what exists beyond the carved-out pieces.

Here lies the challenge and the usefulness of objectification. There is more to the world than we can conceive of it or calculate about it through the abstracting mind. That is its beauty. And that is what we need to pursue if we want to really understand what's going on. A door can lock us in, but it can also let us out. It can lock us out, but it can also let us in. It depends on which side of the door you have locked—if indeed you have.

Chapter 4

A NEW CONCEPTUAL FRAMEWORK FOR SCIENCE: Some Thoughts on Where and How to Begin

He who [likes to] think must [first] turn himself into an object
[of his thoughts,] in keeping with original nature.
Plato

Our notions of physical reality can never be final. We must always be ready
to change these notions—that is to say, the axiomatic structure of physics—
in order to do justice to perceived facts in the most logically perfect way.
Albert Einstein

Certain scientific anomalies are recognized only after they are given compelling explanations within a new conceptual framework.
Alan Lightman and Owen Gingerich

In the last chapter we sampled some of the breakthroughs and thoughts of 20th century scientists, to the extent that they impact on science in general and on consciousness in particular. These particular breakthroughs and thoughts point directly to the need for a new approach to the understanding of nature. Such a new approach will allow scientists to do two important things: first to conceive the world more realistically than currently possible, and second to explore what are the roots of this approach.[113]

[113] Established science prides itself on sticking only to facts. Since the latter mostly represent conclusions conceived, fragmented and investigated according to prevailing theory, they reflect an idealised picture. Nature constitutes an indivisible whole expressible through ever-shifting parts. Any self-locking objectification of these removes the seal of realism from them. When somebody abolishes wholeness from the description of facts, he perceives them as something *less* than they actually are. He therefore diminishes their realism.

In this chapter we will become a little more specific. The goal will be to explore how we can use the breakthroughs and thoughts of scientists for creating the outline of a new conceptual framework for science as a whole and for scholarship more generally. We will start from a particular difficulty encountered when scientists' work calls on them to break the old habits of conceiving and handling nature. The realization that the discoveries of these scientists themselves point to new ways of thinking, doesn't help. There develops a resistance to novelty, even when there is every reason to accept it.

Why then is there a resistance to justified novelty? The problem starts from a simple fact. *The breakthroughs of modern science point way beyond its conceptual framework.* This has happened in a dual sense. The first touches on the capacity of researchers to translate their quantitative findings into a qualitative overview of the subject they are investigating. For example, biologists discovered long ago that a sponge (hydra) reassembles in water cell by cell after it has been crushed to pulp and passed through a sieve. Has this discovery inspired any thoughts among experimenting biologists on what may explain the re-assembly, what ordering principle may be involved and how it gets the job done?

The second sense in which the breakthroughs of 20th century science point beyond its conceptual framework, touches on the capacity of researchers to discern the theoretical implications of their findings for science as a whole. For example, ontogenesis occurs in organic matter on a much more complex level of organization than it occurs in inorganic. Has this weakened the belief in reductionism as the royal road to explaining nature? Has it inspired any thoughts on the qualitative link between part and whole, or on how to reach the latter through (and in) the former?

In both cases it is clear that researchers find it difficult to translate what they find into *how* they think. They believe that facts are independent of mind and speak for themselves. Werner Heisenberg has described this tendency in relation to quantum mechanics. "When new groups of phenomena compel changes in the pattern of thought," he wrote, "even the most eminent physicists find immense difficulties."[114] One wonders what he would have said had "the new groups of phenomena" concerned not a mere scientific revolution, like quantum mechanics, but a revolution in the very way that science thinks of, and therefore goes about its business.

One cannot know, of course, how Heisenberg would have reacted. But the fact remains that quantum mechanics has only an empirical base. The reality on

[114] Werner Heisenberg, *Across the Frontiers,* Harper & Row, New York, 1974, p 162.

the ground enlightens the researcher. The researcher enlightens the reality on the ground only if (and to the extent that) he perceives it through its own eyes. So it is probable that Heisenberg would have acknowledged the need for inviting nature to tell us more about itself than we presently allow her. In so doing he would have walked in the footsteps of Leonardo da Vinci. Through the latter's insatiable curiosity for how things work, da Vinci was able to develop an excellent grasp of the underlying wholeness that makes them work as they do.

Not just physics, but biology and scholarship in general have exhausted the possibilities of object-mediated understanding. The latter doesn't only distort the picture of reality. It misleads society. As Arthur Koestler points out: "It has been said that science knows more and more about less and less. But that applies only to the fanning-out process of specialization. One would be equally justified in saying that science knows less and less about more and more."[115]

The power of object-mediated understanding

Some epistemologists may protest against the view that 20th-century advances in science have failed to impinge on the type of scientific thinking that is being cultivated. They may point out that object-mediated conception (not to mention the object-mediated rationality it gives rise to) breaks down in quantum mechanics for the extremely small, in relativity for the extremely fast, in chaos theory for the extremely complex and in fuzzy logic for the extremely distinct.

The protestors may even remind us that the demise of object-mediated conceptualization was predicted as far back as 1720 by William Wollaston who wrote: "Both the beginnings and ends of things, the least and the greatest, . . . conspire to baffle us: which way ever we prosecute our inquiries, we still fall in with fresh subjects of amazement and fresh reasons to believe that there are infinitely more [things] behind [visible reality] that will for ever escape our earnest pursuits and deepest penetration."[116]

How can one answer the claim of epistemologists that the great advances in 20th-century physics have changed the way scientists think? They certainly have a point when they claim that object-mediated understanding hasn't prevented science from discovering that in both the microcosm and the macrocosm one can no longer speak of objects in the usual sense. Careful examination, however,

---

[115] Arthur Koestler, *The Roots of Coincidence,* Picador (published by Pan Books) 1974, p 139.
[116] William Wollaston, *The Religion of Nature Delineated,* I. and P. Knapton, 1720 (seventh edition), p 144.

shows that this view applies only to what relativity, quantum mechanics, chaos theory and fuzzy logic have done to the image of reality. It doesn't apply to how people in the field actually conceive this image, leave alone how (and why) they *construct* it as they do.

For example, scientists know perfectly well that the level of organization on which we humans exist, somewhere between the very large and the very small, is just one of many. But they keep trying to fathom the other levels on the basis of a conceptual framework that has been molded entirely by how the human senses function and what they are able to perceive. Thus, most scientists are still convinced that the breakdown of object-based structures in the distant levels of physical organization (like the very small or the very large) is inherent in nature herself, not in their mode of apprehending it or of categorizing it.

And so, such people go in for continuously more complex patterns of interaction and complicated forms of mathematical investigation to explain what they encounter in these "remote" areas. The many paradoxes appearing at the far ends of the spectrum of understanding are the direct product of this tendency. It looks as though non-objects cannot be treated as objects with impunity.

Thinking about ten dimensions in terms of three

How important this discrepancy has become is evident when one reflects on string theory—a typical product of the tendency to apply object-mediated thinking to non-object-based reality.

Only a few years ago string theory stipulated the existence of 28 dimensions. Now it stipulates "only" ten. But the current conceptual framework has been molded by experiences in a three-dimensional world, i.e., in an object-informed reality. When Einstein seemed to have added a fourth dimension (time) to the other three, there was a negative reaction not only in the scientific community, but in the educated public. People simply could not (and still cannot) conceive of a four-dimensional universe with a mindset molded by three-dimensional experiences.[117]

Einstein's relativity raises many fundamental questions about how we conceive reality, not least because he himself, contrary to Lorentz, had stipulated that there will be a change in the conceptual framework of humans approaching the speed of light. Lorentz had come up separately with the same equations as

[117] Three-dimensional experiences are intimately tied up with three-dimensional objects. The three dimensions are responsible for giving objects distinct boundaries, forms, possibilities and functions. These features appear to be permanent, so that the particular objects they refer to are always recognisable. Furthermore, the features are mutually exclusive.

Einstein but had failed to interpret them properly. As David Bohm and F. David Peat point out, the reason for Lorentz' failure is that "he held on to old ways of thinking in new situations that called for fundamental change." [118]

This wasn't due to some special failure of Lorentz'. According to Bohm and Peat, it was due to "the mind's strong tendency to cling to what it finds familiar and to defend it against what threatens seriously to disturb its overall balance."[119] As for Einstein, he dealt with the problem of thinking about a four-dimensional universe with a three-dimensional mindset simply by unifying space and time into a single dimension: space-time. However, it is difficult to imagine how he would have managed to squeeze a ten-dimensional universe into a three-dimensional conceptual framework.

More than any other, this mental squeezing of physical operations into pre-existing theoretical schemes illustrates the conceptual problem of modern physics. Edward Witten, a string theory protagonist, is so bedeviled by it that seven years ago he told Dennis Overbye of *The New York Times*: "The lesson may be that time and space are only illusions or approximations, emerging somehow from something [even] more primitive and fundamental about nature. It's a new aspect of the theory. Whether we are getting closer to the deep principle, I don't know . . . It's plausible that we will one day understand string theory."[120]

That is a strange situation for a string theorist to have ended up in. There are three reasons for this. The first is Witten's admission that string theoreticians don't really understand what they are doing. The second reason is that, not really understanding what they are working on, string theorists expose themselves to the danger of making a lot more mistakes than others who do understand what they are doing. And the third reason (pointed out by Leonard Susskind) is that "string theory has so many solutions that [it opens up] an incredible landscape of possibilities."[121] This is perhaps why cosmologist Lawrence Krauss, typical of a growing number of string theory detractors, has called it "a colossal failure."[122]

Quite regardless of the above, string theorists are positing a series of interlinked profound epistemological questions without even being aware of so doing. For example, is the current conceptual framework capable of grasping what it means to exist without space and time, as Witten suggests? If not, is

---

[118] David Bohm and F. David Peat. *Science, Order and Creativity,* (Routledge, London, 1989, p 21.
[119] Ibid. p 22.
[120] Dennis Overbye, "String Theory May Explain All, but Scientists Remain Perplexed," *The New York Times,* December 17, 2004.
[121] "A theory of everything?" *Nature,* Vol 433, January 2005, p 257.
[122] Ibid.

it desirable (and of course possible) to broaden scientists' current three-dimensional conceptual framework so that it can deal with a ten-dimensional universe on its terms? If that again cannot be done, is it possible to imitate Einstein's example and enter the perceived extra dimensions into the three-dimensional picture?

In so many words, can the current three-dimensional conceptual framework of physics be stretched in a way that it not only accounts for what happens in a ten-dimensional universe, but assists people to actually experience it?[123] This would represent a very important contribution because the main reason we have such good knowledge of the object-mediated world is that we are able to experience it. Can we be expected to acquire good knowledge of a ten-dimensional world without experiencing it?

The price of self-locking objectification

The first thing we must do if we want to find satisfactory answers to just these questions is to examine not so much what consciousness is, but how it operates, why it operates as it does, and how its operations affect our understanding. If we do that we will soon discover that we all engage in a specific mental practice that enables us to reify both the external and the internal world. Under certain circumstances, this practice can be derailed into an exclusive self-centered focus. It has negative long-term effects on the pursuit of truth in any form—scientific or philosophical.

"Self-locking objectification" unfolds in five stages. In the first we pick out those elements from our perceptions that are relevant both to our survival and our unique personal imperatives.[124] In the second stage we concretize these elements. In the third we abstract them from their natural embeddedness in reality.

---

[123] One way to do that would be to consider the additional dimensions (from No 5 to No 10) as mere extensions of the three originally accepted dimensions.

[124] It is here that the most striking qualitative difference between animals and humans comes to light. In both cases the brain acts like an all-powerful filter. It doesn't only allow a small portion of the electromagnetic and sound waves bombarding the senses to come through. It edits out the vast majority of those that do. Life would be impossible without such a filtering process. However, there is a marked difference in how animals and humans treat the filtering process. Animals blindly accept the relevant selection of waves that are admitted into their brains. They are happy merely to survive. Humans occasionally want something more, consciously or subconsciously. Thus, they not only arrive at the conception of a whole, they develop a passion for actually becoming one with it. That is what explains the need for pursuing unification that informs mystics and scientists. Man knows that nature and his unique persona severely restrict his understanding of reality, but he also seeks ways to get around this limitation.

In the fourth, we lock mentally not just into the abstractions of these elements, but into their most obvious conceptual implications. In the fifth stage, finally, we project the abstractions both on all that we subsequently perceive and on how we make sense of it.

The net outcome of developing self-locking objectification is that we are incapable of seeing the world as a whole, across dimensions, potentialities, activities and formal expressions. We construct it as we carve it up in the light of our experience in the middle world, sandwiched between the micro- and the macrocosm.[125]

For example, if we measure the position of a quantum system we obtain a position, i.e. particles; if we measure its momentum we obtain a momentum, i.e. waves; if we measure its charge we obtain a charge, i.e. energy. But all these self-locking objectifications don't allow us to identify a unity at the base of what we observe. By focusing on the particulars, we lose the general picture. We see in terms of exclusions rather than inclusions; of forces rather than adjustments; of influences rather than interpenetrations.

It is not all that different from the situation referred to by Xenophanes in the 6th century BC. In describing the way we project our patterns of understanding onto what we perceive, Xenophanes observed: "The Ethiopians maintain that their gods are snub-nosed and black, the Thracians that theirs have light blue eyes and red hair!"[126]

Synthesis in terms of analysis

That's not the end of the story. Because self-locking objectification has taught us to analyze in order to understand, we are stuck on analytical thinking. It is difficult for us to develop synthetic thinking, even when we are confronted with the need to put things together. Because we have learnt to perceive things exclusively, we don't really compose them, we merely add them up or place them next to one another serially. It is difficult for us to develop inclusive perception, even when all we perceive cries out for it.

The same applies to other conceptual practices. In the physical world we have discovered many non-linear links, but we still use linear ways to study them. Increasingly, we detect dynamic relationship, but we still see this like a series of

[125] An indication of this mean may be derived from the fact that the two universal extremes are separated by 60 orders of magnitude.

[126] Xenophanis, Fragment 16, translated by G.S. Kirk and J. E. Raven.

static states in rapid succession to one another. We have come to learn that reality is shot through with non-local interactions, yet we still insist on studying these with the help of conceptual tools fashioned for the handling of local phenomena.

Arthur Koestler comments on this in the following way: "It is time for us to draw the lessons from 20th-century post-mechanistic science and to get out of the strait-jacket which the 19th century . . . imposed on our philosophical outlook. . . Had that outlook kept abreast with modern science itself, instead of lagging one century behind it, we would have been liberated from the strait-jacket long ago."[127] Incidentally, this was written some 50 years ago!

Many modes of knowing

Nothing of what has been said means that we need a new paradigm, as many theorists maintain. We just need to learn to think in terms of what we apprehend, so that we can then see it as much as possible in its own light. Conversely, we need to stop apprehending in terms of what we think, so that *what* we apprehend can be free to reveal its face. How can that be engineered?

Through an in-depth investigation of consciousness and the ways in which its operations inform what we feel, think and do, including science. Such an in-depth investigation must have two prongs. The first is theoretical.

Just as an object has many levels and aspects of organization, so understanding involves many levels and aspects of conceptualization. In examining a phenomenon, the first step is to establish which level and aspect of conceptualization is used for which level and aspect of organization. The second step is to become clear about which particular level and aspect of both organization and conceptualization are used as starting points for understanding.

Different people start from different levels and emphasize different aspects. It depends on their idiosyncrasy and on circumstance. So long as they are sensitive to the presence of other levels and aspects in both organization and conceptualization, there is clarity and there is communication. Just as nature points to more than form, language points to more than meaning. The problem never is exhaustive analysis. The problem is what informs the analysis, why and how.

Tacit awareness of other levels and aspects below, above, around or beyond the one on which a phenomenon is conceptualized, helps the investigator grasp it far better than if he perceived it in isolation, or through one conceptual framework alone. Phenomena are best understood when apprehended both in

---

[127] Arthur Koestler, *The Roots of Coincidence,* Picador (published by Pan Books) 1974, p 138–9.

themselves and in their embeddedness. One then gets to appreciate them simultaneously, through different modes of knowing.

Thought doesn't depend on bringing together just object-mediated abstractions of the type science exclusively relies on. Other modes of knowing also contribute to the process of thinking, among them prehensions of fuzzy entities; glimpses into the ebb and flow of nature; intuitions of intractable units or patterns; and non-conceptual experiences of things, events or actions. Ordinary objectification, non-local receptivity, intuition, feeling, contemplation and mindfulness all conspire to illumine nature through their silent and seamless interpenetration.

The one mode of knowing doesn't obscure, adulterate, or exclude the other. It deepens, broadens and complements it. One perceives phenomena as they manifest because one also perceives in them more than they manifest—and more than they achieve. Inter-level, inter-aspected, inter-conceptual and inter-attitudinal understanding represent the first steps to a type of holistic approach that doesn't get trapped in image, lost in parts, or stuck in mechanics—*assuming* such exist.

Have consciousness studies failed?

The second prong of an in-depth investigation of consciousness is experimental. It started already in the early eighties through the pioneering work of such people as John Searle, Francis Crick, Antonio Damasio, Joseph Le Doux, Suzan Greenfield, Stewart Hameroff and others. Today, more than 30 years later, we have accumulated lots of information on how the brain works. Even so, we have yet to understand what consciousness is or how it appears—*if* synaptic firing produces it, *if* synaptic firing merely correlates with it or *if* consciousness generates synaptic firing so that the brain then focuses it and enhances it.[128]

The reason we haven't come up with answers to these questions is that our conceptual framework is object-dominated. All the major people involved in consciousness research go about their business as though consciousness is some virus or unknown force that can be discovered and investigated like other viruses or forces. They think in terms of self-locking objectification. Consciousness, they believe, is an objective entity or state—elusive perhaps in its nature like the neutrino—but an entity all the same. With more refined machinery and more sophisticated analysis it cannot but yield its secrets.

---

[128] The planet Venus correlates with the darkening of the sky every evening. But Venus neither produces the darkening of the sky at night, nor is it produced by the darkening of the sky.

Little attention has been given to the fact that consciousness must, before anything else, act like a mirror to its own self. It bridges the famous subject-object divide. We cannot examine it without at the same time becoming conscious of what we are investing in that examination. As Aristotle put it, "understanding is the understanding of understanding."[129]

So let us briefly look at where this notion of self-reflection comes from and how it can help us in our quest of a new conceptual framework for physics to begin with, and for science as a whole a little later.

A consciousness conscious of itself

Aristotle wasn't actually the first exponent of a self-reflective epistemology. It was Socrates. He criticized the thinkers before him because they expounded on nature without first examining their own selves. Without such an examination, Socrates maintained, it is impossible to know what you project from, edit out or value in your perceptions—leave alone your conceptions. As both Plotinus and Goethe reformulated the Socratic principle: the understanding of the knower must be adequate to the thing known.

Of course, on the face of it, science does seek self-reflection. It must be critical of its operations or it fails to achieve what it is supposed to do. However, today self-reflection in science refers mainly to research protocols, to the accuracy of collected information, or to the tampering with results. It doesn't refer to the conceptual foundations underlying research itself.

There isn't even agreement on what exactly constitutes a scientific fact. Andrew Marino points out that science today accepts several kinds of evidence as "scientific." However, people don't agree on which kind is appropriate for which area of research.[130] The old classical saying that "a fact is a fact *is* a fact etc. ad infinitum," seems not to be true after all. A fact is what we agree is a fact.

A degree of self-reflection on the part of future consciousness researchers would allow them to establish a level of discussion that will be better suited for examining their findings. This should also take into account two additional components. The first is experimental data showing robust interaction between

---

[129] Aristotle, *Metaphysics,* 11. 1074.

[130] Andrew Marino, "In the Eye of the Beholder: The Role of Style of Thought in the Determination of Health Risks from Electromagnetic Fields," *Frontier Perspectives,* Vol. 9, No 2, Fall 2000, pp 22–27.

human intention and animate, as well as inanimate, systems.[131] The second factor is the various mental attitudes, professional interests and paradigmatic constraints which shape most thinking in the scientific discussion of consciousness.

Both these components demand of the consciousness researcher to go much deeper than paradigm, psychology, brain research, air tight protocols or even epistemological concerns. A level of understanding needs to be accessed which, for lack of a better word, is here called "pre-epistemic." What exactly happens on that level?

A pre-epistemic examination of objectification

Conception is not possible without perception; perception is not possible without recognition; and recognition is not possible without reification. Thus, if epistemology is concerned with how we know what we know all the way down to representation, pre-epistemology is concerned with how we objectify what we objectify, so that we can know what we do know. Usually objectivity is believed to apply only to how we think about things. It should be applied also to how we apprehend them to begin with. You cannot be objective about the world without being objective about objectivity itself.

The question of objectification relates specifically to Heisenberg's Uncertainty Principle. People usually take it to mean that knowledge in the microcosm is uncertain. Here Heisenberg's principle is taken to mean that we can never know the microcosm in its entirety, or even only a portion of it, through objectification. The same probably goes for the macrocosm.

Of course, objectification is imperative in science. But we need to understand the processes whereby it occurs. Throughout his many papers and books, consciousness researcher Max Velmans has repeatedly drawn attention to the issue of gradual objectification from the unconscious to the pre-conscious and the conscious.[132] Objectification processes in the brain are gradual, in both electrochemical and temporal terms.

---

[131] William A. Tiller, Walter E. Dibble Jr. and Michael J. Kohane, "Exploring Robust Interactions between Human Intention and inanimate/animate systems," *Frontier Perspectives,* Vol. 9, No 2, Fall 2000, pp 6–21. The work of Tiller and collaborators is similar to that of Bob Jahn at Princeton between 1979 and 2007.

[132] The main volume in which Velmans elaborates this theme is his *Understanding Consciousness,* Routledge, London, 2000. Other papers in which Velmans touches on the same theme, are "How Could Conscious Experience Affect Brains?" Imprint Academic, Exeter and "Goodbye to Reductionism," in *Towards a Science of Consciousness II: The Second Tucson Discussions and Debates,* ed. S. Hameroff, A. Kaszniak & A. Scott, MIT Press, Cambridge, Ma, 2008.

The many aspects of objectification

It means that objectification has many aspects and involves several questions. They all need to be thoroughly investigated. We must learn how we objectify the world so that we can then better secure the objective understanding of it.

One question that comes up is how we distinguish among fully objectified entities and entities that haven't yet objectified themselves fully.[133] A second question is whether we ourselves have fully objectified these entities or not. A third is what causes objectification to begin with. Does it depend on the ontological predilection of the apprehending individual, is it an independent process, or is it perhaps a combination of the two? What are the conditions for an external or internal event to thrust itself on our attention regardless of personal predilections?

More importantly, where does the objectification process begin? Could it start during the initial sensing stage, when we merely suspect that something like a virtual particle may be articulating itself? What then is the feeling associated with this initial sensation and to what extent is it woven into the objectification process itself?

Equally important is whether we choose to objectify certain entities rather than others. Or whether (and why) we choose to objectify certain kinds of entities rather than others. Or how we evaluate what we objectify both in itself and in relationship to other entities. Who or what dictates the criteria informing this evaluation?

A language adequate to what it describes

A good part of the answer to these questions depends on whether we extrapolate from vision onto how we work our objectifications into representations, as Aristotle did.[134] Do we perceive our objects as building blocks, or as local manifestations of the whole? This needs to be thoroughly looked into. If we see objects as local manifestations of the whole, we need to examine whether we

---

[133] By "fully objectified entities" are here meant those units of perception which have reached the full expression of their formal potentialities.

[134] Alfred North Whitehead wrote a whole book (*The Concept of Nature,* 1920, *Whitehead Anthology,* Northrop and Cross, eds, Macmillan. New York, 1953) to show that even such seemingly objective concepts as time and space actually originate in the senses and are therefore aspects of conscious experience. They cannot be considered objective components of reality. To illustrate how much we edit what comes in through the eyes, Evan Harris Walker mentions in his "The Nature of Consciousness" (*Mathematical Biosciences,* Vol. 7, 1970, pp 131–178) "that the information carried by the optic nerve occupies ten-to-the-fourth channels [fibers], each capable of transferring about ten-to-the-sixth bits per second!"

are accessing wholeness on its own terms, or we are accessing it only through an expansion of, or reaction to, fragmentation.

Which also forces us to ask: do we really apprehend anything as it is? Can we claim, like Socrates, that there exist "things in themselves"? More significantly, can we say that our abstractions of objects reflect the same qualities as the objects themselves, and if not to what degree? Can we create such symbols as will allow us to both specify and point away from specification, without losing their specificity in the process?

But the most significant question is: do we release our objectifications after they have served their purpose, or do we lock into them, thereby influencing future objectifications? The fact that on the whole we don't release our objectifications, has bedeviled civilization ever since the invention of alphabetic writing, if not earlier. By not releasing our objectifications once we are done with them, we extend the rationale of what we conceive in one area, or at one moment, into other areas or other moments, glossing over possible differences.

Is there objective knowledge?

The little that has been said about the domain of pre-epistemology shows that epistemology too requires fundamental rethinking. This is a theme to which we will be returning throughout this book. The propriety of information cannot depend on some pre-determined conception. It can depend only on the living relevance of you, the researcher, to the circumstances surrounding the subject matter you are researching. That covers equally the present state of the subject you are researching; its relevance to you personally; the whole informing both the object and yourself; and finally, your willingness (and ability) to be critical of all these without wallowing in either doubt or self-assertion.

The universe is multi-aspected and obliging enough to respond to any inquiry into its ways—provided the inquiry has been initiated by the universe itself. The latter must act this way because, as Karl Gustafson points out, "each of us is a relatively coarse observational filter upon a world far more complex and rich than our perceptions will ever allow us to know."[135]

[135] Karl Gustafson, "Time, Temporality, Now," *Journal of Scientific Exploration,* Vol 16 No 2, Summer 2002, p 278–280.

It follows that we can understand the universe only to the extent that we invite it to illumine us.

This doesn't mean that we should abandon the well-tested methods of observing and studying physical reality. It just means that we should stop seeing objectivity in terms of objects. Instead, we should start seeing it in terms of a keen interest in how natural and personal bias skew reality. Since organizational bias is responsible for how nature has evolved and personal bias is responsible for how we bias that bias, getting to know where the first ends and the second begins is the key to objectivity.

That is why the common mathematical language describing reality has only limited applications. As Tony Rothman and George Sudarshan put it: "Because we can make a precise mathematical description of a phenomenon, we fool ourselves into thinking that we have described the physical world."[136] In reality we have described very little of it. Bertrand Russell writes on that: "Physics is mathematical not because we know so much about the world, but because we know so little: it is only its mathematical properties that we can discover."[137]

The scientific philosopher and the philosophical scientist

Not just every object differs; every piece of knowledge does. Specific knowledge constitutes as much a unique entity as the object it illumines. It changes as much as the object. When reality appears tentative, so appears the knowledge of it; when reality appears permanent, a permanent watch is kept over it just in case it turns out not to be permanent. Willard Van Orman Quine says: "Even our epistemological convictions about what it means to acquire knowledge and about the nature of explanation, justification and confirmation—i.e. about the nature of the scientific enterprise itself—may be subject to revision and correction."[138]

Ultimately only three things matter in the pursuit of scientific knowledge. The first is that we keep systems and minds open. The second is that in fragmenting and abstracting nature, we never lose sight of its oneness. The third is that

---

[136] Tony Rothman and George Sudarshan, *Doubt and Certainty,* Helix Books, Reading, Massachusetts, 1998, p 39.

[137] Quoted in Arthur Koestler, *The Roots of Coincidence,* Picador, published by Pan Books, London, 1974, p 99.

[138] Willis W. Harman, "Taking Holons Seriously: Toward a More Adequate Epistemology for the Study of Consciousness," paper presented in the 1994 Tucson Medical School conference *Toward a Science of Consciousness II.*

in pursuing the mathematical description of reality we make certain that what we count doesn't dictate for us what counts.

Plato's well-known dictum in the *Republic* that kings should become philosophers and philosophers, kings,[139] needs some editing to meet the needs of improved understanding in science today. Such an edited version might read as follows:

Scientists should become philosophers and philosophers, scientists. Scientists need to learn more about how to think, thinkers need to learn more about how science operates. Both need to learn more about what informs their science and their thinking. Hence the requirement for a new conceptual framework for science. We want to create a system of understanding that doesn't only illumine the world, but itself as a student of the world. It's the only way to develop the kind of certainty that knows both its area of applicability and its limitations, without mistaking the one for the other.

[139] Plato, *Republic,* 5–473c

Chapter 5

LANGUAGE, KNOWLEDGE AND CONSCIOUSNESS: The search for meaning beyond, but not without, words

Watch your thoughts become your words;
watch your words become your actions;
watch your actions become your habits;
and watch these become your character,
which then becomes your destiny.
Ancient saying (as formulated by Chantal Toporow)

Perhaps we are witnessing the "End of Science"—
in the sense of overcoming a type of rationality
that is no longer appropriate for our times.
Ilya Prigogine

The essence of the crisis of our times is that
we are approaching the limits of our knowledge
of what exists—and now need to turn
our attention to consciousness.
Jonas Salk

So far in this text a number of references have been made to the role of language in the transmission of information and (consequently) the unfolding of knowledge. It is argued that the way we use language reflects the way we handle consciousness: how we understand science, philosophy, long-term human welfare, and even naked reality depends on it. But these references to language represent a mere foretaste. We must understand the role of language a lot better before we can continue with this book.

A more comprehensive overview of language cannot be achieved simply by going deeply into linguistics. It can be achieved best by familiarizing ourselves with the function, the subtlety, and the history of language in general. The first of these areas concerns using words for the objectification of reality. The second protects the user against distorting reality through such objectifications. The third helps one handle objectification as a springboard toward areas of interest previously considered unimportant. Finally, the fourth area pushes us to use words as pointers toward meaning and as reflectors of ongoing processes.

By becoming aware of the role played by the above qualities in the multifaceted operations of language we can better familiarize ourselves with the basic orientation of this text. We will then realize why no concern with consciousness and its role in science or society can prove useful without a deeper and broader understanding of language and its potential.

Language as a tool of human empowerment

Language is often accused of distorting reality. This happens only if, and when, words are used in such a manner that the user locks into them conceptually. If words are not locked into conceptually, if they are used as mere tools for focusing attention on presently significant aspects of reality, and if the user is capable of releasing words from self-locking objectification, they don't obscure anything. They make speakers and writers more aware of aspects of reality of which they would otherwise never become aware.

Words don't create things out of nothing, as idealists maintain. They just make us aware of situations. They help us realize what passes among things and beyond them. This is achieved by indicating the limitations of things, by focusing on their mutual relationships, and by pointing to what goes on beyond them in the things themselves.

Incidentally, the above points about language don't represent an original insight into the function or potential of it. Sanskrit, and to a lesser degree pre-Aristotelian Greek, worked along such lines. An email by Vishnu Narayan Namboodiri, expert on Sanskrit, notes:

> In Sanskrit a word operates on four levels. Two in particular are important—one implicit, the other explicit. On the one level, the word evokes in the listener or writer something beyond form and concrete meaning called "para." On the other level, called Vaikhari, the word becomes audible. The listener hears it literally and understands its meaning explicitly. Naturally, through the sound associated with the word, the Sanskrit speaker is able to trace its meaning back to its origins. In this way he penetrates into what abides beyond

> meaning in meaning itself. He touches again, base with the "para" mentioned above.
>
> Upholders of the Vedic tradition say that the "para" level of word expression represents essential experience. We ultimately transcend the limits of language through language itself. Even so, there is one condition: we must heighten our consciousness so that we can tune into the intimations of the implicit level, which language normally carries.[140]

The above outlook on the use of language explains the ancient belief that words can be used as tools of power. By pointing to things, relationships, qualities and absences or failures, words help us understand more about the tangible world than would be possible without them. The more we know about what obtains beyond the tangible, the better—and the more deeply—do we understand it. For the tangible is but the intangible rendered accessible to the senses.

There is a catch, however. Words function in this way vis-à-vis tangible reality only to the extent that no attempt is made to define them. So long as words merely point to something and then inspire us to sense it directly (i.e., in an unmediated fashion), understanding is possible. When the minute language transforms itself from an agent of communion to a tool of communication, this becomes impossible. Language then no longer explains the world. It simply makes it accessible to the senses—and rather poorly at that.

Investigating the investigators

Such language is indicative of the current human plight. Two schools of thought pronounce themselves on the question. The first maintains that what we say or write about science, reality or philosophy is all that matters. The second maintains that what matters more than what we say, is what words invite us to recognize. Where we start out from and why is more significant than where we end up and how. Tell me where you stand and I will tell you what, how far, and in what direction you see.

Let's take this line of thinking a little further.

In reading the numerous articles and books on consciousness currently available, one feels that the authors consider language a given. As long as grammar and syntax are correct and words are properly chosen, language can

[140] Vishnu Narayan Namboodiri, in personal email, March 2, 2009.

represent accurately all that the authors have discovered, and all that can be said, about the research subject.

The belief in the representational power of language needs to be qualified, however, particularly when one treats consciousness as though it is just one more aspect of physical reality. Discussing consciousness without consciousness of what underpins the discussion, constitutes an epistemic error of the first order. It also reflects a conceptual contradiction. As the only term, which bridges the subject-object divide, consciousness demands that we both exteriorize and interiorize what comes to mind, all in one go. Object and subject act as mirrors to one another because both are equally real.

The basic premise behind this position is simple: if we want to be serious about investigating consciousness, we must use language in a manner adequate to the task. That is, we must handle it in the same contradistinguishing manner with which consciousness handles reality, so that language is empowered to reflect consciousness back on us. It abstracts at the same time as it experiences; it embraces at the same time as it transcends; it divides at the same time as it integrates; and finally, it reasons at the same time as it intuits.

This seemingly contradistinguishing aspect of language will help us deepen our understanding in ways that do justice to the non-local, non-temporal, non-linear and super-formal functions of consciousness. We will discover what it means to point to something recognizable, and simultaneously to point away from it.

Contradistinguishing language allows all that to happen—and a lot more. Each moment, event, case, or fact is apprehended not only in its uniqueness, but as an expression of the dynamic processes leading up to it and the interactive wholeness sustaining it. Though seemingly fixed, words also elude their semantic function. They do this in keeping with how nature herself eludes the very forms she creates. We name things and simultaneously we suggest what lies beyond their names, even beyond naming itself.

Reverting to contradistinguishing (or ambiguous) language

We don't need to look for new terms, or new modes of expression, to bring about such an ontological change in our use of language. We only need to rediscover what words are ultimately for, what conceptual mode each usage presupposes and how every mode complements, and enriches, every other. Comprehension shouldn't be a closed circle. It should open up to aspects, susceptibilities and considerations not immediately apparent. It should be inter-conceptual, inter-rational, trans-attitudinal, and cross-explanatory. In other words, it should be multimodal.

How we conceive the world is directly linked to how we use words and think with them. Language molds thinking only to the extent that thinking molds language. If we think differently, words function differently, even when they sound the same. The thinking that has ceded its power to language is the thinking that has stopped being thoughtful. It has defeated its purpose and belied its creative potential. Definition doesn't catalyze meaning. Meaning catalyzes definition.

Of course, abandoning object-mediated language isn't easy for the Westerner. Particularly not in the English-speaking world with its still outspoken preference for logical positivism, language analysis and empiricism. And particularly not since the English attitude toward language is partly justified as a reaction to the conceptual excesses of monotheistic religion, medieval scholasticism and Renaissance esotericism. Despite this justification, a science seeking multimodality upholds the contradictory approach to language.

The power of pre-literate language

How does linguistic contradistinction work? How does it manage to fragment and in the same breath to unify the world? For us today, words are seen as the backbone of communication.[141] Indeed, they are seen as the only vehicle of communication. But that isn't the way other cultures, or past ages, understood and used words. For them it was possible, indeed necessary, to use words in unclear or ambiguous ways.

For example, in the Uroaltaic languages, meaning is far more implicit than it is in the Indo-European group. Whereas in the latter meaning depends on structure and linearity, in the former it depends more on culture, personal involvement and direct experiences. This happens because the Uroaltaic linguistic program works very much in ways informed by the heavily nuanced linguistic practices of non-literate societies.

The Greeks resisted writing for a very long time after its adoption in the eastern Mediterranean. The reason for this is that they wanted to avoid the crystallization of both meaning and expression which alphabetic writing introduces. So strong was their opposition to this that when the Greeks finally succumbed,

[141] In this sense our use of language is out of synch with our neurophysiology.

mainly for practical reasons, to alphabetic writing, they often treated written texts homeopathically. They incorporated the dynamic and holistic features of pre-literate speech into their poetry and prose.

This tendency is exemplified in Plato's definition of wholeness. He says it is that which allows one to establish the proper relationship of parts both to one another and to the larger framework enfolding them. Ambiguous language constitutes the tool by which wholeness expresses itself in partiality without, for that reason, betraying either its own ultimate nature, or crystallizing its own self-contradictory expressions.

From zero to infinite and multiple meaning

Besides pointing to wholeness, self-contradictory language also secures two functional advantages over its conventional counterpart. The first is that it qualitatively enriches meaning by incorporating a sense of what the semantic function excludes by its very nature. Intuition is directly implicated here. The second advantage is that self-contradictory language avoids building up meaning systematically, as Bertrand Russell believed that language should. Very simply, contradiction doesn't admit that there is such a thing as an ultimate unit of meaning.

Instead, ambiguousness starts *from* meaning as an indistinct feeling for something which gradually emerges to view. Once this indistinct feeling has surfaced, the contradictory mind dictates the choice of words; the choice of words doesn't dictate the content of the object that has surfaced. At best they may refine it.

The Greek term "ennoia" (meaning) explains why this happens. "Ennoia" is composed of the prefix "en," which signifies "in," and the noun "nous," which signifies "mind." It follows that meaning for pre-Aristotelian Greeks was what you have *in mind*—literally; it wasn't what comes out of it. One word can signify many things, many words can signify one thing. Which happens depends on the exact mix of conceptions and levels of description that has become relevant at a particular moment and the extent to which this mix remains rooted in wholeness for the person becoming aware of it.

Meaning that becomes meaningful

Experiencing meaning in this non-abstractable manner leads to a special paradox which befuddles linear thinkers. It is that when a person truly opens up to what wells up through him as he talks or writes, even the wrong words carry the right meaning. On the contrary, if the speaker suppresses what emerges, or has nothing welling up in him to begin with, even the right words carry for him the wrong meaning.

Indeed, expression becomes meaningful in the literal sense only to the extent that it links specific conceptions to the whole from which they surge out of. When this link remains active, meaning doesn't only trigger clear writing, it becomes transparent to what the clear writing fails to convey.

Meaning is a product of consciousness. Thus, its expression through language is something that cannot be ignored. Particularly not in a text that argues for a need to establish a *self-reflective interdisciplinary science of consciousness* for striking at the heart of the current plight of our civilization.

We cannot work on consciousness without being simultaneously conscious of how we conceive our task to begin with, and why we conceive it in the way we do. Even if one day we are able to collect all the facts about consciousness and work them into a coherent whole, we still will not have an overview of the subject. Consciousness can be understood in terms of facts only to the extent that facts can be understood in terms of consciousness.

The re-humanization of language

How then are we to proceed?

The first step is to encourage people to become more aware of the relationship between public affairs and consciousness. The more our awareness of this relationship grows, the better will we be able to handle our public affairs, and the better we handle our public affairs, the more will our awareness of this aspect grow. Increased awareness—not just adequate information—will become the key condition for conducting not only public affairs, but personal ones as well.

To push for such a development, two things need to happen. The first is to sensitize ourselves to a more suggestive use of language. At least for the time being, language mirrors the depth and breadth of our awareness. We are totally dependent on words for communicating with one another. Whatever else we do to improve our predicament, we have to start from talking about it, i.e. we have to resort to verbal or written communication.

The second step toward increasing awareness of the role of language in public and private affairs, is to establish the *self-reflective interdisciplinary science of consciousness* this book is essentially about. This will facilitate the use of a more suggestive language, while at the same time facilitate its use as an instrument for our increasing humanization. To attempt humanizing our existence on this planet represents the most urgent task we can pursue.

Language, reality and wholeness

One way to push ourselves toward a more suggestive use of language is to sensitize ourselves to certain qualities built into classical Chinese. A striking example is the famous opening sentence of the Tao Te Ching. It is rendered in Western languages as "the Tao which can be spoken of is not the real Tao."

Some scholars of Classical Chinese disagree with this rendition. One in particular, Tew Bunnag, a Thai mindfulness meditation teacher who studied Classical Chinese in Cambridge, maintains that the above translation of the opening sentence of the Tao Te Ching reflects the either/or logic of the West. It doesn't add up to what a Chinese person of the classical period would have understood by the original Chinese formulation.

Such a person, Bunnag explains, would have interpreted these words as "the Tao which can be spoken of may, or may not, be the real Tao." Which of the two contradictory versions he adopts would have depended on two conditions: how deeply infused by the Tao he was himself in his quest for it, and how able he was not to get stuck in the "messages" he may have received as a result of his ontological connection *with* and love of the Tao.[142]

It follows that the practices of fragmentation and self-locking objectification play an important role in the use of language. They relate closely to the qualitative difference between logic and reason.

Without fragmentation and self-locking objectification there is no logic, in the formal sense. Logic depends on two aptitudes. The first is for isolating self-locking objectifications, that is, cutting them loose from their embeddedness in the whole. The second is for restructuring the objectifications according to the relationships observed by the senses when the individual pushes for utilitarian goals.

Now let us look at reason. It too depends on two aptitudes. But they are different from those applicable to logic. The first is for discovering what kind of relationships one actually obtains in nature. The second is for discovering how these relationships grow out of an emptiness that is sensed rather than intellectually conceived—or if it is intellectually conceived, it is not conceptually locked into.

The living reality of the present

What we comprehend by language, to what purpose we use it and how we take up other additional usages, should help us to understand the difference between

[142] By Tew Bunnag in a private conversation with the author.

logic and reason. But most people don't see that difference. They conceive logic and language as two closely linked exercises in the manipulation of symbols and relationships that are not only objectifiable as such, but generally applicable.

The Western mind assumes that nature works and man thinks like a clockwork orange. But after chaos theory, quantum physics, fuzzy logic and most of all Albert Einstein, Kurt Gödel and Iain McGilchrist, it has become obvious that nature doesn't work like logicians think it does. Their attitude is strongly influenced by the way they understand the use of language. It reflects a totally different approach to that of the ancient Chinese.

Bunnag's take on the sensibilities of classical Chinese is important. It brings into focus what words can trigger in the minds of people and why. Indeed, through classical Chinese we become aware of the key difference between two types of language. The one is informed by the right hemisphere (for example, Chinese, the Uroaltaic group, Hopi, Inuit or very old Greek). The other type is informed by the left hemisphere, as has happened in the West since the triumph of the logical approach after Aristotle.

The art of not being literal

Let us briefly examine the multi-aspected function of language.

The Chinese and the Inuit examples lend themselves particularly well to such an inquiry. Let us first touch on the Chinese case.

The classical Chinese tended to leave important issues open-ended. Ambiguity was not seen as a failure, as it has become in the West. It was seen as a means for comprehending reality more realistically, in the context of the present circumstances. On the whole, specifics were not defined exhaustively. Details were just implied. If there was a practical need for making specifics explicit, this would and could be done. Usually, however, the implied specifics became so self-evident through the seeking process, that there was no need for spelling them out literally.

This meant that things in ancient China were conceived in the living reality of the present moment. They were apprehended in actual space-time, without losing the sense of what eludes space-time. Seekers were helped by language to counteract successfully the tendency of the abstracting mind to identify with its objectifications and then to lock into them. In this manner, classical Chinese (itself a written language) managed to keep alive the dynamic poly-semantics of pre-literate cultures.

This equally explains why for the ancient Chinese the purpose of a dialogue with others, or with nature, was to maintain the openness of the exchange. They cherished a free space in which to dance actuality into manifestation, without needing to choreograph it.

Teasing reality into concrete manifestation

In such a mental climate people were in a position to adapt their formulations to what nature actually demanded. They placed less emphasis on how they themselves apprehended the objectifications of reality. Words were not employed as distinct carriers of meanings. They were employed as *directions in which to look for meaning*, or as indicators of where to look for such directions. Sentences didn't describe the outline of a situation. They suggested the possibility of discovering what the outline is when it became necessary for them to do so.

Another aspect also worth looking at is that what takes place in the dance-space of meaning doesn't affect just the pragmatics of the subject being discussed. It also affects the pragmatics of the other individuals engaged in the exercise. It collapses the framework within which the exercise takes place, and it focuses on the degree to which the seekers are in a position to experience what the messages actually convey.

How amenable seekers are to learning beyond the mere acquisition of information was always a key issue for the Chinese. The ability to be enriched equally by the present circumstances surrounding their search, by the history of these circumstances, and by the understanding of the same on the part of possible fellow seekers, was crucial to the outcome of their quest.

To the Chinese the above issues were extremely important. But we today need to look elsewhere as well.

For example, to what extent and why do objectifications invite new insights by the individuals making them, or by third persons? How sensitive is their understanding of what the other individuals, or nature itself, is able, half-able or completely unable to express? Can such people recognize what we today in the West call "factual reality," irrespective of their specific individual conditioning?

To answer questions of this type we need to delve more deeply into the difference between logic and reason.

Formal logic would have been inconceivable in eighth or seventh century BC China, leave alone earlier. Man still lived in a mythic world, precluding any wholesale utilitarian abstractions of the type that presently form the basis of abstract thought. Indeed, specialists have concluded that 6,000–8,000 years ago there were no nouns—or at least nouns were not used in the same way that Westerners use them today. They functioned as dynamic versions of the static nouns used for hinting at reality. As Chantal Toporow points out, these verb-like nouns "are inherently designed for being in the 'now' as evidenced . . . by the lack of tenses and [the presence of] minimal conjugations."[143]

Nouns embody the par excellence expression of self-locking objectification. They solidify conceptions into permanent "things." Before their appearance, the realities to which they referred to were indicated as manifestations of an ongoing spontaneous creativity. They were not perceived as finished products.

In this sense, very old Greek must have resembled Classical Chinese. It too was a language that felt its way to, and through, reality. It didn't describe things, as it does today. It evoked them in the depths of human consciousness.

This explains why, as the Greek worldview moved from process to structure, their language became increasingly rule orientated. This also explains why Aristotle (and much more Theophrastos) felt the need to model the laws of formal logic on the dictates of Greek grammar and syntax as employed in their days.

Thus, one can cogently claim that Heraclitus, and later Socrates, were attuned to a much more "Chinese" use of language. For these two philosophers, intelligence, along with consciousness, is innate. It manifests through the extent of interest in the external and internal world, beyond the basic biological imperatives for adaptation, survival and procreation.

Where do all these notions of and insights into a pointer language lead?

The limitations of our language are not the limitations of our world, as Ludwig Wittgenstein put it. The limitations of our world are the limitations of our language. Reason doesn't lead to truth. Truth leads to reason.

Language objectifies and abstracts whole blocks of reality. But it does so only to the extent that our culture instructs us to understand things in terms of objectified units.

On the other hand, language equally reveals how our sensibilities make us apprehend reality beyond the words attempting to encapsulate it. Knowledge goes way beyond cognition, especially when we are able to sense what words fail to convey—and why they do.

We are not programmed to lock into our objectifications of reality by nature. Rather, we are programmed to engage it as we need to. Then (and then only) are we able to both think about particular things as they require and to handle them effectively.

[143] Chantal Toporow, in personal email, September 9, 2011.

Of course, cognition can be trustworthy. But only to the extent that the individual constantly maintains his ability to pull the carpet from under his formulations. The individual then knows what he doesn't, and because he doesn't. It all becomes a question of how and why such a person objectifies the world. He doesn't comprehend the particular without at the same time sensing the whole that informs it, surrounds it and compels it.

He realizes that each of us creates his own prison, including the key to unlock it.

Chapter 6

THE EVOLUTION OF CONSCIOUSNESS AND ITS REVERSALS: From the big bang to date

We may be on the verge of a historic understanding of our minds,
both the conscious and the unconscious sides.
Bernard J. Bars

Often it becomes necessary to try very hard intellectually for before humankind
is able to understand a concept in its purest form—
i.e. move all those irrelevant additives
from the concept that have veiled it from . . . people.
Gotlob Frege

The historian is likely to have a better insight into the
thought process of a scientist than the scientist himself.
Albert Einstein

This chapter presents a selective chart of the evolution of consciousness from the beginning of its operation to date. The chart attempts to stimulate an interest to familiarize the reader with both the pitfalls and the opportunities on the road to ever-increasing objectification, which lies at the heart of evolution. By enabling the reader to become aware of these pitfalls and opportunities through the chart, he may avoid the first and embrace the second. Stripped of self-locking practices, objectification represents the key to the opening up and the qualitative transformation of consciousness.

We humans once existed for the sake of interpenetrating with the world, and thus for rendering it meaningful. When we focused on particular entities or states, we sensed the whole informing them. Thus, the fragments we worked with reflected the quality of wholeness. Once we began locking into the objectification of particular entities, we lost this ability. Suddenly things were only things. Satisfaction grew out of possessing them or knowing them, not out of contemplating the wholeness underlying them. From merely sensing that which existed, we moved to making sense of it.

Our task today is to learn how to do both these things simultaneously. We need to make sense of entities on the basis of what we sense their relationship to wholeness is. Familiarizing ourselves with this will express the essence of our humanity as both rational and intuitive beings. By intuition, which arises through communion with the whole, we will penetrate to what is going on in the entities themselves. By reason, which arises through communion with the parts, we will handle that which is going on in the entities to their best advantage.

On their own, objectifications are never the problem. Indeed, without them we wouldn't be able to exist or grow. As suggested repeatedly in this book, the problem always is that we don't know how to deal with the objectifications once they are formed: how long we should retain them; how to apply them in our daily life; how they should shape our thoughts and actions; and under what circumstances we should allow them, or invite them, to change.

A liberated person uses objectifications as much as one trapped in his conditioning. But the liberated person is aware of the limitation of his objectifications; he doesn't allow them to eclipse non-objects. For such a person, language becomes just as transparent to what can be said as to what cannot. Understanding for him covers both the immediate and the eternal, the part and the whole, the tangible and the intangible. It transcends information, since without a self-locking mechanism, objectification naturally points to what lies beyond its specifiable content.

The stations in the evolution of consciousness presented below are those illustrating most revealingly the close relationship between the ways reality is objectified and the extent of our ability to comprehend what goes beyond its objectification. To facilitate the process of understanding this, the passages most relevant to the opening or the closing of the mind are presented in bold letters.

However, the reader will have to interpret himself the two major implications of the close relationship between the ways reality is objectified and the extent of his own ability to sense the whole informing objectified reality. He will have to discern by himself if each specific station reveals an important twist in his consciousness, as well as how this twist relates to previous or subsequent similar changes.

The reader will also have to decide what this specific twist may have contributed to the expansion or the contraction of his consciousness in the period it took place, and if merely acknowledging what happened in this respect satisfies him as a concerned human being.

In other words, the reader shouldn't abandon himself either to the author's judgement, or to a linear comprehension of the unfolding of consciousness. He will have to become as conscious of his own thinking about it as the author is about his. Just as one cannot write a history of consciousness without becoming conscious of what criteria and assumptions he is investing in the enterprise, so one cannot read that history without becoming conscious of what his own criteria and assumptions are, and why.

There can be no reflectivity without self-reflectivity—all the way down to what goes beyond the self in the self itself.

Chart of the evolution of consciousness

Here now are listed some of the stations in the long and convoluted history of the unfoldment of consciousness. Numerous stations could be added. Those have been chosen that bear more significantly on the case for a consciousness that grows both dynamically and in dialogue with itself. For some of the information reflected by these stations, the author is indebted to Richard Tarnas. His *The Passion of the Western Mind: Understanding the Ideas That Have Shaped Our World View* has been an eye-opener and guiding light for the author ever since it was first published in 1991.

The list of stations in the unfoldment of consciousness runs as follows:

- 13.8 billion years ago. Physical reality rises to **a new order of existence**. Time and space inject themselves into formerly compact matter, breaking it up and pushing it (initially) toward chaos.

- A short while later. Former compactness gives rise to **attraction among dispersed particles**. They link up in space and time as non-spatial and non-temporal connections reassert themselves.

- A short while later. Gases collapse into vortex-like formations and then separate out into stars. Some 50 billion galaxies are created. **Formlessness begins to work itself back into form.**

- 12.5 billion years ago. Quarks **assemble** into electrons and protons, these into atoms, elements and molecules and these into all that today concerns physicists, chemists and cosmologists.

- 4 billion years ago. The Earth comes into being as a further stage in the process of restoring lost primordial compactness. Matter organizes itself into **ever more complex aggregates**.

- 3.5 billion years ago. Life appears on Earth through primitive single cell organisms to start with and cells with nuclei later. Ability to **sense external events at a distance emerges**.

- 2.5 billion years ago. A great oxidation event restructures the atmosphere. A new kind of single cell emerges. Life is now capable of changing its background. From product it becomes producer.

- 500,000,000 years ago. Appearance of first multi-cellular highly varied organisms. Recognition of the biological advantages in establishing and promoting **cooperation among cells**.

- 400,000,000 years ago. First appearance of animals capable of storing food and seeking shelter. **Mind emerges** as the physical mechanism whereby this task is carried out.

- 365,000,000 years ago. Some fish begin to hoist themselves out of the sea to eat plants and arthropoids on dry land. First **sign of non-local knowledge** in the service of survival.

- 20,000,000 years ago. Enter Afropithecos, Turkanapithecos, Proconsul and Nacholapithecus. Their **brains are mostly larger and more complex** than those of other mammals of similar size.

- 9,000,000 years ago. Ardipithecos Ramidus arrives on stage. He is able both to move from tree to tree like the apes and to walk upright. **Curiosity pushes him to explore** more of his environment.

- 8,000,000 years ago. Proto-man makes his entry in ape-like garb. His mobility appears greater than it need be **and his intelligence is more pronounced** than mere survival demands.

- 6,000,000 years ago. Proto-man strengthens earlier primate social interaction patterns. He introduces ways of permanently securing **mutual stimulation and awareness**.

- 5,000,000 years ago. Childhood is extended throughout life in proto-humans. **Curiosity** becomes cardinal feature of existence, as it encourages **seeking**, triggers intuition and invites **play**.

- 4,500,000 years ago. Extension of sexual drive in females beyond the yearly cycle to match a similar male drive. A **pattern-breaking tendency increases exposure to different stimuli** and qualities.

- 4,000,000 years ago. Bipedalism becomes principal agent of locomotion in primates. **Overview** of surrounding terrain, **awareness** of changing horizons and spatial **perspective** now a reality.

- 3,500,000 years ago. First anatomical signs of language capacity strengthen brain lateralization, as well as parallel functions. Cognitive skills and symbolic uses begin to outstrip **genetic information**.

- 3,000,000 years ago. Language capacity enhances curiosity and broadens understanding. **Learning becomes life supporting and skill enhancing.** To secure it premature birth is introduced.

- 2,500,000 years ago. Birth of Homo Habilis, first skillful tool maker. He provides indications of **volitional brain activity**, as opposed to that of animals, which is predominantly autonomic.

- 1,700,000 years ago. Birth of Homo Erectus. Roaming broad areas, he becomes more aware of **nature's extensive variability**. A sense of wholeness seems to guide his every move.

- 1,600,000 years ago. Major improvements in stone implements. Their abrupt, widespread and (relatively) concurrent appearance suggests **a more pronounced non-local-mind-effect** at work.

- 1,500,000 years ago. Beginning of great exodus from Africa—not only as a result of climatic change. **Wandering on foot stimulates wondering** (and opening up) **of mind**.

- 1,100,000 years ago. Use of hand axes extends to new human needs. Methods for igniting fire discovered. Capability for **recognizing possibilities and opportunities in nature** grows.

- 1,000,000 years ago. Many well-crafted unused hand axes discovered. **Seen as a manifestation of the power of wholeness**, these axes become veneration objects, later called "gods" by the Egyptians.

- 500,000 years ago. A site in Boxgrove, England, reveals greatly improved butchering skills. The orderliness they reflect shows **a capacity for increased abstraction and rational action**.

- 400,000 years ago. Highly effective wooden spears found near Hamburg, Germany. They indicate an **understanding of aerodynamic principles** and a specified use of tools for their production.

- 300,000 years ago. Speech becomes more articulate and symbolic. Information is transmitted in vague terms, thus inviting individuals to **sense specific reality without abstracting it**.

- 250,000 years ago. The Levallois carving technique triggers a conceptual leap. Recognition of accidental flint shapes is replaced by **recognition of potential shapes *before* chiseling**.

- 100,000 years ago. Brain reaches maximum capacity of 1,500 cc. Senses interpenetrate synaesthetically, reflecting **the ontological interpenetration of nature herself**.

- 90,000 years ago. Relative absence of artefacts signals an **age of contentment** in simplicity. No need for further improvement felt. Man is at last happy to live from day to day with what he has.

- 75,000 years ago. Evidence of shamanic practices in the Ukraine. Symbolism consciously used for combating unnecessary objectifications and for pointing to non-objectifiable reality.

- 70,000 years ago. First signs of representative art in the garb of painted and carved images. **Form signals what goes beyond it.** Man sees himself as responsible co-creator of the world.

- 50,000 years ago. Haematitis mines dug in Africa. Conception of cosmos in terms of a female being (not a goddess.) **Heaven, Earth and man probably viewed as inseparable whole.**

- 42,000 years ago. Eruption of creativity in bone, wood, stone, ceramics and weaving in Africa spreads beyond it. Utilitarian **abstraction** and **manipulation** becomes even more evident than earlier.

- 40,000 years ago. Sophisticated artistic carvings appear on deer-horns, stones and ivory. Non-utilitarian, these carvings suggest a **longing for the wholeness** symbolized by the carvings.

- 35,000 BC Cro-Magnon, an individualistic and technologically advanced human specimen from central Asia, moves west and south. **He is cunning, creative, sophisticated, and ruthless.**

- 32,000 years ago. First cave paintings in southern France. Beginning of **initiatory practices**. Mystical experience used for stemming increased signs of cultural self-locking **objectification**.

- 25,000 years ago. Small statues found of cosmic beings in the form of women, one of them with an initiatory veil over her head. Once again, **oneness of humans with the universe** is implied.

- 25,000 years ago. Carved bone found in France, which could have been used for keeping a track of seasons: a proto-calendar. **External technology begins to supplant innate knowledge.**

- 13,000 BC. Introduction of animal domestication and husbandry. Handling of practical affairs stops being intuitive. Not only are **concepts objectified**, but thoughts, goals and strategies as well.

- 10,000 BC. Agriculture invented. Self-locking objectification begins to transform culture. **Homes, horizons and practices are now fixed.** Economy, laws, gods and cities assert themselves.

- 9,500 BC. Farming and town building begin to favor **objectively-informed rational action**, whereas earlier hunting and fruit gathering practices had favored **free-flowing interaction**.

- 9,000 BC. Emergence of female earth goddesses. People start forgetting symbolic nature of myths. They **interpret them literally**. Human and animal sacrifices are thus introduced.

- 9,000 BC. First archaeological evidence for **systematic warfare** along the northern coast of Africa from west to east. War technology improves. Building of the walls of Jericho.

- 8,500 BC. Birth of abstracting science through geometry and astronomy. Realization that **objectification reveals as much as it conceals** introduces notion of sacred science.

- 8,000 BC. First tool for abstracting science found in the Congo: **a calculator** consisting of a bone with etched lines and a small blue stone wedged into one of them.

- 7,000 BC. Older balance of the two brain lobes begins to change. Right brain, with its emphasis on intuition, starts to fall under the sway of the left **objectifying brain**, with its emphasis on reason.

- 6,000 BC. Showcase for a benevolent society in Chatal Huyuk, Turkey. Self-locking objectification consciously guarded against through **mystery plays and ceremonial practices**.

- 5,500 BC. Effective irrigation systems and cereal mutations or hybridizations introduced in Iran. Mere existence no longer suffices. **Exploitation of opportunities becomes a skill.**

- 5,200 BC. Patriarchal Semitic tribes from the Zagros mountains invade large areas in the Middle East, killing off other tribes and devastating the land. **Land grabbing and greed become endemic.**

- 4,500 BC. Environmental disaster in the Sahara forces humans out of Africa. Survival now invites even more violent ego-mediated solutions. **Objectification hardens**, informing all human action.

- 3,600 BC. New technological explosion. The wheel, plough, animal-driven locomotion, new building techniques and irrigation systems become dominant. Man increasingly **manipulates** nature.

- 3,500 BC. **Individualism asserts itself even in death.** In earlier times people were buried in communal graves. Now they are buried in individual tombs, with their personal belongings.

- 3,300 BC. Invention of pictographic writing. Increase in overt self-consciousness—and self-locking objectification. **Systematic knowledge further undercuts experienced reality.**

- 3,200 BC. New conceptualizing and problem-solving capabilities invite **increased abstraction and organization of activities**. Systematic observation leads to geometry, the calendar and astronomy.

- 3,100 BC. Vyasa composes the epic *Mahabharata*. It describes **the battle between light and darkness**, plus the help extended to the former when dedication to light is whole-hearted.

- 3,000 BC. Monotheism, sacred books and **absolute truth are born**. Objectification gets entrenched. Belief takes over from experiential religion. The latter dwindles or goes underground.

- 2,800 BC. Egyptians start building pyramids holistically. They use a non-objectifiable **trial-and-error method**, without mathematically pre-calculating shapes, angles, stresses etc.

- 2,700 BC. Egyptians and Persians try to **restore the initial conditions of creation** for worshipers. These conditions are believed equal to what existed **before self-locking objectification set in**.

- 2,000 BC. Minoan civilization reinstates sacred society of Chatal Huyuk. **Images point toward, as well as away from, what they show.** Central authority not visible, but present behind the scenes.

- 1,500 BC. Menhirs and stone circles set up in Britain and continental Europe as epiphanies of divine powers. Worshippers assisted in **re-experiencing the divine in wild nature**. Stones symbolize spirits.

- 1,450 BC. Overtly utilitarian approach to nature introduced in Greece. Earth Goddess cult abandoned. Mycenean civilization implodes by **totally destroying Greek south**.

- 1,300 BC. Invention of alphabetic writing. Left hemisphere grows larger. In addition, **erosion of "right" qualities by left quantities** undermines their nature and function.

- 9th cent. BC. First sacred Hebrew texts enhance power of the written word. Through the Tower of Babel myth, such texts also **warn against the unheeding objectification of truth**.

- 8th cent. BC. Babylon introduces **first complex mathematical calculations**. They are perceived as accurate symbols of reality, capable of providing man with an improved representation of it.

- 8th cent. BC. Citizens in Greek city-states display **an aptitude to criticize social structures and beliefs**. Democracy and philosophy are born. From now onward nothing is considered a given.

- 7th cent. BC. Using mythical terminology, Hesiod outlines in his *Theogony* **the first history of objectification**. Zeus is thereby conceived as unifier of opposing forces.

- 7th cent. BC. Another Vyasa composes the *Brahma Sutras*. In them he resurrects the philosophy of his great older namesake. **Non-duality** is proclaimed as desirable for the second time.

- 7th cent. BC. **Myth in Greece begins to lose its symbolic role.** Result: religion is divested of its self-initiatory role. Two centuries later classical theatre attempts to revive it.

- 6th cent. BC. Buddha, Lao Tse and Heraclitus speak out for universal flux and uncertainty. It is unrealistic to cling to anything. For the three sages, this is **the only knowledge worth obtaining**.

- 6th cent. BC. For the first time, Thalis of Miletos **replaces intuitive mythic accounts with rational scientific explanation**. Demonstration appears not only desirable, but possible.

- 6th cent. BC. Anaximander scores three firsts: an **objective account of creation, a theory of evolution, and the notion of the quantum vacuum**. Things emerge from it, but also return thereto.

- 6th cent. BC. Confucius speaks out for **harmony**. He believes it **can be objectified in rules** which, in addition to wisdom, goodness, respect and courage, bode for a good society.

- 6th cent. BC. Pythagoras becomes the first thinker to advocate **a theory of everything** by claiming mathematics to be—and to describe—the essence of all. He introduces the term "philosophy."

- 6th cent. BC. Kanaada in India encourages reductionism by claiming for the first time that **all matter is made of atoms**. Change occurs only in the forms binding matter together.

- 5th cent. BC. Xenophanes expresses twin belief that human understanding is completely Conditioned. However, **freedom from conditioning is not only possible, but desirable**.

- 5th cent. BC. With roots in a much earlier age, the universal flood myth warns against **the dangers of adopting a purely object-mediated** (and thus utilitarian) **approach** to life.

- 5th cent. BC. Zenon of Elea confounds objectifying philosophers by introducing his famous paradoxes. Their purpose is to show that self-locking **objectification contradicts itself**.

- 5th cent. BC. Socrates uses **philosophical homeopathy** to undercut objectification. He launches **a secret war on reason** by revealing the limitations of definable entities, concepts and relationships.

- 4th cent. BC. The myth of the Hyperboreans offers the blueprint of an **enlightened society**. Plato discusses Atlantis as **a warning against anything that is less than enlightened**.

- 4th cent. BC. Aristotle invents **formal logic**. At the same time, he warns that several "languages" are required for understanding nature, not just mathematics. **Concepts can entrap the mind.**

- 4th cent. BC. Pyrro of Elis introduces Jain mystical teachings into Greece in the form of Skepticism. **Man should avoid all judgments** and live unperturbed as each day requires.

- 4th cent. BC. Perhaps influenced by Parmenides, Hippocrates first introduces concerns for the proper **relationship of theory to experience and observation** in his treatise *Precepts*.

- 3rd cent. BC. Eratosthenes of Alexandria calculates the Earth's circumference. **Indirect scientific thinking introduced** under the guidance of constructive rational analysis.

- 2nd cent. BC. Latin translations of Greek philosophy restrict its experiential message in favor of a conceptual one. **Meaningfulness loses out to meaning, thoughtfulness to logic.**

- 1st cent. BC. Romans mold a system of **logic based on rules inspired from their strict legal system**, rather than those drawn from grammar and syntax, as the Greeks did.

- 1st cent. AD. Teachings of Jesus of Nazareth and of Mahayana Buddhism pronounced. **Love tied to understanding**, while **compassion is seen as evoking profound personal insight**.

- 2nd cent. AD. On its way to becoming formulated, Christianity too divests myth of its older self-initiating function. **Literal interpretation** now prepares the ground for **dogmatic assertion**.

- 238–276 AD. Mani of Persia epitomizes all older o**bjectivist dualisms** about good and evil. His fundamentalist teaching brings together Parsiism, Buddhism, and Christianity.

- 325 AD. Emperor Constantine ensures that Christianity becomes a religion operating along the lines of Roman law. Truth is seen as a question of **right belief**, not of direct experience.

- 391 AD. All pagan religions prohibited by emperor Theodosius throughout the Roman Empire. **Fundamentalism introduced into religion.** Brainwashing institutionalized.

- 415 AD. Library of Alexandria burnt to the ground by fanatic Christians. Example of what happens when people **entertain the belief that truth is exclusive**, and they **alone** possess it.

- 529 AD. Emperor Justinian shuts down Plato's Academy and Aristotle's Lyceum in Athens. Henceforth **philosophy would be prohibited on penalty of death**. The Dark Ages set in.

- 550 AD. (circa) Hui Neng, 6th patriarch of Zen Buddhism in China, composes the Platform Scripture, proclaiming **the end of ideation** and the importance of **living in (and for) the moment**.

- 683 AD. Fa Tsang, 3rd patriarch of Hua-Yen Buddhism in China, starts to teach and spread the doctrine of **unhindered interfusion of all things, including the universal and the particular**.

- 13th cent. AD. Thomas Aquinas proposes **marriage between reason and mystical insight**. Society reflects a "universitas" and overrides all other concerns, particularly individual ones.

- 13th cent. AD. The Japanese Zen master Dogen reveals his teaching according to which reality is a stream of discontinuous realities (dharma moments), each of which consists of a pure "**being-in-time**."

- 13th cent. AD. First steps in the direction of modern **experimental science** taken by Roger Bacon. Doctrinal truth, based on hallowed texts and great "authorities," is subtly undermined.

- 14th cent. AD. William of Ockham, father of nominalism, presents **society as an association of individuals**. The latter and their consciousness are thus seen as carrying special weight.

- 14th cent. AD. Invention of mechanical clocks, and therefore of linear time and machine efficiency. Faith develops in **man's ability to control most things by timing them**.

- 1455 AD. Gutenberg invents first printing machine. The way opens to further entrapment of man in his mental creations. **Printed word is canonized, spreading** of ideas is facilitated.

- 1486 AD. Inspired by Ficino's *Theologica Platonica*, Pico della Mirandola publishes his ***Oration on the Dignity of Man***. He thereby jump-starts the Renaissance, enthroning humanism.

- 15th cent. AD. Through his treatise on *Learned Ignorance*, Nicholas of Cusa introduces the so called "via negative" into the West: "Absolute **truth cannot be 'this' or 'that.'**"

- 1600 AD. Giordano Bruno burned at the stake for promoting heliocentrism, extraterrestrial life and other "magical arts." To save himself from a similar fate, **Galileo Galilei retracts** his proof of Copernican solar system theory. The Royal Society begins operation.

- 1619 AD. Rene Descartes has a mystical revelation about a new type of science. It is based on the belief that **reality is really a big machine**, and can, therefore, only be treated as such.

- 1620 AD. Francis Bacon publishes his *Novum, Organum*. Deductive **logic needs to be based on empirical evidence**. Beginning of Enlightenment secularization and tangible pragmatism.

- 1687 AD. Isaac Newton publishes his *Principia*. Time and space are considered by him objective and independent. They introduce distinct **limits in our ability to know and understand**.

- 1710 AD. George Berkeley maintains that **we become aware of all qualities in the form of ideas**. Whether these correspond for him to actual objects remains an open question.

- 1719 AD. G. W. Leibniz publishes his *Monadology*. Fragments are seen as mere **local manifestations of wholeness**. Mind alone can discover truth and make effective use of it.

- 1747 AD. J. O. La Mettrie publishes his ***L' Homme-Machine***. He claims that man is, literally, a machine. Modern molecular biologists (and not only they) have taken him on his word.

- 1781 AD. Immanuel Kant publishes his *Critique of Pure Reason*. Space and time not found in nature. They are **categories invented by man**, as and while he deals with nature.

- 1807 AD. G. W. F. Hegel publishes his *Phenomenology of Mind*. **Cognitive categories are indivisible from human nature.** History is driven by all affecting over-arching meaning.

- 1819 AD. Arthur Schopenhauer publishes *The World as Will and Idea*. Buddhist notions first hit the West. Since **mind defines all**, it needs to be understood, before all and in relation to all.

- 1859 AD. Charles Darwin publishes his *Origin of Species*. The study of life and man is transferred **from one object-mediated discipline (theology) to another (science)**.

- 1873 AD. J. C. Maxwell's electromagnetism starts **the process of dis-objectifying nature**. Poincaré, Planck, Einstein, Bohr, Heisenberg, Bohm and Feigenbaum follow suit.

- 1890 AD. William James publishes his *Principles of Psychology* and twelve years later, *The Varieties of Religious Experience*. **A modern thoughtful approach to consciousness** begins.

- 1900. Edmund Husserl kicks off a new school of thinking: "phenomenology." **Focus here is on the experience of being itself**, with all its ambiguities (when intellectualized).

- 1900. Sigmund Freud publishes his *The Interpretation of Dreams*. **Psyche reduced to a causally functioning machine**, fueled by the repression of childhood experiences.

- 1904. Reversing his older stand, and ignoring the sensibilities embedded in the original Greek term, W. James reacts angrily to the **excessive objectifications of "consciousness."**

- 1905. Einstein formulates both special relativity and contributes to the development of quantum theory. In either case, **patterns of relationship matter more than what actually relates**. Non-local ties suspected.

- 1912. Karl Gustaf Jung publishes *Psychology of the Unconscious*. Investigation of consciousness seen as necessary. **Archetypes are transpersonal, and therefore objective.**

- 1918. Oswald Spengler publishes *The Decline of the West*. Some forces shaping the Western civilization are singled out. The **West is unable to react to its shortcomings**.

- 1921. Bertrand Russell publishes *The Analysis of Mind*. Mind, like any other subject, can be understood by **rationally investigating its various components**.

- 1925. A. N. Whitehead publishes *Science and the Modern World*, and four years later, *Process and Reality*. **Consciousness is present in nature from the start, guiding evolution.**

- 1927. Werner Heisenberg formulates his principle of uncertainty. **Totally objectified knowledge in microphysics is impossible.** It should therefore not be pursued.

- 1928. Rudolf Carnap publishes *The Logical Structure of the World*. **Equating logic with nature**, he avoids asking epistemological questions about either.

- 1929. Vienna Circle publishes its manifesto as *The Scientific Conception of the World*. **Faith is expressed in the ability of science and logic to enlighten absolutely everything.**

- 1931. Kurt Gödel publishes his *Incompleteness Metatheorem*. **There are always some undecidable propositions in mathematics.** Proof does not lead to truth and vice versa.

- 1934. Karl Popper publishes his *Logic of Scientific Discovery*. **Every proposition has a flaw** and it is the scientist's duty to find it and correct it. Self-criticism is indispensable.

- 1943. J. P. Sartre publishes *Being and Nothingness*, a manifesto for existentialism. **Thinking is one thing and awareness another.** Man is (hopelessly) trapped in between.

- 1943. T.S. Elliott publishes the *Four Quartets*, re-inventing pre-Socratic thought. He **shows how and why the rationale of Western thought fails to approach experiential truth**.

- 1945. Erwin Schrödinger publishes *What is Life*. We **cannot research consciousness** through a science that has expelled it from both its terminology and its thinking.

- 1946–48. Ludwig von Bertalanfy publishes a series of seminal texts demonstrating the relevance of **a systems view of the world**: from atoms to the universe itself.

- 1953. Martin Heidegger publishes his *Introduction to Metaphysics*. An ontological plus semantic challenge to metaphysics is presented, revealing the depths of **cultural relativism**.

- 1954. Joseph Needham publishes his *Science and Civilization in China*. For the first time, the West is exposed to an entirely different type of reasoning, built on **non-object-mediated premises**.

- 1960. W. V. O. Quine publishes his *Word and Object*. He provides an analysis of **the extent to which words define objects,** objects define words and both define each other.

- 1962. Thomas Kuhn publishes *The Structure of Scientific Revolutions*. Science depends on the **"paradigms" that inspire researchers to find the facts** in the first place. Unanimity reigns supreme.

- 1962. Rachel Carson publishes *The Silent Spring*. A rude awakening to the fact that humans are **destroying the environment** on a planetary scale at an ever-faster rate. No action followed.

- 1967. Jacques Derrida publishes *L'Ecriture et la Difference*. A well-grounded epistemology **deconstructs the belief that language can carry secure meaning.** This of course includes his own.

- 1969. Fritz Perls publishes *Gestalt Therapy Verbatim*. **Awareness of the power of mental patterns** and suggestions on how to break them. Freeing the human spirit is thereby promoted.

- 1975. Fritjof Capra publishes *The Tao of Physics*. The important **breakthroughs of modern physics parallel some of the profoundest insights of ancient oriental cultures**.

- 1980. Ilya Prigogine publishes *From Being to Becoming*. **If one analyses systems in disequilibrium systematically, features of order emerge.** Of course, the opposite holds as well.

- 1982. Alain Aspect **experimentally proves the existence of non-locality** in physical existence. Particles are indeed structurally entangled beyond the confines of space, time and causality.

- 1987. Robert Jahn and Brenda Dunne publish their *Margins of Reality: The Role of Consciousness in the Physical World*. Experiments showing man able to influence sensitive random physical processes yield a **plausible quantum metaphor of consciousness**.

- 2000 and onwards: **The age of entanglement and connectivity.** The Internet provides a medium of non-locality available to everyone, everywhere at all times. Science encounters subjectivity and inevitably Consciousness unfolds, heralding a new era of understanding.

A self-reflecting society

The above list of some 150 stations in the evolution of consciousness raises many questions. One concerns the trust society has placed in the ability of objectification to describe reality accurately. This trust has led to an outlook eloquently described by George Gilder: "The highest purpose of the leading universities seems to be to reduce philosophy to a mechanistic positivism, to reduce history to statistical fluctuations and class exploitation, to deconstruct literature to a flux of words and writers' neuroses and to banish heroes from human life."[144]

The question naturally arises: are we going to allow this outlook to influence all we do and think? Has Western Civilization reached the stage where it is unable to react constructively to its own excesses, as Arnold Toynbee insists all civilizations do once they have reached the peak of their development?

---

[144] George Gilder, *Microcosm: The Quantum Revolution in Economic and Technology*.

We have not arrived at such a stage—yet. On the contrary, the fantastic development of the Western mind since the Renaissance has taken us to an important cross-road. We are now in a position to make the following statement about our achievements as a civilization:

Since the Enlightenment, we have delved deeply into matter in all its manifestations—small, large, medium, simple, complex, tractable and intractable. Each time we secure a major breakthrough in any direction, however, we stumble on the same unnerving situation: two eyes stare back at us from the depths of the physical reality into which we have penetrated. General relativity, quantum mechanics, genetic engineering, chaos theory, the subconscious, black holes, fractals, non-locality, dark energy and dark matter may be real enough. But do we allow them to tell us their full story? Or do we force them, through our self-locking objectifications of them, to conceal it?

It is true that we have achieved much. It is equally true that these achievements also have generated so many additional possibilities and previously hidden inter-connections that we are now unable to perceive the prospects of an end to our pursuit. We seem to have reached the opposite position exactly of what was put forward more than one century ago by Lord Kelvin. He claimed in 1900 that science had unraveled all that could be known about the world to such a degree that there was no purpose for a young man to study physics anymore![145]

Of course, the answer to the question of blind human progress is that the eyes we find staring back at us from the depths of physical existence are the ones we use for observing it. Nature appears to us as it does because we have carved her up in the particular way we have. The greatest sages and scientists of the last few centuries—Leibniz, Kant, Boole, Maxwell, Planck, W. James, Einstein, Bohr, Heidegger, Schrödinger, Wittgenstein, Eddington, de Broglie, G. Bell, Jung, Kuhn, Popper and others—have said as much. As Heisenberg summed up their collective wisdom: "What we observe is not nature itself, but nature exposed to our methods of questioning."[146]

The fact that the way mind objectifies, classifies and strings reality together influences the appearance of matter cannot be denied even by the most hard-nosed reductionist. It doesn't follow that everything is relative, as post-modernists claim. The relativism introduced by 20th-century critique into science, philosophy and literature represents a contradiction in terms. If all is relative,

[145] Five years later, Albert Einstein wrote his famous paper on special relativity.
[146] W. Heisenberg, *Physics and Philosophy: The Revolution in Modern Science* (1958) Lectures delivered at University of St. Andrews, Scotland, Winter 1955–56.

then this applies equally to the criteria used for saying so. There is no safe yardstick by which to judge it.

Four points can be made in view of this epistemological quagmire:

First, some insights are perhaps not relative at all, Kant, Foucault, Derrida, Feyerabend, and Kuhn notwithstanding. Second, we cannot rely on others to tell us what these insights are; we need to discover them ourselves. Third, we must search for these insights in full awareness of both the relative soundness of relativistic criticism and its logical inconsistency—as is evident from this sentence.

Fourth, and perhaps most important, we must abandon any belief that certainty is a question of proof. Certainty, like completeness, can be found only in the act of identifying with something. Such certainty will then spill over to its description, provided the sense of oneness in the speaker is enough to inform his words with what exceeds their meaning.

This type of certainty is far from impossible. It becomes evident each time we engage in a direct personal experience and speak from it, compelled from within. A self-aware language reveals what it is unable to convey at the very moment it fails, both for the speaker and for the listener.

Nothing of this means that we must now abandon the intellectual pursuit. It means that we must start using our mind as a servant rather than as a master. Evolution has pushed us to develop an intelligence so that we may use it not only to study and handle nature, but to become aware of our own limitations in so doing. That is what makes the times we are living in so exciting. We have come to realize that a mindset that doesn't invite us to see through its modes of operation is not the most trustworthy. It has stopped doing what it is supposed to.

The moment has arrived to start using our intelligence in this three-fold capacity. We need it equally to illumine the world, to illumine our illumination equipment, and to illumine our own selves as illuminators.

We also need our intelligence to help us translate what we have learned from 20th-century physics into equivalent qualities of perception. We cannot detect wholeness in nature and think about it in fragmentary ways. We cannot observe non-locality in the heart of matter and think about it in terms shaped through local and temporal experiences. We cannot realize that the laws governing each level of physical organization are not transferable to another (as chaos and complexity studies show) and in the same breath insist on a logic applicable to all.

To learn this lesson and live by it, we need to start experiencing reality again: knowingly and humbly, locally and globally. It doesn't mean we should stop abstracting. It means that in abstracting we should remember what we are abstracting *from* and *why*.

By the same token, in formulating our abstractions in the light of such experiences, we should allow ourselves to be inspired by nature's examples. We can be only as perceptive in our observations and wise in our thinking as our openness allows us to be, and our sense of measure prevents us from getting stuck in.

In the introduction of his book *The Phenomenon of Man*, Pierre Teilhard de Chardin distinguishes between man and ape. "Ape knows. Man knows that he knows."[147] The time has arrived to add something to this distinction. Knowing that we know makes us responsible for our knowledge. We must be in a position to handle it in such a way that we don't get caught in the labyrinth of unheeded objectifications.

The time for acting on profound self-reflection has arrived. It needs to be carried out in all we think and do, in private or in public.

[147] P. Teilhard de Chardin, *The Phenomenon of Man*. Harper Torchbooks, The Cloister Library, Harper & Row, Publishers, 1961.

Part II

A SELF-REFLECTIVE INTERDISCIPLINARY SCIENCE OF CONSCIOUSNESS

CHAPTER 7

A NEW DELPHIC ORACLE: Unifying the conception and the experience of wholeness

In every case the mind which is actively thinking is the objects which it thinks.
Aristotle

Hitherto, it has been assumed that all our knowledge must conform to objects. But all attempts to extend our knowledge of objects by establishing something in regard to them a priori, by means of concepts, have, on this assumption, ended in failure. We must therefore make trial whether we may not have more success in the tasks of metaphysics, if we suppose that objects must conform to our knowledge.
Immanuel Kant

When we look at the world through our theoretical insights, the factual knowledge that we obtain will evidently be shaped and formed by our theories.
David Bohm

Modern physics has rediscovered an ancient truth: not only individual things, but man and things, interpenetrate. There is a difference, however: ancient man experienced the interpenetration. He sensed it happening all around him. Modern man conceptualizes it. He tries to understand it.

This is the reality from which any effort to tackle the problems facing science and society must start. It is true that we need to break out of the reductionist fragmentation into which our self-locking mindset has pushed us. But we can do that only by first comprehending the problem intellectually. We therefore need to tread carefully—"interpenetration" shouldn't become one more slogan. We shouldn't fall into the trap of fighting the enemy on his own territory. The ancients lost sight of the unity of existence when, from experiencing it, they began to conceptualize it. We today risk losing the prospect of re-establishing unity if, in addition to conceptualizing it, we don't also start to experience it.

Experiencing the unity of existence will be much tougher on us than it was on our forefathers. They had not yet fully developed the objectifying penchant, so sensing reality in its oneness was easy for them. We have developed such a penchant. More importantly, we cannot, indeed should not, undo it. Objectification now permeates too deeply our way of living and thinking for us to be able to manage without it. What we need is equally to conceptualize, to experience, and not to confuse the two. We should conceptualize as we experience and we should experience as we conceptualize.

In the end, unity of existence applies less to the world and more to us. The more we fuse experience with conceptualization in the depths of our being, the more does the world fuse its opposites. We become receptive to the realization that we are all joined in a shared experience. As William James wrote: "Out of my experience, such as it is (and it is limited enough) one fixed conclusion dogmatically emerges, and that is this, that we with our lives are like islands in the sea, or like trees in the forest. The maple and the pine may whisper to each other with their leaves... But the trees also commingle their roots in the darkness underground, and the islands also hang together through the ocean's bottom. Just so there is a continuum of cosmic consciousness, against which our individuality builds but accidental fences, and into which our several minds plunge as into a mother-sea or reservoir."[148]

In this chapter we will present some ideas on how to mobilize the rediscovery of unity of existence in our times. We will dwell on two major theoretical issues. The first is concerned with what the increasing preoccupation over wholeness may point to. The second is concerned with what wholeness may actually mean in itself. Following the clarification of these two issues, we will examine how to put wholeness to work for us in creating and sustaining a new discipline called a *self-reflective interdisciplinary science of consciousness* or SRISOC for short. The means for achieving this is inter-personal dialogue.

Beyond monism and dualism: What wholeness is not

The most basic questions to ask in dealing with the rediscovery of wholeness in our times are these: Does it imply that we are moving away from dualism and fragmentation? Are we abandoning the "either/or" approach that has haunted us since the invention of formal logic?

---

[148] W. James, "Confidences of a 'Psychical Researcher,'" *The American Magazine*, Vol. 68 (1909), p. 589.

The answer is this: Not quite—yet. Sensing that wholeness obtains something beyond fragmentation is one thing. Experientially including our self- awareness in it is another. Pre-literate man used to experience this type of interpenetration. He sensed it happening all the time. We today merely conceptualize it. We are no longer capable of discerning the difference between knowing something to be true and experiencing the truth.

The reason for this is that wholeness cannot be approached on the theoretical level alone. It exceeds the sum of its parts and their relationships.

For example, when Einstein, Hawkins, Weinberg and the other great physicists worked on a unified field theory, they left consciousness out. Thus, their theoretical approach to wholeness was incomplete. Whatever else one says about consciousness, it is part of the universe. Therefore, a theory of everything that leaves it out belies its claim: It covers everything minus one. The work of Gödel and Chaitin makes this clear.

Wholeness transcends the subject-object divide.

Including consciousness in a theory of everything

How might a theory of everything look if it included consciousness and subjectivity?

A lot of givens would have to be reformulated, a lot of thinking redone. Perhaps the most important change would be that we would understand categories in a different way. Nowhere would this be more pronounced than in the categories referring to monism and dualism.

In common parlance today these two categories are considered to represent the most basic opposites conceivable. Under various guises and across the planet, they have inspired philosophers and religious teachers right from the beginning of recorded thought. However, a theory of everything that included consciousness wouldn't necessarily consider monism and dualism as opposite. It wouldn't even consider them complementary. It would conceive them as trans-functional. Monism and dualism would express mere conceptual differences on the various levels of description used for understanding and handling relevant reality.

Data in any given system may be recognized by everyone as being the same. What differs is assessment: "The art of handling the same bundle of data as before," to use Butterfield's words, "but placing them in a new system of relations with one another, thus giving them a different framework."[149] Nature herself

[149] H. Butterfield, *The Origins of Modern Science 1300-1800*, New York, 1961, p 32.

builds up her structures in this way. Aristotle points out that "matter . . . can never exist without quality and without form."[150] P. Weiss observes: "Take a gene out of an organism and it has no more meaning than a particular set of cards has outside . . . a game of poker or bridge. Both information value and function are context dependent."[151]

A theory of everything that included consciousness in its equations wouldn't use symbols denoting just specific states, relationships or tendencies—always restricted to being the same. It would use symbols that are entirely context dependent, as Ian Marshall might say. They would signify different things on different levels (or aspects) of description, merely suggesting (but not exhausting) what Christine Hardy calls a "dynamic constellation of meanings."[152]

Even this approach, however, doesn't take the issue of wholeness far enough. One more thing is needed. It is all very good to incorporate consciousness in a theory of everything. How about reversing the equation? If it is necessary that wholeness incorporate consciousness, should it not be equally necessary that consciousness incorporate wholeness?

Non-local contemplation

This notion has to do with perceiving the implications of non-locality (and its attendant non-temporality) for a world that includes man as its conscious contemplator. Such an embedded contemplator wouldn't apprehend non-locality as some kind of substratum. That would still be dualistic. Rather he would apprehend non-locality as something woven into the very fiber of locality, temporality and the way these are apprehended.

Indeed, for such an embedded contemplator the question wouldn't be whether reality is monistic or dualistic. Monism and dualism, as currently understood, are concepts belonging to a mindset informed by self-locking mental objectification, which the embedded contemplator will have abandoned. The question rather would be whether such a person is in a position to sense what the interweaving of non-locality with locality and non-temporality with temporality entails.

---

[150] *De gen.* 320b15.

[151] Mentioned by R. Root-Bernstein and P. Dillon, "Molecular complementarity I: The complementarity theory of the origin and evolution of life," *Journal of Theoretical Biology* 188, p 449.

[152] Christine Hardy, *Networks of Meaning: A Bridge Between Mind and Matter*, Praeger/Greenwood, 1998.

Who gets to the bottom of this difficult question realizes that distinct states, though conceivable as separate, can exist in the same or in different places at the same time. Conversely, the same state, though conceivable as unitary, can exist in different places at different times. Wholeness doesn't imply sameness.

More importantly, inclusivity doesn't deny exclusivity. Reality can be inclusive in one aspect and exclusive in another. It can be different from one angle and the same from another. Inter-penetration exists because of ontological differentiation. It doesn't work like a steam-roller that flattens everything into uniformity.

Why wholeness needs fragmentation

That is why the entities abstracted as a consequence of observation or calculation in science can inter-penetrate physically only up to a certain point. Beyond it there would be no differences to span, no qualities to exchange, and no imbalances to adjust. The universe itself would not exist. John Barrow explains why this must be the case. He writes:

> The fact that there is a limit to the speed at which information can be transmitted in Nature—that of light—has all sorts of unusual consequences. It is responsible for our astronomical isolation. The enormous times needed to send or receive light or radio waves from other star systems in the Universe is a consequence of the finite speed of light.
>
> It is also responsible for our own existence that may not be at first obvious," Barrow continues. "If the speed of light were not finite, then radiation of all sorts would be received instantaneously after it was emitted, no matter how far away its source. The result would be a reverberating cacophony. We would be dramatically influenced by signals from everywhere. Instead of local influences dominating over distant ones, we would be affected simultaneously by changes occurring on the other side of the Universe. The impossibility of transferring information faster than the speed of light, makes it possible to discriminate and organize any form of information.[153]

[153] John Barrow, *Impossibility: The Limits of Science and the Science of Limits*, Oxford University Press, 1999, p 25.

The one and the many minds

Non-locality of mind, then, has nothing to do with physical extension. It has everything to do with instantaneous ubiquity. Our local minds are nothing but excitations of a single field, as Einstein might have called them. The one ubiquitous mind has the ability to conceive physical states and imperatives as they rise to formal expression. But what particular states, what particular imperatives, is left to the local mind. It is for this reason that we must learn to perceive trans-locality, intuit trans-temporality, and sense trans-qualities without getting confused, or carried away, by our provisional mental objectifications of them.

Such clarity of understanding can be achieved only if, in addition to *conceptualizing* what we encounter, we are able to also sink into an all-pervading experience of it. Knowledge without experience is as misleading as experience without knowledge is useless. If we cannot approach non-linear reality with linear consciousness, as Ilya Prigogine told me some years ago, we cannot comprehend non-local reality with a localizing mindset. Our understanding must become as trans-conceptual as the world is trans-objective and trans-systemic.

Unifying conceptualization with experience

We have got used to believing that dualism and fragmentation are about the world. As a result, our minds now operate along similar lines to those envisaged by Heisenberg's uncertainty. We are able to describe accurately how reality is structured or behaves. But we are unable to feel the same reality at the same moment from within its actual being. Or if we do, we get lost in the feeling, unable to translate it into meaningful description. To solve this problem doesn't entail abandoning the conceptualization of wholeness.

But how can experiencing and conceptualizing be simultaneously exercised? The method is simple: we join objective participation in the world (including one another) to experiencing its interwoven wholeness. The first practice requires willful choice. The second requires willful abandonment. On the level of phenomena, we actively join hands. On the level of non-phenomena, we allow the whole to articulate itself through us, as circumstances may dictate.

For conscious participation in the world and experiencing its interwoven wholeness to interpenetrate successfully, the first must invite, and subsequently yield to, the second. Emerging as they do out of wholeness, phenomena can be handled properly only when the handling is consciously informed by wholeness. That is why meaning goes beyond definable content and reality beyond thingness. That is also why mythic gods are either dual-aspected, like Kali, or establish close links with their apposite numbers, like Apollo, lord of light, who lies with Persephone, mistress of death, to become a healer.

Bringing heaven to earth

What has been suggested so far clarifies the question of how to establish ourselves in qualitative wholeness, or ubiquity. It has been shown that wholeness reflects not the addition of all things, but a non-measurable experience of them on the level of interpenetration. We are now able to ask: How can the experiencing of wholeness lead to something more than just a personal feel? And if so, how can society benefit from this development in concrete terms?

Wholeness training and society

First, the very realization that wholeness doesn't constitute only a mental abstraction or article of faith, but represents a qualitative aspect of reality, makes people more open to the idea of incorporating their personal consciousness into it. This allows them to partly identify with the entire human predicament on the one hand, and with other expressions of existence on the other.

Participating personally in positive public activities then no longer appears to them as an expression of human concern. It appears as an imperative personal need. It's your own child that is dying in East Timor, not someone else's; it's your own ignorance that is over-cultivating the land, not some ignorant peasant's in Erythrea.

Second, for those who cannot naturally transcend their self-locking mind, there exist various exercises and ways of practicing meditation, which are capable of transmogrifying their theoretical understanding of wholeness into a lived experience. These techniques can (and should) be used in a very conscious way for bringing the sensibilities of wholeness to bear on science, society and education.

Third, people can be of increased usefulness to society when they place their awakened experience of wholeness at the service of common efforts, in addition to radiating it in their personal relationships. Such sharing of wholeness-experience can be of two kinds. The first applies to the common action needed for realizing specific projects. The second applies to obtaining the proper advice necessary for conceiving and planning such projects.

Both types of serving society are important. But the first merely touches on *how* something is to be pursued. The second type of serving society touches on *what* is going to be pursued—and more importantly, on *why*. In ancient societies this second type was expressed both through council decisions, as those taken today by indigenous tribes, and through oracles, personal or collective. It is with a combination of these two means of obtaining wholeness-informed advice that we are here concerned.

The hope of putting wholeness to work

By obtaining the best ideas on how to meet the challenges it faces, a civilization can prevent itself from imploding. Such a readiness, however, has not been displayed by civilizations in the past. Once headed for destruction under the influence of their slumber, nothing seems to have been able to stop their downfall. The few sages like Lao Tse or Marcus Aurelius who foresaw the dangers and offered solutions, were not listened to in the long run.

Today things may develop differently. Ancient sages foresaw such a possibility when they conceived of cleansing cities either through ritual enactments, through special action dictated by oracles, or through powerful city-cleansers, such as the famous Epimenides from Crete. The body is capable of healing itself through the immune system, as guided and focused by the psychological state of the person. Why not society? And why not our society in particular?

After all, this age is the first that can claim three qualitative differences with the past. The first is a broadly based instant communication system. The second is a penchant for self-examination. The third is the power of public awareness. Combined, these three may yet prove our saving grace. At the very least, our chances of collective self-healing today are far better than those of other civilizations in the past.

Dipping into collective wisdom

Please don't think that what is here proposed is a return to some form of shamanism. On the contrary, what is proposed here is something quite different: a new Delphic Oracle. It encompasses a system of obtaining much needed guidance on the major issues of science, society and education from the collective unconscious, and then offering that guidance to the public. To generate such a system of public service, two preparatory stages are necessary:

The first is investigation. We must thoroughly research how inter-personal dialogue works in tribal societies, how it has worked in ancient times, and what guidelines we today can cull from our own experience with Bohmian dialogue. The insights gained from such a thorough investigation will be collected, cross-referenced and composed into a single new method for obtaining collective wisdom. It will incorporate the most useful aspects of the aforementioned partial systems, and possibly other techniques.

The second stage is adaptation. It will consist of seeing how the new composite version of inter-personal dialogue will be used consciously for obtaining insights from the collective unconscious. Our future is too precious to leave to mere technocrats, politicians or professional interests. We need to contextualize all public (and private) action. Practicality needs to be fused again with beauty, immediate needs with long-term goals, democracy with responsibility, progress with creativity, and economics with self-articulation. Above all, creativity must once again be honored in all human beings and consciously utilized to pave a more rewarding path to the future.

The actual steps

Because the collective unconscious is in touch both with the reality at hand and its interwoven wholeness, it is in a position to yield pertinent information and advice on how best to handle current problems and opportunities. But how is this information and advice to be obtained in practice?

The following ideas reflect an outline of how this might be achieved.

Each time there is a major problem, challenge, or opportunity open to public debate, a core of humble, well-informed and dedicated individuals, willing to establish a field among themselves through some form of inter-personal dialogue, will be convened to discuss it. Who is to participate will be determined by the exact mix necessary for examining both the issue at hand and its dynamics. Not all participants will need to have received some form of wholeness training to engage in such a form of dialogue. But one or two persons with some experience of it should be included in every dialogue session. Their presence will assist in the smooth and focused development of the discussion.

Following the group's convocation, there will be an attempt to clearly formulate the particular questions to be discussed. Though the subject will be vaguely known in advance, no attempt will be made to specify it before the discussion begins. Defining and redefining the exact area to be covered is the ongoing business of those dealing with it, not those organizing the meeting. It frequently happens that as one exchanges ideas on a particular aspect of an overall theme, other particular aspects will come to view, which had been ignored not only by the organizers, but by the first speakers.

After the group has marked out its direction, each participant contributes the most significant information he is aware of on the subject as currently perceived. As others do the same, each will offer, through silence-punctuated dialogue, the most thoughtful insights into the continually re-adjusting dissuasion.

Exchanges will be pursued with one sole purpose—that of obtaining the best answer possible to the question debated. As long as there is not only a firm understanding of this, but a firm intention on the part of most participants to see it through, the rest will be done by wholeness itself. It will articulate its relevance to the present moment and the present interests by bringing to the foreground some of the hidden aspects. The willingness (and ability) of the dialoguing individuals to keep their ego out of the exchange, will lead to this without effort.

Learning from the past and the collective

The oracle at Delphi advised cities and individuals through the collective wit of priests, who made sense of the inchoate pronouncements of the entranced Pythia. Herodotus mentions that something similar occurred in an oracle dedicated to Amon-Ra in Egypt. Priests there divined the will of God by interpreting together the movements of children playing freely in the temple precinct.

This is also how the brain operates when giving birth to creative thinking. Through their lively interaction, billions of neurons suddenly throw up significant insights. In some cases, these insights turn out crucial—both for us personally and for society as a whole.

Indeed, all great practical inventions, experiences of enlightenment and creative inspirations in art, science or poetry originate in and through such neuronal interactions. Dana Zohar calls these flashes of spiritual intelligence, which she describes as ". . . the intelligence with which we address and solve problems of meaning and value, the intelligence with which we can place our actions and our lives in a wider, richer, meaning-giving context, the intelligence with which we can assess that one course of action or one life-path is more meaningful than another."[154]

We have been so thickened by our obsessive practice of self-locking mental objectification, that we have forgotten this happens all the time inside our brains and among us. But the experience of thousands of years, plus the practice of thousands of tribal councils and board meetings in Japan and elsewhere, are proving that we can indeed access the knowledge, the ingenuity, and the wisdom

---

[154] Dana Zohar, *Spiritual Intelligence: The Ultimate Intelligence,* Bloomsbury Publishing, 2012, p 4.

dwelling in the depths of our collective mind. This means that we should leave no stone unturned to rediscover the key for unlocking not only this hidden treasure, but its constructive uses.

A new approach to consultation

One of the fastest growing services today is the consulting business. In practically every area of human endeavor there seems to be a need for advisers and consultants. The time has come to inject some collective intelligence into this activity. Inter-personal dialogue, as described here and as refinable through future practice, can promote this enrichment not only in the area of business, but in the area of meaningful survival.

There is nothing metaphysical about this. Nature has developed its partiality through its practice of wholeness. She sees to it that the hidden lies on the surface, that appearance takes you straight to the non-phenomenal, that the formulation of opinion engineers for you the experience of truth.

However, there is a requirement: You must abandon the practice of self-locking mental objectification. The non-phenomenal is 100% embedded in the phenomenal. Truth is 100% embedded in the passing statement. Thus, it is up to you, the user of language and the doer of deeds, to see this. When you do, the particular becomes transparent to the general, the many to the one. No conflict arises, no confusion, no misunderstanding. If in the course of dialoguing some differences remain, they are experienced as such. The starting point of the dissenting speaker recalls for you the starting point of all creation, and because it does, you take the issue no further.

Differences make no difference in inter-personal dialogue. They cannot, and need not, be resolved. They can either be dissolved in the non-objectifiable field which the dialogue brings to your attention, or they can act as reminders of the unity they are pointing away from.

Modern physics tells us that Nature is a self-organizing system. This includes not only our body, but our brain. But there is a catch in what physics tells us: Given enough time, space and complexity, everything in Nature eventually evokes its opposite. So it happened that the human brain developed into the only natural system that can double up on itself and look at what it is doing, how and why. This development throws up a question of ontological proportions:

Are we humans going to develop from a self-organizing system into a self-creating one? Are we going to prevent, in our case, the natural forces of chaos to eventually break onto the scene of order and disrupt it, as always happens in inanimate matter? The challenge posed by this question is enormous. It entails nothing less than overthrowing the blind dynamics of Nature and its all-pervading habits. Are we up to the task? And if we are, are we able to actually get around Nature's habits?

Nobody knows. It is worth trying though. In the words of Parmenides: "What's needed is for you to learn all things—both the unshaken heart of persuasive Truth and the opinions of mortals, in which there is nothing worth trusting at all. But even so, this too you will learn: How beliefs based on appearance ought to be believable—as they all travel through all that exists."[155]

[155] Parmenides Fr 1.

Chapter 8

THE SCIENTIFIC RATIONALE FOR A SCIENCE OF CONSCIOUSNESS: A pre-epistemological approach

If you can paint one leaf, you can paint the entire world.
John Ruskin

Trying to understand vision by studying only neurons is like trying to understand bird flight by studying only feathers. You need a theoretical conception of what neurons (or feathers) do to decide which facts are even relevant.
David Marr (as quoted and explained by Alva Noe)

The human mind has been given the ability to grasp things in their entirety, to create and shape coherent wholes out of disparate elements.
Samuel Taylor Coleridge

Consciousness has been an object of intense scientific scrutiny since the early 1980s. But the results obtained have not made us much the wiser about what consciousness is, how it works, or why it has the effects it has. This limited progress is due to the fact that up until now, consciousness studies were premised on classical deterministic assumptions. Depending on the researcher's particular interests, training, attitude, interpretive skills or point of view, consciousness was seen as a by-product of either brain complexification, of DNA instructions, of biochemical accident, or of causation from either the top or the bottom of the organizational scale.

In so many words, consciousness was portrayed as not too different from any other specific subject being submitted to scientific scrutiny, and therefore researchable as any other specific subject. This flattening attitude restricted the scope of consciousness studies right from the beginning. The appropriateness of the investigative approach, or of its epistemological foundations, was never questioned. Both had repeatedly been proven effective in other disciplines, so science could safely study consciousness in similar ways. It could ignore what informs the study itself and its premises. No wonder then that the new discipline didn't illumine consciousness all that much. Where no care is taken to investigate the assumptions behind an assumption, no results can reasonably be expected.

The approach adopted by a *self-reflective interdisciplinary science of consciousness* for the investigation of consciousness is very different. Consciousness needs to be researched both as factual reality and motivating force; as quantity and quality; as cause and effect. It will thus be possible to study the subjective element of consciousness, so that researchers can then understand and handle more effectively its objective counterpart.

Alva Noe points this out in a striking passage when he writes: "It is a mistake to think that the new neuroscience of consciousness has broken with philosophy or moved beyond it. In fact, as we have been discovering, [Francis] Crick and other neuroscientists have taken a specific family of philosophical assumptions for granted—so much so that their own reliance on them has become all but invisible to them."[156] Alva Noe here describes a basic tenet of the objectifying human mind. Unless there is a good deal of self-awareness, this objectifying tendency turns context-dependent intimations into axiom-dependent rules. The provisional nature of the first is transmogrified into a fixed approach for the second.

A new approach to scientific investigation

To function on a deeper level, a *self-reflective interdisciplinary science of consciousness* will have to push for four specific goals. The first is a new version of reductionism. Writing about neuroscience's explanatory gap, John Horgan notes: "Like a precocious eight-year old tinkering with a radio, mind scientists excel at taking the brain apart, but they have no idea how to put it back together again."[157] Horgan's insight suggests that the new brand of reductionism here suggested needs to push the analytical process all the way down to the wholeness that holds the reducible parts together, qualitatively as well as structurally.

Neuroscience deals with neurons. Unless it is disentangled from its present deterministic computer model of the brain, however, and made more responsive to its far superior non-mechanical sensibilities and possibilities, it cannot make proper use of its findings.

---

[156] Alva Noe, *Out of Our Heads: Why You Are Not Your Brain and Other Lessons from the Biology of Consciousness,* Hill and Wang, a division of Farrar, Straus and Giroux, New York, 2009, p 8.

[157] John Horgan, *The Undiscovered Mind: How the Brain Defies Explanation,* Phoenix (Orion Books), London, 2000, p 23.

The second goal that a *self-reflective interdisciplinary science of consciousness* will have to pursue is to stop considering repeatability a necessary condition for validating experiments. There is already a plethora of indications that, even in chemistry, some experiments are not literally repeatable. Environmental components differ, often in unpredictable ways.

Complex variability applies even more to the investigation of organic matter. A recent study of 4.9 trillion of human genome bases from 800 individuals, carried out with the help of scanning equipment of the latest technology,[158] shows that the human genome is far more differentiated than previously thought.

In particular, fifteen million variations of the so-called "letters" occupying discrete places in the human DNA chain, were recorded. A good chunk of them refer to the mapping of those chain sections which codify for the composition of vital proteins. This deeply affects the way our brain works. As John Horgan points out, "the putative cornerstone of science is the ability to replicate experiments and thus results. But replicability poses a special challenge to mind-science because all brains and all mental illnesses differ in significant ways."[159]

This situation is exacerbated by the fact that not all genes are active but get to be so depending on a huge variety of interacting circumstances. These also interact among themselves, so that in the end we have such a complex and unpredictable web of interactions that even the most perfect computers cannot come up with a clear picture of what's happening in or to biological systems.

Wholeness as an investigative tool

The third goal is an offshoot of the second. Though reductionism will always remain a useful tool for certain measurable jobs in science, it no longer can be seen as the only valid tool for investigating nature, particularly living nature. There is need to introduce an alternative tool, and that is wholeness. This will prove useful particularly in biology and neuroscience for the reasons explained above.

At the same time, a sense of wholeness can help neuroscience discover the reality and usefulness of non-measurables like intuition, aesthetic satisfaction, empathy or remote cognition, which reflect important functions of consciousness. Furthermore, a sense of wholeness will help neuroscience to jump the conceptual barrier separating non-measurables from measurables.

---

[158] *Guardian* report published on November 5, 2010, of a story in *Nature* under the title "The One Thousand Genomes Programme."

[159] John Horgan, *The Undiscovered Mind: How the Brain Defies Explanation,* Phoenix (Orion Books), London, 2000, p 35.

Fourth, and finally, a sense of wholeness will help neuroscience see that if it would fathom the role of quantity in consciousness research, it must first develop a taste for, and an ability to access, qualitative understanding. Accurate description of what happens in the brain cannot be held up as a sample of quality. The technique created to promote this kind of investigation must remain conscious not only of the kind of discipline it is developing into, but of how the said discipline may continue to develop without getting stuck on what it discovers in the present. Consciousness investigators will thus empower themselves to constantly translate their findings into new premises, theories and methodologies as a matter of course.

By definition, consciousness represents the one state that bridges the subject-object divide. Like traditional Chinese medicine, with its emphasis on body-mind interaction, consciousness touches both the observer and the observed, the thought and its material substrate. As stressed in previous chapters, the one reflects the usefulness, and function, of the other.

There can be no examination of consciousness without a consciousness of that examination. Indeed, there can be no science of consciousness that is not at the same time conscious of the science it is developing into. What matters in consciousness research is not only the findings. It is also the finder. Anthropologist Clifford Geertz told John Horgan "that debates about human nature, unlike questions in nuclear physics or molecular biology or 'harder' fields of science, cannot be unambiguously resolved through an appeal to empirical evidence."[160] Geertz has argued that his own field of anthropology is, and may always be, "a half literary and half scientific enterprise."

Self-reflection and the "hard" problem

Presently active consciousness researchers may respond to this that they *have* successfully broached the subjective aspect of consciousness. They have done so by dividing their area of research into "hard" and "easy" problems, as David Chalmers calls them. The "hard" problems pertain to how we experience things, each in our unique way. The "easy" problems pertain to what happens to our brain when (and as) we have the experience. In the opinion of many contemporary researchers, both objective and subjective elements are equally considered in this scheme.[161]

[160] Ibid, pp 70-71.

[161] David Chalmers discusses this theory at length in his *The Conscious Mind: In Search of a Fundamental Theory*, Oxford University Press, Oxford, 1997.

The hard-easy distinction doesn't stand up to epistemological scrutiny, however. Dealing with the hard problem is not equivalent to self-reflection. Indeed, it obfuscates the entire issue of subjectivity.

For one thing, it is far from certain that the brain causes consciousness without being itself caused by it. Something of this nature happens in the nucleus of atoms where particles maintain one another in mutual existence. For another, subjective experience becomes "hard" only because the investigator has objectified it into a hard entity to begin with.

In actual fact, what Chalmers calls the "hard problem" is neither hard nor a problem. It isn't even a proper subject for discussion. We feel or think because our neurons fire and our neurons fire because we feel or think. It all starts from what chaos theorists call "infinite sensitivity to initial causes." Observation cannot penetrate this layer of reality, mind cannot compute it. As a measurer of all things, consciousness constitutes the most important non-measurable in the universe.

Equating preoccupation over the hard problem with self-reflection results from the fact that so far investigators have not gone beyond what happens when consciousness manifests in a particular way—the specific photons or sound waves, the specific childhood trauma, the specific information that causes X reaction. Researchers have not yet examined what allows or invites the brain to focus on something to begin with. A process takes place, thanks to which entities, states, fields or relationships are objectified in such a way that they become susceptible to representation, perception, conception or (eventually) thought. But how and why this happens, and what fuels it, remains unknown.

We need to cultivate an awareness of this objectification process. We need to investigate how and why things are born to thing-hood in the mind. Moreover, we need to ask ourselves if we allow what we objectify on that deep structural level of perception to influence our judgement or feelings and what is needed to stem such influences in the interest of objectivity. It stands to reason that the more we are dominated by operations we are unaware of, leave alone we don't see the beginning of, the less are we liable to understand them.

Accommodating serious objections

The same sensitivity and openness needs to be cultivated toward all sensible criticisms of the theoretical and practical framework of a *self-reflective interdisciplinary science of consciousness*. Such sensitivity and openness need to be carefully nurtured and systematically pursued. Consciousness researchers are as yet disinterested in examining criticisms of their thinking, in looking at what informs such criticisms, and in accommodating them in a complementary fashion within the operational frame of their own thinking.

This will be very different for the here-proposed *self-reflective interdisciplinary science of consciousness*. Acceptance and integration of an epistemological criticism on a continuing basis will enable the new discipline to handle its material in a fuller and more flexible manner. In addition, acceptance of epistemological criticism will mark an important departure from the practice of other disciplines, where the either/or attitude reigns supreme.

If consciousness investigators feel that there is only one way to do their job (through reductionism to ever smaller units), or one way only to interpret their findings (through comparison with computer-like operations), they are unconscious of other sensibilities, possibilities and angles that play an important role in the operation of consciousness. As Joseph LeDoux remarks, "cognitive science is really a science of only part of the mind, the part having to do with thinking, reasoning and intellect. It leaves emotions out."[162] People who use this kind of reductionism in their consciousness studies should rethink it.

A science adequate to its task

Scientists have been frustrated for some time now over their inability to find a purely scientific approach to illuminating the consciousness issue. Some attribute their failure to its intangible nature. They are mistaken.

As stressed earlier, the culprit is no other than the insistence that investigating nature is possible through one type of science only: that mediated by the tendency to conceive everything in terms of objects. So John Searle may well be right when he points out that "consciousness is one of the rare philosophical problems that will have a scientific solution."[163] Science is definitely required to illumine consciousness. The question is what kind of science?

The least that can be said about such a different kind of science is that it will *have* to be substantially different from the one currently practiced. A holistic operation like consciousness can be addressed only by a consciousness of what wholeness ultimately is and how it relates to time, locality and fragmentation.

---

[162] Quoted by John Horgan in *The Undiscovered Mind: How the Brain Defies Explanation,* Phoenix (Orion Books), London, 2000 p 23, from Joseph LeDoux, *The Emotional Brain,* Simon and Schuster, New York 1996.

[163] Searle made this remark on June 27, 2005, at the conference of the Association for the Scientific Study of Consciousness in California.

The medium has to be adequate to the subject mediated.[164] We cannot look at atoms through a telescope.

Of course, a holistic operation, which re-articulates the unity of all things before the creation singularity, and space, which expresses their separability after it, is difficult to reconcile conceptually. We have been conditioned too much by linear, local and object-mediated thinking to be able to achieve such a reconciliation. But we can learn from nature. It has brought wholeness and fragmentation together in its systems approach. Nature's systemic interactions articulate non-local and non-temporal wholeness in local and temporal terms.

Science and the reconciliation of opposites

It is then no accident that consciousness emerged as a subject worthy of scientific investigation at the same time as the discovery of the systemic interaction among subatomic particles during the 1920s. Neither is it an accident that the first scientists to recognize the importance of consciousness studies for their work were physicists. Quantum physics and consciousness both articulate wholeness by localizing it. Whitehead's "process philosophy" and Prigogine's "self-organization" are reflections of this. A seamless bond links every specific entity with its framework and its history, as it recedes into ever less perceptible characteristics through an infinite sensitivity to trans-functional or initial causes.

Things are their extensions and their stories to a much larger degree than they are to their constituent parts or their mechanics.[165]

Systemic self-organization plays a key role in the functioning and evolution of physical units because it constitutes a par excellence reflection of the relationship developing between matter and action or form and dynamics. Every operation of an entity ties in with the operation of every other—pretty much as Geoffrey Chew stipulates in his bootstrap theory.[166] Every type of operation

---

[164] Both Plato and Goethe warn us against the danger of using inappropriate instruments for studying a subject. Goethe's famous pronouncement on this is: "There must be something sun-like in him who would study the sun."

[165] In ancient Greek there were three words for what we today call science. One of them was "historie"—history. Everything is the product of a movement. Knowing starts from familiarising oneself with how this movement started and developed. Things depend more on their development than on their origins or their present structure. They are not composed of elements. They are composed of stages and interactions.

[166] The bootstrap theory had gained some prominence in the mid-seventies. But then it lost its appeal. It regained some of it twenty years later as a result of Ilya Prigogine's work on self-organisation in systems lacking equilibrium.

also ties in with its seeming opposite, as Heraclitus maintains.[167] The observable interpenetrates with the non-observable, the one with the multiple.

This is why the science required for dealing with a *self-reflective interdisciplinary science of consciousness* will require a different epistemological base. In order to advance effective consciousness studies, there will be a need for understanding the oneness of being and becoming, just as in order to cultivate an understanding of the oneness of being and becoming there will be a need for advancing more effective consciousness studies. The one cannot happen without the other.

Being, like oneness, arises to prominence in consciousness when the person avoids objectifying the world. Becoming, like multiplicity, arises to prominence when the person objectifies the world. The issue is not conceptual. It is experiential. We can succeed to be while becoming and we can succeed to become while being, provided we are able to also experience things in addition to thinking about them. The unity of experience with thought is something we must re-discover and learn to protect like a precious jewel.[168]

Self-reflective epistemology

It all goes to show that the self-reflective part of a *self-reflective interdisciplinary science of consciousness* will prove invaluable for science generally. Relativity, quantum mechanics, Bohr's complementarity, Heisenberg's uncertainty, Gödel's metatheorem, Chew's bootstrapping, complexity theory and fuzzy logic all cry out for a new understanding of the physical world that is dependent on self-reflection, multiformity, direct experience and profound intuition.

It isn't as if from an understanding of things as static, separate and structured we are now driven to an understanding of them as flexible, interdependent and procedural. It is rather as if we have now come to realize that several modes of thinking (often seemingly contradictory) are required for approaching reality in either its local or its non-local manifestations.

---

[167] In fragment 67 Heraclitus expresses this idea as follows: "Out of all things there comes a unity and out of a unity all things."

[168] We need to distinguish three kinds of experiences. The first is of things or situations experienced through the abstractions we have made of them. The second is of things or situations experienced away from any abstractions whatever. The third, and most difficult kind of experience is that of things or situations experienced simultaneously both in themselves and through some abstraction. It is characteristic of this third kind that the individual also becomes aware of what he has projected on the thing or situation experienced, why he has done so and what kind of truth or reality, if any, may be found in it.

We simply cannot continue to treat numbers, fields, tendencies, dimensions or indirect influences using the light of our understanding of how strictly delineated objects behave and how they relate in linear time or container-space. Vision-mediated comprehension (and its offshoot object-mediated reason) limit the interpretation of data.

Of course, conventional concepts can be stretched and modern science has engaged extensively in this practice. But at the end of the day the stretching of concepts can go only so far. Seeing beyond the seen isn't secured by extending seeing. It is secured by seeing differently, and by seeing what vision cannot reveal.

A cross-rational mindset

Openness comes naturally to human beings because it allows them to access what obtains beyond that which they are currently able to perceive or understand, and on which they are ultimately dependent. Natural openness explains why the twentieth century de-reified both the higher structural level of the universe (general relativity) and the lower structural level (particle physics.) Without this de-reification, even the limited comprehension of the macrocosm or the microcosm that we have developed would have been impossible.

But natural openness is not enough to complete and safeguard on its own the task of restoring wholeness to our view of both consciousness and reality. The damage done by object-mediated understanding is too extensive and entrenched to allow such a restoration. As Heisenberg puts it: "The Cartesian partition has penetrated deeply into the human mind during the three centuries following Descartes and it will take a long time for it to be replaced by a really different attitude toward the problems of reality."[169]

That is why it is so important to establish a *self-reflective interdisciplinary science of consciousness*. It can shed light on what really causes object-mediated understanding and reverse it.

That is also why we need an interdisciplinary overview of theoretical physics, theoretical biology, social and physical anthropology, epistemology, history of civilization, philosophy, psychology and philosophy of mathematics. To properly pursue a self-reflective interdisciplinary science of consciousness, data from these sources are as indispensable as are subtler ways of evaluating them. They can help us restore wholeness to our vision.

---

[169] Werner Heisenberg in conversation with Fritjof Capra, as reported in Fritjof Capra, *Uncommon Wisdom: Conversations with Remarkable People,* Flamingo, London, 1989, p 19.

Incidentally, by "sources" here we don't only mean the variety of disciplines just mentioned. We mean such natural and mental components as the properties of fields, the successive levels of organization, informed intuition, information coming through non-local (and non-temporal) conduits, and indirect interdependencies. Together, the data from such sources can weave a multi-layered, trans-informational, inter-conceptual, inter-functional and cross-rational web of understanding, that will make far better sense of both consciousness and the world than the present object-mediated rationale allows.

Scientists or scholars working on consciousness or other subjects in other disciplines simply cannot continue to be unaware of the way their perceptions are formed, their conceptions arrived at, their theories construed and their insights validated. Too much work has gone into the investigation of these issues for it to be further ignored.

That is the big task confronting consciousness studies today. If we are not sufficiently aware of what we invest in our consciousness research, we are simply not going to do with it what we claim we want to: investigate consciousness. We will be researching just an abstraction of consciousness, as it has been molded by the established use of language, the technical inquiries of philosophy, and the laboratory tests in medicine, neuroscience and cognitive psychology.

Lacking a consciousness of what molds our understanding and why, we cannot develop an understanding of what informs our consciousness and how. That, in a nutshell, is the most important argument in favor of a *self-reflective interdisciplinary science of consciousness*. Without a willingness to go deeply into epistemological questions—including the pre-epistemological layer—we will be unable to preserve a civilization that has pushed our curiosity so far that we are now attempting to investigate the very mindset that created it.

It is indisputable that in the past civilization influenced the way consciousness operates. The moment has come to reverse the trend. Consciousness must now start influencing the way civilization operates. Without such a reversal of roles there may soon be no civilization to influence, or to be influenced by.

Chapter 9

FUNDAMENTAL QUESTIONS FOR AN AWARE SCIENCE: The extent of philosophical involvement

The energy required to observe a system has been shown to interact with the energy within it in ways that make it disconcertingly impossible to describe the system independently of the observation process.
Werner Heisenberg

There may be always another reality to make fiction of the truth we think we have arrived at.
Christopher Fry

It is paradoxical that more than one half century after the advent of relativistic physics and the formulation of quantum mechanics . . . our neurophysiological models of the organism, our psychological and psychoanalytical concepts about "the mind", are located in Euclidean space and conform essentially to mechanistic, Newtonian causal-reductive concepts.
Jan Ehrenwald

We will now discuss some questions of fundamental philosophical importance to a *self-reflective interdisciplinary science of consciousness.* Philosophy plays a key role in science in the sense that it underpins how science thinks, if not what it actually does. However, most scientists are not aware of its role. They earnestly believe that they are not philosophizing when they stipulate that "only" the tangible is real, "only" measurements can assess it, and "only" facts can describe it. That insignificant little word "only" reveals their philosophy. It reveals it at least as much as their notions of tangibility, measurement and factuality.

The list of fundamental questions bearing on philosophy is long and covers a great many subjects. Thus, we will restrict ourselves to an indicative treatment.

One of the first philosophical questions that can be asked after a *self-reflective interdisciplinary science of consciousness* has become operative, is whether there are scientific domains where awareness of the consciousness component makes no difference. If it is found that such domains in fact exist, how do they differ from others where research can be conducted fruitfully only if the consciousness component is purposefully taken into account?

Related to this is the following subject. What are the circumstances, if any, under which good will, reliable information, healthy inquisitiveness and honest objectivity are sufficient in themselves for carrying out constructive research? In other words, is an awareness of the consciousness component indispensable for properly investigating nature?

Another subject now comes to mind. Is it possible to invite the unknown to somehow suggest the appropriate conceptual tools for investigating it? Since we already suspect enough about it to decide to research it in the first place, greater familiarity with the consciousness component might enable us to become aware of what hopes, past experiences and ideas we project onto the unknown.

If reality is so much more unpredictable than we can predict, as complexity theory now claims, then research into the unknown should be consciously open to what goes beyond predictability—*without* diminishing the importance of predictability for that reason.

Vagueness or specificity?

Closely related to predictability is the question of vagueness. In our times it has become fashionable to belittle it as "unscientific." Vagueness is perceived as almost synonymous with unimportance and scientists go to extraordinary lengths to avoid it, or circumscribe it. A lot of unhelpful analysis and mind-boggling complexity are the end product of this terror of vagueness.

Being widespread in nature, vagueness shouldn't disqualify the subjects it affects for scientific investigation. Perceiving where vagueness starts, or why it is there, is as important as perceiving where specificity reigns and what it leaves out of the picture. Things are clear or vague for reasons of their own, and in each case, we must come to know what these reasons are. We must see whether specificity is inherent in the object studied, or in the studying individual. In some cases, vagueness may turn out to be more revealing than specificity—simply because it is truer to the situation actually at hand.

Vagueness has to do principally with us, nature's investigators. Manifesting through open-ended and ambiguous formulations, nature requires of us a correspondingly open and sensitive mindset. But our culture doesn't encourage us to develop such a mindset. Since the triumph of rational objectivism after Newton and Descartes, our flexibility of perception has fallen out of step with nature's dynamic operations. Love of structure imprints itself on perception of process; need for continuity fills in arbitrarily the gaps of discontinuity and explanations in one area are drafted for answering problems in another.

So, since it is often procured at the expense of realism, specificity cannot be viewed as a desirable virtue of scientific investigation in itself. Indeed, if vagueness is inherent in the object under scrutiny, the way to go about it is not to reduce it to a describable quantity, procrustean style.

Our understanding should grow to the size of nature. Nature shouldn't be shrunk to the size of our understanding. Some formal operations conceal essential differences in the same sense that some formal differences conceal essential similarities. In the words of Boltzmann: "We must not aspire to derive nature from our concepts, but adapt [instead] the latter to the former."[170]

Beginnings shrouded in mist

Alfred North Whitehead approaches the same issue from a different angle. "The aims of scientific thought," he writes, "are to see the general in the particular and the eternal in the transitory."[171] Here Whitehead can be seen as anticipating what chaos theory stipulates about the starting points of all physical systems. Nature, chaos tells us, is infinitely sensitive to initial causes. These however are so imperceptible that we cannot arrive at knowing them, regardless of physical, conceptual or computational tools and skills. When perchance we think we do know them, we discover, to our surprise, that the causality chain is always longer than we had originally thought it would be and goes always deeper than we had initially suspected it can.

Understanding more just reveals that there is always more to reality than understanding can enlighten. "Things manifested are a vision of the unseen," if we are to believe Anaxagoras.[172] It's not a question of nature maintaining secret pockets of reality hidden from our view. It's a question of how our consciousness operates. The freer we are from pre-conceived notions about nature or our mind,

---

[170] Ludwig Boltzmann, *Theoretical Physics and Philosophical Problems,* translated by P. Foulkes and edited by B. Mc Guiness, Reidel, Boston, 1974, as quoted by Arthur I. Miller, *Imagery in Scientific Thought,* The MIT Press, Cambridge, Massachusetts, 1986, p XI.

[171] Quoted in Mark Buchanan, *Ubiquity,* Weldenfeld and Nicolson, London, 2000, p 85.

[172] Anaxagoras, fr. 21a.

the more clearly we apprehend her. "Truth," as Democritus phrases it, "abides in the deep."[173] In the deep there is darkness, and darkness serves understanding because it doesn't allow the senses to be caught up in the appearances of things, and judge them accordingly.

Unconscious of consciousness

Another subject could be: the premises of research. We absolutely determine its outcome and use. Kant brings this point up in his *Critique of Judgement*, when he writes: "When we study nature in terms of its mechanism, we keep to what we can observe or experiment on in such a way that we could produce it as nature does, at least in terms of similar laws: for we have complete insight only into what we can ourselves make and accomplish according to *concepts*"[174] (italics added).

Elucidating the role of premises is important for two reasons. The first is that it invites better use of insights into reality whenever they occur. *How* we think depends more on *what* we are able to conceive and less on what we are conceiving, or on what mental processes we use in so doing. The quality and level of our conceptual apparatus influences the scope of our insights. Strictly speaking we are not what we perceive. We are as we perceive. As Marlene Mary Hanna puts it: "What you see depends on *how* you look."[175]

The second reason for delving into the question of premises is that it has today become far more important than our object-mediated understanding suggests. That is particularly true of quantum and post-quantum physics. Their findings call the object-mediated approach into question.

The same goes for the new strands of molecular biology. Biologists are increasingly discovering what Pier L. Luisi calls "the tautology of molecular Darwinism . . . [which] is unable to elicit concepts other than those from which it has been originally constructed."[176] Biologists are also discovering the sway of systems over isolated units—of interaction over single action and of dynamic patterns over stable structures. As Andrew Packard formulates it in describing the connectivity of cells: "The primary datum is the pattern of collective activity

---

[173] Democritos, fr. 117.

[174] Quoted in Hans-Jorg Rheinberger, *Toward a History of Epistemic Things,* Stanford University Press, Stanford 1997, p 128.

[175] In personal letter to the author, June 1998.

[176] Quoted in Jeremy Narby, *The Cosmic Serpant: DNA and the Origins of Knowledge,* Jeremy P. Tarcher/Putnam, New York, 1999, p 144.

throughout a given area or field."[177] And as Antonio Damasio observes: "Consciousness involves the whole body, not just the brain."[178]

Strangely, the researchers who have not yet begun to learn this lesson are those most closely involved with consciousness studies. These people are the ones least conscious of the role played by their premises both in pursuing their research and in theorizing about it. It is as though medieval school men have re-incarnated as modern cognitive scientists and neurophysiologists. The doctrine may be different. But the unquestioning belief with which it is expounded remains the same. Cognitive science and neurophysiology query everything—except their own fundamental assumptions.

Understanding our understanding

As mentioned earlier, the accepted translation of the Tao Te Ching's first sentence, "the Tao which can be spoken of is not the real Tao," does not reflect the intentional ambiguity of the original Chinese text. The opening sentence should read: "The Tao being spoken of may be, but also may not be, the true Tao." The difference between the two being the fixed nature of the former and the dynamism of the latter. The Tao always depends on the prevailing circumstances. If both speaker and listener are at one with the Tao on a qualitative level, the Tao will be 'true.' If they are not at one with it, the Tao will not be 'true.''[179]

So too, knowledge that can be expressed, may or may not be true knowledge. True knowledge is not expressible without experience. It comes through and because of total oneness with the world.

The reason for this judgement is that every piece of express knowledge (or understanding) is informed by seven interconnected layers of abstraction, which restrict communion with what exists. These layers are mostly buried in the unconscious. They are engineered by two sets of concepts. The first pertains to general notions, the second to individual limitations.

In the first set we have four successive layers of abstraction from physical reality. They are shared by all members of a culture or civilization. The deepest of these layers touches on two aspects. The first is what nature's constraints

[177] Andrew Packard, "One man's contribution to the whole: Can squids show us anything that we didn't know already?" unpublished paper.
[178] Antonio Damasio, interviewed by Clive Cookson under "Public view of a private subject," *Financial Times*, June 30, 2001.
[179] Tew Bunnag (see chap. 5 footnote 144)

allow our senses to perceive. The second is how the brain identifies what the senses in fact pick up.

In other words, the first layer of abstraction from physical reality reflects man's common biological inheritance.

The second layer up from the bottom pertains to how we objectify what we perceive in the first. Is it relevant to my current state? What do I include from what I perceive; what do I reject and for what reasons? For how long do I want to retain an objectification? In which pigeon hole do I place it? How do I relate it to my overall past experience? How do I recreate it when I need to remember? Do I perhaps avoid objectifying certain states or aspects of reality—and if so why?

In short, the second layer touches on questions of pre-epistemology.

The third layer up pertains to how we think in the light of what we objectify. What do I learn from the way I objectify reality? What general principles can I deduce from it concerning the way the world works and the rules governing it? To what extent do I structure these principles into logical schemes? How do I use them to judge things and handle them?

In short, the third layer touches on questions of rationality.

The fourth layer is the one closest to the conscious state. It pertains to how we validate what we objectify in the light of the rules we have isolated in layer no 3. Is my rationality the real judge? Is it perhaps the servant of intuition or prejudice? Am I willing to assign increased validity to particular objectifications rather than others—and if so, why?

Whatever the choice, what we have here is an epistemology. We develop a kind of blueprint from our experience of the world and use it for evaluating and validating further conceptions. Our epistemology is the guide—conscious up to a point, unconscious mostly.

We come now to the second set of notions. It is all about how individuals color their particular understanding and handling of the world, thereby also restricting communion with it. There are three successive layers in this set.

The deepest contains the inherent sensibilities, psychological traits, prejudices and preferences underlying the unique persona. What makes one identical twin, brought up in the same environment and with the same care as his sibling, react differently to the same stimuli? Does this difference come through the genes, through the environment, or from some third source not currently identifiable by science? How receptive or closed am I to intuitions not relevant to any of the accepted abstractions—and why?

The second layer up from the first is the family background, both in the biological sense and in the cultural. How far does family influence the quality of my perceptions and actions? Does it cultivate the sensibilities and sensitivities underlying my knowledge and understanding or not? How does it influence my choices, reactions and behavior?

Finally, we come to the third layer, that closest to the conscious level. It pertains to the influences received by the individual from his broader social context. This context is composed of the religious, the philosophical, the political. and the educational background. What is the prevailing public ethos? What are the contrary ideas? To what extent does society, or the individual, make it possible to follow neither? Do either friends or individuals in the public eye influence my thinking?

A *self-reflective interdisciplinary science of consciousness* needs to investigate all these layers of abstraction from physical reality to the best of its ability and from all possible angles. This shouldn't be done only for the sake of better understanding human nature and human potential. It should be done for the sake of better understanding what informs science and society. If we have learnt one thing from the history of science over the past 100 years, it is that objectivity is not a question of blindly following rules and procedures. It is a question of accessing equally what underlies the rules and what escapes their regularities.

Heraclitus was right when he maintained that "nature loves to hide." She also loves to confuse us, when we objectify what we should not and extend what we cannot.

The mind-brain debate

The next philosophical question a consciousness-mediated science could try to elucidate deals with a much-debated neurophysiological issue. How does the brain fashion a single perception out of the thousands of scattered synaptic firings taking place in it? What enables these firings to trigger a unified picture, and the individual to develop the sense that he is actually perceiving it?

It might be assumed that this is a technical issue, but actually it is a philosophical issue. We deal with some of the technical aspects involved elsewhere in this book. For now, we deal only with the philosophical aspect of the mind-brain debate.

The reigning theory here is that of cognitive science. It was epitomized by brain specialist Joseph LeDoux in an interview with science writer John

Horgan. LeDoux muses: "That to me is the big question: how our brain makes us who we are."[180]

Colin Blakemore, another eminent scientist, is even more explicit: "The human brain," he writes, "is a machine which accounts for all our actions, our most private thoughts, our beliefs. It creates the state of consciousness and the sense of self. It makes the mind . . . To choose a job, a religious creed—or even to choose to rob a bank—is the peak of a causal chain that runs back to the origin of life and down to the nature of atoms and molecules."[181]

Like most scientists, Blakemore doesn't, of course, realize the implications of what he is saying. Physical existence doesn't start structurally from the atom. It starts way beneath it, in the particle interactions that quantum mechanics describes.

But the quantum mechanical particle interactions are not the beginning of the process either. They arise out of the quantum vacuum, which underlies the quantum mechanical operation. Might then not consciousness have originated on that level of organization? And if so, might not the quantum vacuum itself have originated in consciousness rather than the other way around? In other words, is it not possible that if consciousness goes "down to the nature of atoms," nature actually starts with consciousness? With its emphasis on infinite sensitivity to initial causes, chaos theory suggests the possibility that it *is* so.

These questions are legitimate in the light of Blakemore's and LeDoux's logic, even though neither of the two ask them. Mechanistic reductionism simply undermines itself theoretically the minute it stipulates that consciousness is determined by the smallest (or oldest) possible physical units. The process that is there *from* the beginning, simply is the beginning.

Mind creates brain

There is another aspect to this. LeDoux applies the wrong metaphor to brain activity when he claims that it is a "machine." Binding doesn't constitute a neurophysiological operation, as he, Crick, Chalmers and others insist, any more than writing is a function of the paper on which it appears. Brains grow in size and complexity under their own steam and in response to environmental stimuli. All other components being equal, machines don't.

[180] John Horgan, *The Undiscovered Mind,* Phoenix, London, p 30.
[181] I am indebted to David Lorimer for this quotation, who mentions it in his *The Radical Prince.*

There is a mass of evidence showing that the brain reacts to events external or internal to the body in unique, or at least in highly idiosyncratic, ways. Machines don't. Or if they do, their reaction has been programmed in advance. Human beings are capable of reacting in totally unpredictable ways. As G.E. Pugh explains: "If the human brain were so simple that we could understand it, we would be so simple that we couldn't."[182]

The following analogy will illustrate how the mind articulates itself through brain and what the brain does to facilitate the exercise. For example, these lines derive their meaning from the specific words used to the extent that the specific words are already an expression of the meaning. The words are the tools of a semantic imperative which articulates itself *through* them but is not created *by* them.[183] At best, the words reveal the ins and outs of this imperative in a way that calls for self-correction. By saying what you don't want, you become aware of what you do. The right choice is made possible through the wrong choice, but both are mind products nonetheless. If left to their devices, the words can do a bad job if they become coherent at all.

Brain as amplifier?

These considerations force us to look for the origins of mind, which thus becomes the third general question a *self-reflective interdisciplinary science of consciousness* could attempt to elucidate. The new project should definitely start from an examination of the epistemological and theoretical aspects of this subject. But the examination shouldn't stop there. Account should also be taken of the pertinent data, like the correlations between brain events and unified perceptions, the procedural patterns of mind and where (if anywhere) mind begins to shape up.

This third investigation should also concentrate on the possibility that the above components are so closely intertwined that they cannot be treated separately.

For example, on the quantum level there is no such thing as cause and effect. Many scientists think that this also applies to more complex levels. Roald Hoffmann has pointed out that "even in two 'hard natural science' fields as close

---

[182] G. E. Pugh, *The Biological Origin of Human Values,* Basic Books, New York, 1964, p 38.

[183] As every writer knows, this doesn't mean that words cannot trigger meaning. They do. But then this meaning already pre-exists in the author's mind in a latent form. The proper words merely make him aware of what he knows. They don't create meaning ex nihilo. If you are not inclined to accept something, no barrage of clever words or facts will convince you—as every reductionist reading these words will realise.

to each other as chemistry and physics, even here there are concepts in chemistry which are not reducible to physics. Or if they are reduced, they lose much that is interesting in them."[184] Consciousness, as normally perceived, can only appear on a certain level of complexification. If it doesn't operate in the way we are familiar with, if it expresses itself in simpler forms, we are just not in its presence. Consciousness is either as we know it to be, or it is something else. It cannot be "self," "other," "less," or "more."

Hoffmann's insight appears to differ from that of Herms Romijn. The latter boldly asserts that consciousness "already existed in a very elementary form as a fundamental property of the omnipresent virtual photons, i.e., of matter."[185] That is, consciousness as a potentiality was present right from the beginning of evolution.

If Romjin is right, neurons merely act as particularizers and organizers of a ubiquitous primal potentiality-thrust, a consciousness strange attractor. In that case not only is consciousness present everywhere; it literally reflects *the bringing together of forms after the big bang*—quantitatively on the level of inorganic matter, and qualitatively on the level of its organic follow-up.[186]

Pre-consciousness and the two ontological functions of brain

The mind-first hypothesis involves numerous and complex issues, with which a consciousness-mediated science needs to grapple. At the very least, such a science should investigate how mind creates brain. It also should investigate how the latter's roots in the former affect its processes and dynamics. The most promising metaphor here is that of an amplifier. It takes in extremely weak and vague emanations only to give out much enhanced and clear-cut impulses.

Let's go even deeper. As conceived in this book, the mind-first hypothesis stipulates that brain has two ontological functions. The first is to modulate and focus what, for lack of a better word, is here called "pre-consciousness." This is a non-measurable quantity, akin to the virtual particles or the zero-point energy inhabiting the quantum vacuum. At this stage pre-consciousness is so weak and unfocused that it can affect the "things" it comes in contact with only very little.

---

[184] Roald Hoffmann, *The Same and Not the Same,* Columbia University Press, 1995, p 20.
[185] H. Romijn, "Are Virtual Photons the Elementary Carriers of Consciousness?" *Journal of Consciousness Studies,* Vol 9 No 1, 2002, p 61-81.
[186] The original Greek term for consciousness, "syneidesis" denotes just this: the bringing together ("syn") of forms, plus the knowledge thereof (eidesis).

That is why scientists are incapable of detecting it. The only entities known to be affected appreciably by pre-consciousness are the neurons, which probably have been so designed as to be able to pick up its stirrings, enhance its imperceptible thrust, and then constructively interact with it.

There is no direct evidence that this is actually so. However, something similar happens with other cells closely related to neurons. These comprise the outer layer of the retina. They absorb photons and amplify their energy at least one million times before transferring it in the form of nervous impulses to the back of the brain, where the visual cortex is.[187] The same might well happen with neurons.

We can now deal with the second ontological function of the brain, as stipulated by the consciousness-first hypothesis here advanced.

It is that the brain reshuffles its own operations. Once contact with the neurons has been established, pre-consciousness is transformed by them into what can be called life-supporting consciousness. From that moment on, brain builds itself up through a process of trial and error into the kind of mechanism that serves the direct and indirect needs of the organism it inhabits. Consciousness sees to it that things happen in the best possible way for the particular individual, for the species the individual belongs to, and for the evolutionary stage the species occupies.

The homeopathy of self-conscious becoming

If the second ontological brain function directs and protects life on all its levels of expression, how does it manifest in humans? A tentative answer suggests itself but needs to be tested both on the conceptual and the actual level.

The trial-and-error dialectic among pre-consciousness, consciousness and brain becomes ever more pronounced and effective as increasingly complex life forms evolve. But a stage is eventually reached when, through over-complexification, over-population and over-effectiveness, one life-form—humankind—begins to destroy the subtle balance of the environment on which depends not only its own survival, but that of the other species.

A new evolutionary twist thus sets in. Consciousness gradually makes humans realize that they cannot continue to be passive players in their own

[187] Mae-Wan-Ho and Fritz-Albert Popp, "Biological organization, coherence and light emission from living organisms," in *Thinking about Biology,* W.D. Stein and F. J. Varela eds., pp 183-213, Addison Wesley, New York, 1993.

evolution. This inspires them to react to the excesses of their own becoming. There is a realization that in order to continue on their path, humans need to become both students and stewards of nature. The old animal imperative for mere survival transforms itself from within. Mere survival is now perceived as no-survival. It changes into meaningful survival so that it becomes worth having.

Of all animal species, man is the one that *can* survive by becoming aware of the fact that he is about to kill himself. His very ability to destroy himself empowers him to save himself, just as his very need to promote himself enables him to transcend himself. Eve had to eat the apple from the "tree of knowledge of good and evil" so that she should get a bad tummy and not eat from the same tree again! We are paying a heavy price for her being such a poor student.

The deficiency of the present approach

This train of thought highlights what is wrong with the brain-first school. Epiphenomenalism arises from an inability of consciousness investigators to think about what they are doing in a manner appropriate to their task. There are quite a few examples of their failure.

One is that consciousness investigators ignore the now considerable evidence (like for example non-local and non-temporal connectivity on a very deep structural level) that the three famous constants limiting physical existence can be violated under certain circumstances. Writing about this, A. K. Mukhopadhyay mentions Max Planck's constant, which excludes continuity of events; Albert Einstein's constant, which excludes simultaneity of events; and entropy, which excludes the identity of events.

The inability of investigators to take these violations of the three basic constants into proper account when studying consciousness, hampers their effort to research it on the non-mechanistic level it requires. Their inability also handicaps their effort to understand the outcome of their research in the proper spirit. You cannot understand artful painting in terms of house painting, just as you cannot understand words in terms of the letters composing them.

A second example offered by Mukhopadhyay on the inability of consciousness investigators to think about what they are doing in a manner appropriate to their subject, is that they "work within the boundary of a universe that is, in turn, determined by the boundary of the cerebral cortex". The result is that the cerebral cortex of consciousness investigators locks into its objectifications in a manner that is incapable of apprehending reality in different, and perhaps more faithful, ways.

A third example is that "consciousness occupies the subjective realm, while science works with the objective." The subjective and the objective are not just seen as separate. The subjective is seen as objectifiable in the same way as everything else, and therefore also apprehensible in the same way as everything else.

These examples—and more could be added—show one thing. Scientists investigating consciousness need "personal transformation" if they are to operate on the qualitative level necessary for really advancing (and not just using) their science. Just as you cannot understand chemistry unless you have studied it, you cannot research consciousness unless you have developed the sensibilities and epistemology that consciousness requires. Mukhopadhyay's thinking ought to be compulsory reading for any future consciousness investigators.[188]

Wrong level of description and direction of approach

Another epistemological shortcoming also needs to be addressed with respect to the brain-first hypothesis: epiphenomenalism examines the mind on the wrong level of description.

Brain-first theorists presume to know what it is they are looking for, when it is their very ignorance of consciousness that has pushed them to search for it. Furthermore, contrary to sound scientific practice, brain-first theorists are unwilling to explore a different approach that might get them out of their current theoretical quagmire. One such different approach would be to treat consciousness as a presence rather than a structure; a tendency rather than a phenomenon.

The consciousness-first hypothesis conceives mind as a non-reducible state. For example, it is quite true that mind represents nothing but a bundle of interacting neurons. It is equally true that Bach's "Passion According to Matthew" represents nothing but a collection of black dots and lines on large white pentagram sheets. Does this collection of black dots and lines really constitute Bach's masterpiece? Is mind the shifting interaction of the 100 billion neurons that each of us carries? Can it be identified *with* this interaction or is it the *cause* of it?[189]

---

[188] A.K. Mukhopadhyay, "Science for Consciousness: Five Reasons for Failure and Five Ways to Make it a Success," *Frontier Perspective,* Vol 11, No 1, Spring 2002, p 33.

[189] Non-reducibility here doesn't diminish the importance of the "history" of a state. You can see *how* the present emerged from the past, but this doesn't mean that the past *caused* the present. As Teilhard de Chardin observes, man is not descended *from* the ape. He has ascended *through* it. Indeed, one could go so far as to propose that man 'created' the ape so that he could use him as a ladder for reaching his abode.

As music articulates itself through the notes, so consciousness articulates itself through the neurons. They manifest its action on their level. They don't manifest consciousness itself.

The fallacy of equating location with origin

Of course, epistemologically naive scientists cannot give up looking for a mechanical explanation of consciousness. Thus, following in the footsteps of Max Planck, Francis Crick and Christof Koch, they have devoted lots of research to finding what they called "awareness neurons" and where they operate from.

For many years research along such lines yielded no result. However, in March 2003, Crick and Koch announced what they considered to be a major breakthrough in consciousness research. As reported in the *Sunday Times* on the basis of an article published in *Nature*, the two men now claim "to have found the group of cells responsible for generating consciousness and an individual's sense of self." Koch clarifies that "it is clear consciousness arises from biochemical reaction within the brain." Earlier Crick is reported to have said: "The scientific belief is that our minds—the behavior of your brains—can be explained entirely by the interactions of nerve cells."[190]

Both say that we are the products of synaptic firing, in the strict sense of the word. However, this reflects only half the story. The full story needs to account for why this happens. What makes the synapses fire in the particular ways that make us feel and think as we do? The discovery of Crick and Koch just proves that the two scientists have isolated which area in the brain gets activated when consciousness is triggered into specific manifestation and the sense of self arises. It doesn't prove that Crick and Koch have found what consciousness is, or even only what triggers it.

The question of equating correlation with causation has been the subject of profound discussions among theorists for a long time. They clarify that, from the standpoint of reason, isolating the location of something is not synonymous with discovering its origin or ultimate nature. Location and origin are not mutually reducible to one another. It is no truer to claim that a particular group of neurons generates consciousness than it is to claim that the moving grasses in a meadow generate wind, or that brushes create masterful paintings.

Of all scientists, consciousness investigators shouldn't concentrate only on appearances; it undermines the particular quality of the subject they are studying.

[190] Jonathan Leake, "DNA pioneer locates 'cells of our soul.'" *The Sunday Times,* March 9, 2003.

They should concentrate as much on what *triggers* the appearances as on why they are there to begin with. Machines don't explain engineering. Engineering explains machines, and human needs objectified explain engineering.

Bias for consciousness?

That is not the end of the story either. Investigators should concentrate at least as much on the way neurons change their firing patterns, as on the structure of the patterns themselves. Probably consciousness is tied to some natural bias for enriching such firing patterns. Probably too this bias is not an added peculiarity of the brain but represents its most fundamental feature. Most living matter mirrors bias for change. In man, the process seems to have become that much faster, more pronounced and more intricate than in other creatures.

A *self-reflective interdisciplinary science of consciousness* will probably consider useless any further research into the physical origins of consciousness. Nevertheless, it will continue trying to find out the physical mechanism through which consciousness interacts with the brain and the rest of the body, as new technical means facilitate the search.

This will be done in the belief that only by taking analysis to its bitter end can it be discovered whether science is in a position to throw light on what Koch calls "the puzzling aspects of consciousness," or on the contrary, whether consciousness is in a position to throw light on the puzzling inability of cognitive scientists and neurophysiologists to search for answers where they can be found to start with.

There always comes a moment, as you follow a path, when you realize that you have taken the wrong turn. But this realization presupposes that you have walked long enough on the wrong path to realize that it is wrong. It takes as much patience to find where you've made a mistake as it takes to find where you've made the right choice.

As Erwin Schrödinger points out, we cannot evict consciousness from the scientific arena and then claim triumphantly that we haven't found it by applying the scientific method! You cannot find what you are not disposed (or able) to look for,[191] and a very important step will have been taken by scientists when they begin to incorporate this realization into their work. A *self-reflective interdisciplinary science of consciousness* will be as much about finding out about reality as it will be about finding out what it is that prevents us from so doing.

---

[191] Erwin Schrödinger treats this in his in *What is life? Matter and Mind,* Cambridge University Press, Cambridge, 1967.

CHAPTER 10

DEVELOPING FUNDAMENTAL SENSIBILITIES: Self-reflection and the ways of nature

Let yourself be silently drawn by the strange pull
of what you really love. It will not lead you astray.
Rumi

People say that what we are all seeking is a meaning for life. I don't think that's what we are really seeking. I think that what we are seeking is an experience of being alive, so that our life experiences on the purely physical plane will have resonances within our innermost being and reality, so that we actually feel the rapture of being alive.
Joseph Campbell

Our human consciousness does not merely make possible
the question "why." It insists that the question be asked.
The urge to know is a defining feature of humanity.
Richard Leaky

Answering the questions raised in previous chapters doesn't exhaust the list of tasks a *self-reflective interdisciplinary science of consciousness* will be able to undertake. To the contrary, each answer will lead to new questions, and each of these in turn will lead to even more. By broadening and deepening your understanding you can see further, and by seeing further you become aware of how much more there is for you to see—indeed how much more there is to seeing than seeing itself. Aspects you hadn't even suspected existed until they come to the foreground; details you had hitherto considered marginal, suddenly occupy center stage.

Let us look at some of the questions that may become pertinent if the subjects relevant to a *self-reflective interdisciplinary science of consciousness* are addressed in depth:

What types of consciousness research are called for if mind is not reducible to the brain activity correlating with it? What is the role of consciousness in the ladder of evolutionary complexification? How does it differ from one level of organization to the next? Is this difference a result of how things work on that level, or is the way things work on a particular level the result of consciousness influencing them? Pierre Teilhard de Chardin may have had an inkling about this when he wrote that "the mind sleeps in the mineral kingdom, breathes in the vegetable kingdom, dreams in the animal kingdom and awakes in man."[192]

The list of questions arising from the realization that consciousness plays a role in the ladder of evolutionary complexification is long. For example, when we say that the role of consciousness changes from one level of organization to the next, do we mean there is a common thread in the way consciousness transforms from one level of organization to the next? And if there is, how can this common thread be identified? Is it the function of consciousness to influence the very structure of things on each level? Could consciousness be operative in the quantum vacuum, "dictating" from there the very patterns energy assumes once it rises to the level of measurable particles?

Another line of questioning may concern the nature and character of scientific research. If consciousness has been around since the beginning of time, it must also inhere in the objects researched. That is, we are looking at states, situations or relationships in the physical world that stare back at us, albeit in a different way to how we stare at them. What then should we be looking for? By what criteria and indicators should we identify consciousness in the physical world? What specific kinds of research should we pursue once we have found the answer to this question, and by what standards of validation should we judge them?

It stands to reason that if consciousness is taken to be a given in nature, the premises and role of science change. It must now try to fathom how consciousness opens the path to creation and by what means. Which of nature's inherent drives have their origin in consciousness and to what extent do they dominate the evolution? Is meaning something projected onto things, are things projected onto meanings, or are meanings and things perhaps the two sides of the same coin?

I. RE-WHOLIFICATION

The first general research project a consciousness-mediated science could undertake, once it has dealt with the questions outlined above, is to find ways for re-introducing people to the significance, the quality and the experience of wholeness. There are two reasons for going into this kind of project. The first is that in our

[192] Quoted in ibid from P. Teilhard de Chardin *The Phenomenon of Man,* Paris, 1947.

times most science has been trapped in a fragmented view of reality. As a result of branching out into an ever-increasing number of disciplines and sub-disciplines, it cannot approach wholeness even as an overview of all available information, as it did in earlier centuries.[193]

David Bohm and David Peat describe the mechanism involved in this process of gradual alienation from wholeness in the following way:

> In their day-to-day work, the neurobiologist and the theoretical physicist have little to do with each other's activities. It is not surprising that research into elementary particles and the nature of black holes does not draw upon concepts involving nerve synapses and neurotransmitters. It could hardly be called a serious barrier to communication. The danger arises when it is assumed that, in their deepest levels, these subjects have no true relationship to each other and that the world really does consist of separate parts which can be identified and studied on their own. This is the very assumption that underlies fragmentation.[194]

This means that in addition to knowing as much as possible about their field, scientists must also turn to sensing things. Wholeness can no longer be seen as a question of adding all the parts, or of making out all the interactions. It is a question of sinking qualitatively into that level of physical organization from which the parts emerge.

You no longer connect everything in an abstract manner. You feel the connectedness. You invite it to inform you and to guide you. It invites you to become one with it as the ultimate means to understanding its own nature. Wholeness is no longer viewed as conceptually or functionally opposite to fragmentation. It is viewed as that which underlies it—and informs it.

Feeling and fragmentation

Bohm realizes that fragmentation is much more involved with mind than with reality. "What can be done," he asks, "to end the prevailing state of fragmentation?

---

[193] In ancient times, the main proponent of fragmentation was belief-based religion (mainly monotheism) and absolutist philosophy. The modern scientific belief in fragmentation is mainly derived from the patterns of thinking introduced by doctrinal Christianity. Mystical Christianity, as mystical Islam and mystical Judaism, are innocent of this charge.

[194] David Bohm and David Peat, *Science, Order and Creativity,* Routledge, London, 1989, p 71.

At first sight this may seem to be a reasonable question, but a closer examination leads one to see that [it] has presuppositions that are not clear."

"Generally speaking," he continues, "if one asks how one can solve some technical problem . . . it is presupposed that while we begin not knowing the answer, our minds are nevertheless clear enough to discover an answer. . . But if our whole way of thinking is penetrated by fragmentation, this implies that we are not capable of reaching an answer, for fragmentary perception is in essence a largely unconscious habit of confusion around the question of what is different and what is not. So, *in the very act in which we try to discover what to do about fragmentation, we will go on with this habit and thus we will tend to introduce yet further forms of fragmentation*"[195] (italics added).

One way of dealing with this mental problem is to address people's subconscious concerns over it. We could start from making the point, as Celsus did when he anticipated modern systems theory in the second century AD, that "everything has been calculated to serve not one the other, but the whole."[196] We could go on to explain that wholeness is not the addition of all parts, but the drive shaping the parts and keeping them together. A third point could be that if this is the case, wholeness cannot, and therefore should not, be defined. Its presence can only be felt in and behind the phenomenal world.

In this connection, it could be pointed out that feeling, in fact, underpins all true knowledge. Indeed, some scientists and thinkers like Daniel Goleman, Antonio Damasio, and Susan Greenfield are addressing this question on the research level. Damasio has amassed a wealth of information and insights on the topic in his *The Feeling of What Happens* (1994). Goleman refers extensively to the role of the limbic brain (seat of emotions) informing thoughts (seated in the neocortex.) in his *Emotional Intelligence* (1996).

Most scientists who have dared to research feelings on the neurophysiological level, however, have retained the self-locking reductionist approach, exactly as Bohm points out above. Thus, their work enlightens part of the question only—and not the most significant part either. Petros Lezos understood this when he said that "you cannot know something unless you are able to really feel it, as you cannot feel something unless you are able to really know it."[197] The trick is to feel for feeling while researching it; to feel for knowledge as it rises

---

[195] David Bohm, *Wholeness and the Implicate Order,* p 23.
[196] Celsus, *Alethes Logos (The True Word),* Epiloge, Athens, p 64.
[197] Petros Lezos, an old friend of the author, expressed this view to him in October 1979.

through feeling; and most important of all, to appreciate the creative interaction between the two while engaged in scientific enquiry.

As David Loye formulates it: "We think of the 'intellect' as one thing and 'feelings' as another. But as the seminal work of Silvan Tomkins[198] makes massively evident, in all real-life operations, the two not only work closely together, but also are generally something new that is both thought and emotion, as bronze is an alloy of copper and tin."[199]

Wholistic fragmentation

Another point also needs to be made in relation to the re-wholification project. Readers may think that the idea of wholeness has religious connotations. It hasn't. In its present expressions, religion—with the possible exception of very few exponents of the mystical path—is too involved with culture, doctrine, tradition, emotion, power politics and history to be in a position to apprehend wholeness on the qualitative level here suggested. Re-wholification is a job for a *self-reflective interdisciplinary science of consciousness*. It is not a job for religion.

Being safely grounded in conceptual thinking, the scientific ethos is able to take people beyond it. You need to reduce to the very small before you can get the larger picture; you need to be based in factuality before you can suspect what passes among the entities emerging through the facts; you need to know what can be described before you can guess what may constitute an explanation. Science alone has the know-how, the rigor and the means to pave the way for such a qualitative understanding.

The other reason why re-wholification should be undertaken by people steeped (but not trapped) in science is that, having triggered the movement toward ever greater fragmentation, scientists are now responsible for redressing the imbalance. That is, at any rate, what the Delphic Oracle would advise if it still operated. One of its most famous pronouncements was that "he who wounds also heals." Having abstracted fragmentation into an article of faith and supreme explanatory tool, science is now well equipped for fathoming what really happens to be the case in and through physical reality.

It knows only too well that wholeness reflects nothing but the ontological involvement of the universe with itself. This self-involvement was materially

---

[198] David Loye is here referring to Silvan Tomkins' book *The Positive Affects, The Negative Affects*, in which he speaks of the physiological and psychological inseparability of emotion and thought.
[199] David Loye, *The Sphinx and the Rainbow*, Shambhala, Boulder, 1983, p 62.

shattered 15-billion years ago when the big bang broke up what originally existed in compact form. The major forces around in that original universe are still present in its post-bang successor. They appear in the guise of gravity, energy, noise, non-locality, procedural interpenetration and others. So, scientists can base their re-wholification project on these by-products of the big bang. Portraying the whole in action on, and among, the parts, these ubiquitous by-products will enable us to speak of wholeness without implying a metaphysical principle.

Re-educating for wholeness

Explaining in depth what wholeness is and manifesting its numerous applications will be useful on two counts. The first is psychological and social. Re-educating people in wholeness will restore a harmonious relationship between the activities initiated in each of the two brain hemispheres: the right inclined toward holistic experience and the left inclined toward fragmented perception.

In other words, wholeness education will integrate what Susan Blackmore calls "the spiritual insights with the scientific." It will "reveal what kind of illusion we live in, how the illusion comes about and perhaps even [how we can] see our way out of the illusion."[200] Once again people will be able to think and act in the light of what lies behind the phenomena—in the phenomena themselves.

The second reason why educating for wholeness will be useful is philosophical. Such education will clarify the important point, evident from the preceding section, that wholeness is *not* in fact opposite to fragmentation. Understanding wholes is of a different order to understanding parts. Just as you cannot judge atoms from what particles do, or molecules from what atoms do, so you cannot judge wholes from what parts do. The whole is what enables the parts to function properly; the parts are what enables the whole to reveal itself. Injecting wholeness into the understanding of parts counteracts the hold of the parts on conception and action. Wholeness needs to become a state of mind before it can be appreciated as a state in nature.

It follows that wholeness education must assist people to develop, retain and increase the feeling for wholeness. It is developing this feeling, rather than merely talking about wholeness, that will give the re-wholification project real substance and proper direction.

David Orr puts his finger on this when he writes:

---

[200] Susan Blackmore, *Journal of Consciousness Studies*

> The great ecological issues of our time have to do in one way or another with our failure to see things in their entirety. This failure occurs when minds are taught to think in boxes and not taught to transcend those boxes. We educate many in-the-box-thinkers who perform within their various specialties rather like a dog kept in the yard by an electronic barrier. And there is a connection between knowledge organized in boxes, minds that stay in those boxes and the inability of those minds to perceive the causes of degraded ecologies and global imbalances. The situation is tragic in that many suspect where all this is leading, but believe themselves powerless to alter it.[201]

II. WHAT IS QUALITY?

Since wholeness is closely linked with quality, launching an in-depth investigation of the latter could be the next major task for a *self-reflective interdisciplinary science of consciousness*. The first thing here would be to discuss what quality means.

One distinct possibility is that quality represents an accidental trend in nature, which progressively lifts physical existence out of the mire of chaos simply by promoting more effective patterned interactions. This would verify the meaning of the original Greek term for quality, "poeotis," which denotes just "doing" (or "creating"). Quite literally, beauty, balance, complexity and many other states could be the "doings" of nature with respect to how things evolve, relate and structure themselves.

Any discussion of what quality is, however, must also take into account three further possibilities. The first is that, like so many other key concepts, quality ultimately lacks a single identity. The second possibility is that, to the contrary, quality has many identities, even conflicting ones. The third is that as a force behind the scenes, quality merely "nudges" things into developing an identity of their own, which then becomes nameable. In this latter sense quality merely provides the impetus toward identity formation.

Inviting quality to manifest

Once the issue of what quality actually is has been settled one way or another, it will be necessary to deal with how it manifests. Obviously, quality "occurs" *in* or *about* things. It also occurs *through* things. That is important because it

---

[201] David Orr, "The Marriage of Mind and Nature," *Resurgence* No 166, pp 6–7.

indicates its intangibility. For example, there seems to be nothing special about the molecules making up the neurons. Most of the neurotransmitters are common amino acids that show up in other parts of the body as well. The same goes for the hormone regulation or the food components responsible for the survival and differentiation of neurons.

So what determines the very special function of the firing patterns in the brain? Indeed, what makes the brain brainy? Does quantity follow in the wake of quality, quality in the wake of quantity, or perhaps both?

The hypothesis favored here is that quality expresses itself through large numbers. For example, it has been calculated that there are 10^{80} atoms in the universe. Furthermore, the average human brain numbers some 100 billion neurons. In particular, the area of Einstein's brain that dealt with mathematics was 30% more voluminous than that of ordinary people.

Probably quality operates through large numbers in two distinct ways. In the first it plays an active role. Something previously latent becomes suddenly articulate on its own, so that certain components or aspects are selected by it from a pool containing a lot more. These components or aspects are then woven into a pattern, or even an altogether new composite unit which is endowed with new characteristics, and therefore new possibilities.

Quality and the spontaneous re-arrangement of patterns

In the second way, quality seems to play a more passive role. It emerges from a large number of basic units. At some stage, perhaps as the result of a random event that catalyzes a lasting feature, these basic units re-arrange themselves into new patterns, or develop characteristics they previously lacked. The large numbers involved make new states possible and so quality manifests.

But the question doggedly persists: Is quality there before the numbers, do the numbers "create" quality, or do perhaps the numbers and the quality reflect one another? Conversely, can quality be found in ultimate simplicity?

If it is found that quality comes first, a line of other questions become pertinent. How does quality actually "incarnate"? If there is such a thing as choice for quality, doesn't that involve an ability to discriminate? And isn't discrimination a feature of organic matter only? The one certainty is that by understanding better what quality is, what it isn't and how it influences the way physical structures form themselves and behave, we will be in a position to invite more of it into our science, our thoughts and our actions.

III. INVESTIGATING HUMAN NATURE

Since on our level of organization quality is very much a question of human awareness, launching a serious investigation of what are the most outspoken characteristics of human nature could become the next task for a *self-reflective interdisciplinary science of consciousness.*

We have endless discussions about human rights; we have a whole branch of learning called "the humanities;" we have psychology, religion, anthropology and the social sciences. Do we know what it actually means to be a human being? Do we know how we differ from the other higher primates? Indeed, *can* we know the difference so long as we have only our human understanding to go by?

The starting point of such a research project could be the fact that we humans are the only species that inquires into its own nature. Animals don't seem to think about what they are; they just are. More significantly, perhaps, animals don't try to correct themselves. We do. We go so far as to become aware of our conditioning, to inquire into nature and to attempt getting rid of our fixations.

Another starting point for the investigation of human nature could be the question of intelligence. What is it really? Is there a difference between doing things intelligently and conceiving their inter-relationship with other things? Are we more intelligent than animals, or just differently intelligent?

A third starting point could be evolution. Animals change as species and subspecies appear. Humans change within their species. They even evolve as individuals. A fourth starting point could be the scientific thinking on the subject—human evolution, neurophysiology, biology, psychology, anatomy.

Civilization and humanness

A fifth starting point for the investigation of human nature could be civilization. Is our humanity derived from it? If so, how about the many hundreds of millennia during which we roamed the mountains and valleys of the Earth as hunters and fruit-gatherers, without having developed civilization? Were we then barbarians? Or were we gentler than we are now? Is gentleness an inherent characteristic of human nature, like intelligence or self-knowledge? Does it go hand in hand with nobility and spirituality? Are these characteristics exclusively human, or just more pronounced in humans?

A sixth starting point for the investigation of human nature could be the fact that each person seems to have a very specific character. Can one isolate any stage of development, from embryo to adulthood, at which it can be said that a person receives passively incoming messages through the senses? Are selection and projection always tied to previous experiences and if not, what influences them? Is character uniqueness a product of the selfish gene and meme, as Dawkins and Wilson claim? What may be the unknown component, which according to Darwin, shapes evolution in addition to natural selection and beyond the provisions of chaos theory?

Finally, the last starting point worth investigating could be language. Does it really differentiate us from animals? They have been shown capable of forming concepts. They have also been shown to exchange information at a distance. One particular chimp has even been taught to use a vocabulary of 700 words. In some human societies the average vocabulary is roughly 500 words! Does our unique capacity for articulating speech increase our capacity for understanding and handling the world? Does ideation depend on language? Or does language depend on ideation?

As was hinted in an earlier chapter, human language differs from both animal language (and incidentally from analytical philosophy) in that it doesn't only convey specific meaning. That is a point all consciousness investigators must keep in mind. Chimps may be able to master a few hundred words, but they cannot go beyond these while using them. Human beings can, and do. That is what makes them human. By going beyond the words, humans give them greater meaning. When, upon occasion, they happen to stick to the words they are using, they restrict even the little meaning the words do have.

This explains why real ideas are so elusive. Also, why ideas need to be *lived* and not intellectualized. When words are taken too literally they transform ideas into ideologies and divest them of meaningfulness. Words deprived of their beyondness are simply incapable of revealing the essence of a thought. They debase it into an abstraction and turn it into a recipe for truth rather than a hint of it, an article of faith rather than an experience.

More than can be specified

Another consideration is also pertinent. Investigating human nature isn't only a question of starting points. It is also a question of angles. If we really want to find out more about who we are, we must equally inquire into how we think we are. This would entail asking many people from different paths of life, different cultures, and different social and family backgrounds what they feel about the essence of their humanness. It would also entail researching the history of civilizations for clues on how people actually thought about human nature in the past.

In all probability no clear picture will emerge from such a wide-ranging project. Indeed, drawing an unclear picture will be one guarantee that the researchers of human nature are on the right track. Man is not a finished product like the ant, which hasn't changed in 50 million years. Man is a creature always in the making and that is both his glory and his danger.

The fear of ending up with an unclear picture shouldn't deter us from undertaking the inquiry into human nature. It is important to reach the limitations of what we can know about humankind. It is even more important to investigate whether these limitations are inherent in the subject itself or in our approach thereto. By pursuing our inquiry into human nature to the limits of our capacity we may see whether there is something beyond these limits that we haven't thought of before.

We may also reflect on what lies behind the answers we do obtain, what to do about them on the social level, and how they affect existing disciplines like anthropology, sociology, psychology, economics, medicine and education. As C. G. Jung formulates it: "The answer to human life is not to be found within the limits of human life."[202]

IV. INVESTIGATING INTUITION

Western science takes it for granted that we have only one way of investigating nature. It is our five senses and their technical extensions. Henri Bergson flatly denies it. He claims there are two ways of investigating nature, not one. They are the five senses, *plus* deep intuition. So, the next, and last, general investigative task for a *self-reflective interdisciplinary science of consciousness* should be to research this phenomenon. If it is true that intuition has contributed to science, as the scientists themselves admit, then the time has come for science to contribute to intuition.

This shouldn't be done just because the subject is fascinating. It should be done because intuition plays a key role in all human affairs, from art to daily living and from thought to play. As Philip Goldberg writes in a book exclusively dedicated to the subject, all creative revolutions have emerged as a result of intuitive leaps of one kind or another. They owe very little to direct information.

Goldberg quotes massive evidence in support of his position. Among others he mentions Einstein, who coined the expression "intuitive leap," Paul Dirac, Henri Poincaré and G. Kekule. According to their own admissions, these

[202] Quoted in David Lorimer, *All in One*. Arkana, London, 1990, p 220.

men owe their significant discoveries to "sudden pictorial revelations" from the unconscious.[203]

Other examples are also available. Plato speaks of "sudden insight" in his *7th Letter.* Descartes had what he describes as a mystical experience concerning "the order of all sciences." Karl Marx had a catalytic insight into what's wrong with society before he wrote *Das Kapital.* Robert Lewis Stevenson spent years looking for a story that would fit "his strong sense of man's double being;" however, the plot of *Dr. Jekyll and Mr. Hyde* was revealed to him during a dream. Hindeki Yukawa speaks of "his intuitive understanding of nature," which he inherited from the old Taoist masters he studied in his youth—particularly Chuang Tzu.

A *self-reflective interdisciplinary science of consciousness* is the best instrument for discovering what triggers intuition and why. Do we intuit through our familiarity with things, or because of the things themselves? Is our intuition the product of something coming together in our existing understanding, or of something reflecting a completely different understanding? Is it feasible to cultivate intuition, not to mention the possibility of willfully inducing it? Can one devise a form of training for intuition—some exercises perhaps that will sensitize one to it?

Distinguishing intuition from imagination

Investigating intuition will have to go through three preparatory stages. They are all connected to the fact that, like so much else, intuition cannot be pinned down sufficiently to become researchable in the "normal" sense of the word. If intuition wasn't vague, it wouldn't be what it is. But vagueness, as fuzzy logic has shown, can, and should, be factored into the picture of reality as the gateway to interpenetration.

The first preparatory stage for investigating intuition will be to come up with some working definition of the subject. In the light of what has been discussed in this book, it would appear that intuition arises when the mind unwittingly sidesteps the self-locking objectification system under which it normally labors. Intuition then expresses the underlying power of wholeness, as it informs the particular fragments that are relevant to you the researcher. It hasn't only become the subject of your search, it has become your best guide in conducting the search.

The second preparatory stage will be to secure the appropriate criteria for distinguishing between intuition and imagination.

[203] Philip Goldberg develops this idea through a plethora of examples in *The Intuitive Edge,* Turnstone, Wellingborough, 1985.

Intuition always leads to something real. Imagination always leads to something wishful. The good researcher is he who, by applying the scientific method within an appropriate epistemology, is able to tell the two apart. Intuition shows him what to look for and why it is significant to do so. It acts like a time-saver. If after several trials the scientist fails to find tangible evidence for his intuition, he knows that it was no more than imagination.

However, by and large this will not happen if the researcher has developed discernment and self-discipline. Genuine intuition, the product of the free-flowing connection of everything to everything else, not only tells you what to look for. It tells you what experiments to conduct and how to interpret the facts you come up with. It also tells you which practical and theoretical considerations to leave out of the picture. Intuition often carries its own rationale, which may be different, or even opposite, to the rationale you had been following until that moment. You must be in a position to adopt it.

The third and last preparatory step for investigating intuition will be to consciously cultivate your sensibilities. They will keep open your channel of communication with the whole, which is indispensable if you want to study intuition and have it guide your steps. It will also make certain that no aspect of your study is formalized in a way that prevents the upsurge of the unexpected. Nature is far too subtle to allow herself to be trapped in any pattern, including the pattern of no-pattern. The name of the game is openness—openness to everything, even to contraction when contraction prevents openness from spending itself into chaos.

Inquiring into the nature of intuition exhausts the list of general projects which a *self-reflective interdisciplinary science of consciousness* could undertake after reaching maturity. It is no longer possible for science to ignore the consciousness component. Researchers must learn to see what they project on the subject they are studying, but also what unmediated nature projects on them. Therein lies the challenge and opportunity of a *self-reflective interdisciplinary science of consciousness.* New information requires new eyes to perceive it—and a strong heart to feel it.

Part III

A SCIENCE TOWARD THE LIMITS

Chapter 11

TRUTH, REALITY AND OBJECTIFICATION: Toward an epistemology and pre-epistemology of consciousness

He thought he saw a Banker's Clerk
Descending from a bus:
He looked again and found it was
A Hippopotamus:
"If this should stay to dine," he said,
"There won't be much for us."
Edward Lear

There is no inductive method which can lead
to the fundamental concepts of physics.
Albert Einstein

We find pleasure in manipulating the world so that it fits into a
symbolic Procrustean bed—and when it does fit and seems to
obey symbolic rules, we find the result comforting, even beautiful.
Terrence Deacon

Many researchers claim that thanks to the new highly sophisticated brain scanning techniques, the investigation of consciousness has now yielded significant results. This is true only if we equate the discovery of mind-brain correlations with consciousness. For those of us who feel that consciousness reflects something altogether more than the mechanics of its operation, the scanning techniques haven't done much.

It thus becomes necessary to approach consciousness research from an angle that promises to yield more interesting results. One way of doing this would be to research consciousness on a non-local level, in addition to the local one that is being currently investigated. Finding out which specific groups of neurons fire when we are in love, or when we solve differential equations, doesn't tell us much about why these neurons get aroused in the first place, or why they (often) fire in synchrony.

It is like claiming that Bach's "Prelude and Fugue in D minor" is rendered audible by the little felt hammers hitting the metallic chords in the piano-mechanism. We may know all about this mechanism without being able to play the piano. Or we may be able to play the piano without knowing anything about the mechanism.

Adding a non-local dimension to the local one in consciousness studies will prove essential for eventually establishing a *self-reflective interdisciplinary science of consciousness* that will consider reference to wholeness as its most fundamental activity. This non-local dimension will have the same significance for the proposed new science as understanding the quantum vacuum has for particle physics today. They both start from something that can only be described as "indivisible existence."

How consciousness objectifies reality

A host of particular questions will have to be answered as we begin to examine consciousness with an eye for wholeness. For example, is dualism only a cultural phenomenon and if so, can an increasingly non-local understanding of consciousness get rid of it? Does rationality arise from dualism and if so, how do the principles informing formal logic compare with those informing other approaches to reality like myth, poetry or intuition? Is it possible to develop a trans-conceptual—and why not, a trans-rational—approach?

One thing researchers will discover early on as they embark on such local-non-local research is the following: not just ordinary things, but all perceptions depend on how we objectify reality, both tangible and intangible.

Objectification is usually assumed to be a straightforward operation. In fact, it represents a subtle and complex process, subject to many constraints and qualifications. Objects are of course real enough in themselves. But they reflect the reality of a self-developing juncture in time and space. They don't constitute a permanent state.

Let us see what justifies this flexible understanding of objectification. Two points need to be emphasized.

To begin with, objectification relates to something we can call "organizational prudence." Nature sees to it that we are always in a position to handle circumstances in the best way possible for what we are. To achieve this, we objectify "things" in a way that allows us to register them as they occur.[204] When we don't need them, the "things" maintain themselves in a state of limbo within our memory. When we do, they automatically recall themselves to active service, informing the way we perceive and handle the new circumstances. Objects don't only re-configure themselves physically as the present changes. They constantly re-configure themselves within our understanding on the basis of where we stand in the present moment.

Second, Heisenberg's famous uncertainty principle is usually taken to mean that knowledge of physical reality is uncertain. Here his principle is taken to mean that one can never know the world in its entirety by objectifying it. The whole enlightens the parts. The parts don't enlighten the whole.[205] We can become conscious only of a tiny fraction of the world at a time and we can become aware of it only in the light of a particular purpose. The whole abides beyond our grasp, quite simply because it is not a "thing" to be grasped in the first place.[206]

An epistemology of objectification

Objectification also relates to perceptual assumptions. We need to know not just what our objectifications include and how. We need to know what they exclude and why. In other words, we need to become aware of what conditions our prehension of both the external and the internal world.

---

[204] "Organizational prudence" was undermined when humans began to lock into their objectifications through the invention first of agriculture, and later of writing. Nature originally just sensitised us to certain reality patterns, so that we could then recall them when confronted with real life situations. We would then be in a position to project these reality patterns onto present entities and situations, thereby getting immediately the picture of how we need to act. But this is no longer possible today. Having endorsed for thousands of years the practice of locking into our objectifications, we recall these rather than the reality patterns that inform them. We are thus unable to draw from bygone experience—to conceive the present circumstances as they are and to react to them effectively. We come up continuously with fossilised messages from a past that doesn't relate to the present.

[205] The one big exception arises when the individual sees the part as a local manifestation of the whole. People were able to do that before they adopted the habit of self-locking objectification after the invention of agriculture.

[206] As John Barrow has called attention to in his *Theories of Everything* (1990), the efforts by physicists to create a unified field theory that would explain everything about creation through one simple equation, are doomed to failure. The degree of generality such an equation would require is so vast that it would become counterproductive. There is much more to creation than can be anticipated or put into an equation. As Ilya Prigogine has pointed out, creativity constitutes an integral part of creation. The universe is not a predetermined clockwork orange.

Here, conceiving reality in terms of unchanging objects plays a vital role. Not everybody views them as the key to understanding. Dante equates hell with a lack of mobility, a sense of being constricted. Karl Marx claims that the world is made up by "activities" of varying intensity and character. Ilya Prigogine sees physical reality being composed of "events." Albert Einstein rejects the conception of particles as "things." He describes them as "local excitations of the one field."

In view of the fact that so many people are intensely preoccupied over such questions, Einstein proposes that scientists go deeper in their investigations than they are normally wont. He says: "Science without epistemology . . . ends up primitive and rudderless."[207] It stands to reason that if one's perception is informed by the notion of hard and unchanging objects, it will yield a quite different picture than if it is informed by the notion of dynamic occurrences.

For Arthur Eddington this realization was an invitation to tackle the role of consciousness itself in the investigation of reality. He speaks of what he calls "selective subjectivism."

David Lorimer sums up his approach in the following words: "Eddington imagined an *ichthyologist* casting for fish in the ocean with a net having two-inch holes. The employment of such a device might lead him to the general conclusion that no sea creatures are smaller than two inches long and that they all have gills. Eddington's point was that the nature of the observer and his instruments limits and conditions the kind of knowledge he can acquire."[208]

Why traditional epistemology doesn't hold

The insights of four great men in physics and one in formal logic enlighten the close relationship between the ways our consciousness operates and what we conceive as "real."

The first great name is David Bohm. "The word 'reality,'" he reminds us, "is derived from the Latin roots 'thing' (res) and 'think' (revi). Consequently, 'reality' means 'everything we can think about.' This differs from 'that which merely is,' as the notion of reality is normally summed up. No idea can capture 'truth' in the sense of that-which-is."[209] Or to use the famous formulation by Parmenides: "Comprehending and being are one and the same."[210]

---

[207] Quoted in Paul Schilpp, *Albert Einstein: Philosopher-Scientist*, Tudor, New York 1949, p 684.
[208] David Lorimer, *All in One,* Arkana, London, 1990, p 253.
[209] David Bohm, lecture to professional physicists in the Lawrence Berkeley Laboratory, April 1977.
[210] Parmenides, Fr. 3.

The second big physicist who has something to say on the mind-matter link, is Niels Bohr. He writes: "An independent reality in the ordinary physical sense can be ascribed neither to the phenomena, nor to the agencies of observation."[211]

The third big name on the list is Werner Heisenberg. His uncertainty principle demonstrates that we can never obtain a full picture of what's going on in particle physics. "What we observe," he points out, "is not nature itself, but nature exposed to our methods of questioning."[212] The same applies to religion and to spirituality. Unless we are mystics of the highest order, we don't experience naked spirit. We experience spirit exposed to the quality of our quest and the types of thinking familiar to us.

The fourth name is Albert Einstein. He makes the important point that what we study in science is the various models we make of nature. These models, Einstein maintains, are nothing but "free creations of the human mind."[213] We use them to express our need for understanding what we perceive in a consistent (i.e., a rational) way. What nature is in her own right, Einstein, like Kant, maintains we cannot know.

Finally, we come to Kurt Gödel, that master logician. Whereas the great physicists of the 20th century point to the fact that we are conditioned in our ways of perceiving and thinking—and therefore need to become aware of the fact—Gödel shows that turning to the logic of a closed formal system will not take us further either. Objectivity is not an intellectual commodity that can be secured by way of strict logical extrapolation.

Through his famous 1930s non-completion theorem, Gödel makes us realize that our formal proof systems are incapable of ascertaining what is true about them in the first instance, and about nature in the second. These formal systems are supposed to be closed to influences not arising from within them. Gödel proves that this is not the case. No formal system can be absolutely closed, or sufficient unto itself, as it is supposed to. It is condemned by the very nature of the objectification process to remain open. Nature's interpenetration is mirrored in theory's interconnectedness.

It would then appear that for all their efforts to the contrary, modern physics and mathematics have not established a fully objective system for investigating nature or for establishing its truth. They have merely introduced a conceptual circularity into their understanding.

[211] Niels Bohr, *Atomic Theory and the Descriptions of Nature,* Cambridge University Press, Cambridge, 1934, p 53.
[212] Werner Heisenberg, *Physics and Philosophy,* Harper Torchbooks, New York, 1958, p 58.
[213] Albert Einstein, *On Physical Reality,* Franklin Institute Journal, 221, 1936, p 35.

Conceptual circularity operates on two levels. On the first, circular movement starts from the scientist as a human being. Biological specification, cultural influences, subconscious disposition, intellectual temperament, education and personal belief all determine what scientists are able to choose as subject matter and how they treat it. And on the second, as Wittgenstein insisted throughout his life, there are aspects of reality which cannot be explored, leave alone understood, by reductionist or mathematical analysis.

Objects and objectivity

That science selects and colors objectivity is obvious from the fact that not everybody interprets the same facts in the same way. B. Alan Wallace brings out a particular aspect of this: "Among the many problems with the realist position," he says, "is the fact that multiple, mutually incompatible theories can often be presented that equally account for a given body of scientific evidence. A philosophically unreflecting approach to science gives the impression that objective reality screens out false hypotheses, leading to only one true theory. In fact, multiple hypotheses are often put forth, and the choice among them is based on various human factors."[214]

The reason for this is that in the minds of too many scientists, objectivity has been equated with the presence, the attributes and the certifiability of objects, as conceived by the senses. This tendency survives in spite of the fact that scientists today know reality differs from what the senses make of it. However, the old understanding of things still persists. It forms the core idea of objectivity.

Five points are relevant here. First, objects are part of what exists; objectivity is part of how we apprehend what exists. Second, both in the fifth century BC and during the 18th century AD, the quest for objectivity arose as a reaction to blatantly false claims to "certain" knowledge on the part of religious authorities. Third, no object is just itself. It ties in with other objects that may, or may not, be detectable. Fourth, any object depends on what the observer is interested in apprehending. It doesn't depend on what is actually there for the seeing. Fifth, forces, feelings, patterns, resonances and relationships in the physical world are seen to have the same characteristics as "hard" objects.

In a nutshell: we can never be absolutely objective. If we could, we would not be observing. By its very nature, observation entails discrimination. And the best way for handling this is to become aware of what lies behind this discrimination, and why.

---

[214] B. Alan Wallace, *Choosing Reality*. Snow Lion Publication, 1996, p 13.

Perhaps in the future we will develop an attitude that will broaden our conception of factuality. If this happens, such a broader conception will not supplant the old one. It will complement it, deepen it and enrich it. It will encompass both what currently appears to be making it to objecthood and what breaks through the confines of object-mediated rationality.

A pre-epistemic examination of objectification

All these theoretical considerations demand of the consciousness investigator to go much deeper into his subject than either paradigm, psychology, brain research or even epistemology allow. A level of understanding needs to be accessed which is here called "pre-epistemic."

The notion of a pre-epistemic inquiry doesn't touch on what we make of our objectifications, as normal epistemology does. It entails studying the process of objectification itself. We find out how we isolate and structure the stimuli we receive through the senses.[215] Following this, we examine how we evaluate these stimuli and what yarn we weave around them.

Conception is not possible without perception, perception is not possible without representation, and representation is not possible without objectification. Thus, if epistemology is concerned with how we know what we know all the way down to representation, pre-epistemology is concerned with how we objectify what we objectify, so that we can know what we do know. Usually objectivity is believed to apply only to how we think about things. It should apply also to how we apprehend the things to begin with.

As already pointed out, objectification is rooted in very deep processes. The most important consideration is how we distinguish among fully objectified entities, entities that haven't yet fully objectified and entities that are merging back into their non-objectifiable origins.[216]

---

[215] Information about objects doesn't necessarily come through the senses operating separately from one another. It can come also through all of them put together in what is known as "synaesthesia." The synaesthetic experience can be direct or indirect. One may conceive an object through all the senses simultaneously, or one sense may dominate while the others "support" it from below the level of actual experience.

[216] By "fully objectified entities" are here meant those units of perception which have reached the full expression of their formal potentialities.

Man continues the example of nature

Another very important aspect is what causes things to be objectified at all. On the surface it appears that objectification depends on the ontological predilection of the apprehending individual. The history of the universe, however, shows that objectification doesn't only happen in the human mind. It starts from nature and forms its backbone.

Nature comes up with something concrete, but it doesn't do so for the sake of concreteness. It does it for the sake of being able to ascertain functionally what needs to be perfected in the entity concretized. That is why nature favors both static and dynamic processes. That is, furthermore, why man needs to emulate how nature operates.

It is perhaps impossible to know how objectification starts outside of us. But it is perhaps possible to know what the conditions are for some external or internal need to thrust itself on our attention, so that we start to objectify it.

Projections, contexts and evaluations

But there also is the question of what we "add" to or change in the subjects we objectify. We can, for example, objectify them in their immediate context. Or we can objectify them in a much broader, or even unsuitable, context. On the other hand, we can isolate the subjects so thoroughly from their environment that we shut out all contexts and remote influences. A lot of modern thinking does exactly that.

An additional issue is: do we perceive objects as building blocks, or as local manifestations of a qualitative and indefinable whole? [217] This question is important because the individuals who sense a whole underlying their particular objectifications, handle them better on the one hand and tend to develop a more inclusive attitude on the other.

In last analysis, the question seems to be: do we actually apprehend anything as it is? More significantly, can we claim that our abstractions of objects reflect the same qualities as the objects themselves? Are we able to pursue an

[217] Alfred North Whitehead wrote a whole book (*The Concept of Nature,* 1920, *Whitehead Anthology,* Northrop and Cross, eds, Macmillan. New York, 1953) to show that even such seemingly objective concepts as time and space actually originate in the senses—and are therefore aspects of conscious experience. They cannot be considered objective components of reality. To illustrate how much we edit what comes in through the eyes, Evan Harris Walker mentions in his "The Nature of Consciousness," (*Mathematical Biosciences,* Vol. 7, 1970, pp 131-178) "that the information carried by the optic nerve occupies ten-to-the-fourth channels [fibers], each capable of transferring about ten-to-the-sixth bits/sec!"

ongoing dialogue between what the objects are and their framework, as, for example, happens between genes and their environment?[218]

Function exceeds structure

The realization that what we apprehend doesn't reflect faithfully either what is going on in the brain, or what is going on in the world, has profound implications.[219] One is that we allow reality to dictate the terms whereby we think of it and work with it, regardless of the older ideas we may have entertained about it.

For example, in inorganic matter the scientist gets wind of what is happening by observing physical and chemical interactions. In organic matter he can do this less effectively. Physicist Walter Elsasser and biochemist Marian J. Wnuk point out why.[220] Organic matter, they claim, is more complex functionally than it is structurally. A complicated operation doesn't require an equally complicated physical substrate of the kind that correlates function to structure in inanimate matter.[221]

One can go even further than Elsasser and Wnuk. One can maintain that the above disparity between structure and function outlines the essential difference between animate and inanimate matter. In nature there is no parity between

---

[218] In order to pursue such a dialogue as an ongoing process, it will be necessary to create new types of symbols that will denote the dynamic character of both the physical and the mental processes. These new symbols will be empowered in such a way that they point to open-ended self-organisation—including potential or implicit states. Thus, the realities of non-linear systems will be absorbed back into their semiography. The mathematical elaboration of process-bound reality will thus be greatly simplified. More importantly, the habit of apprehending relationships in terms of objects will be reversed, so that we start again apprehending objects (mental or physical) in terms of relationships. The old dominant grammar and syntax, with its emphasis on past, present and future tenses, will have lost its stranglehold on our understanding. We will still use it, of course. But it will not dominate our thinking.

[219] See also the special issue of the *Journal of Consciousness Studies* under the general title IS THE VISUAL WORLD A GRAND ILLUSION? (Vol. 9, No 5/6, 2002, especially the articles "Is the Visual World a Grand Illusion?" by Alva Noe, "Visual World: Construction or Reconstruction?" by Donald D. Hoffman and Antonio M. Rodriquez, and "Is Seeing All It Seems? Action, Reason and the Grand Illusion" by Mark Rowlands.)

[220] Marian Wnuk expresses this idea in her "The Electromagnetic Nature of Life: The Contribution of W. Sedlak to the Understanding of the Essence of Life," *Frontier Perspectives,* Spring 2001, pp 32-35. Walter Elsasser expresses the same idea in his *Reflections on a Theory of Organisms,* Editions Orbis Publishing, Frelighsburg, Quebec, 1987, p 41. Having first presented the point that living organisms are much more complex than inorganic matter, Elsasser makes the following observation: "If a complex heterogeneous structure . . . is large enough, the number of possible patterns [of interaction] might vastly exceed the number of members of the class that can exist in a finite world."

[221] This applies particularly to those levels of organisation that are determined by unchanging basic laws—those rooted in Planck's constant.

being and doing. If inanimate matter usually is more than it does, animate matter always does more than it is—and consciousness does even more.

Learning to see in the light of the seen

This forces us to look for the basic principles of objectivity, if such there be. Since science bases on it its very "raison d'etre," then investigation of objectivity should become the next goal. As has already been suggested, to advance objectivity we must take into account all those insights from modern physics, mathematics, and biology which point to a new, dynamic and flexible notion of nature.

Finally, the question will be asked: Is partial objectivity an option, and if so, how much of it do we need before being able to practice reliable science? How flexible can such a partial objectivity be? How about the possibility that there exist such "states" as non-conceptual objectivity and non-conceptual subjectivity? More importantly, is there a way that subjectivity and objectivity can coincide experientially, and thus illumine our understanding?

A new concept of objectivity

The purpose of this kind of questioning is not to get rid of the notion of objectivity. The purpose is to conceive objectivity in more realistic terms. We need to enter dynamics and fuzziness into our conceptualization of objects. Particular objects will then be seen as their stories much more than they are seen as their chemical or structural make-up. The ancient Greek practice of calling science a "narrative" will have become relevant again.

Of course, scientists should insist on objectivity. What they should avoid is to project onto entities on the road toward objectification something abstracted from a different level of either organization or abstraction. No longer should such scientists assume that their own openness of mind, depth of understanding or flexibility of approach exhausts the openness, profundity or flexibility of nature itself.

Even less should scientists assume that what they are able to conceive of reality exhausts its mode of being. Or that it is possible to discover all its modes of being. Nature may be conceivable in many ways—some not available right now and some becoming available in the future through either new tools, or new ways of looking. But there can never be a perfect equation between what exists and what can be conceived.

Some aspects of nature cannot be conceived at all. Others, though conceivable, don't yield accurate accounts. As J. M. Burgers points out when speaking about cellular growth: "The amount of necessary information [for this growth] far exceeds the amount of data available." He adds that the missing data may be available through a "conceptual activity" that is not based on the usual objectification processes.[222]

The inevitability of bias

This shows that objectivity is impaired when we strongly adhere to a paradigm or reigning theory. It is well known that scientists are struck with results supporting a thesis dear to them, while they tend to downgrade other results that don't. Michael Polanyi draws attention to the fact that instead of constantly seeking evidence to check out their ideas, such scientists simply ignore the data that doesn't accommodate their ideas.

The second way reflects a subtler form of bias. Philip M. Merikle mentions impressive evidence showing that we are capable of receiving information unconsciously. This information imprints itself more powerfully on the brain when "personally relevant." Merikle adds that not all individuals are equally sensitive to unconscious perceptions. He concludes that given "we now have the tools to distinguish between the effects of conscious and unconscious perception, it should be possible to tease apart the factors that determine how different individuals respond to unconsciously perceived information."[223]

Absolute objectivity may not be possible, or even useful. But we have two alternatives. The first is to adopt the Delphic admonition "know thyself." It will help us reach the height of objectivity through plumbing the depths of subjectivity. Amit Goswami believes that we have the capacity to achieve this. We can recognize the conditioned part of our thinking for what it is and then ignore it, or even discard it.[224]

The second alternative is to see that our bias doesn't necessarily distort reality. It distorts only a conception of it that is itself biased in favor of a too purist, too mechanistic or too fragmentary understanding. After all, on the molecular

---

[222] J.M. Burgers, "Causality and Anticipation, and Their Meaning for Biology," communicated at a meeting on April 29, 1972, *Proceedings Royal Netherland Academy of Science*, Section B, Physical Science, p 384.

[223] Philip M. Merikle, "Psychological investigation of unconscious perception," *Journal of Consciousness Studies,* 5, No 1, 1998, pp 5–18.

[224] Amit Goswami, *The Self-Aware Universe: How Consciousness Creates the World,* Simon and Schuster, New York, 1993, p 193.

level of organic matter (proteins, amino acids, etc.) there is plenty of bias in favor of faster evolution than randomness allows. The resonances discovered by Prigogine in unstable systems probably play a significant role here.

Be that as it may, after the introduction of fuzzy logic, bias as such shouldn't be the issue in science. The issue should be four interlinked questions. First, to what extent is nature biased in its self-organizing operations? Second, to what extent do we, as observers, introduce our own bias on top of this? Third, to what degree are we able to merely reflect nature's own bias, without adding this something on top of it? And fourth, which kind of bias on our part best supports nature's bias?

Of course, all these considerations outline an approach that is less than the pure objectivity we have been striving for until now. An entity, a relationship, a situation isn't objective when it obeys some set of formal rules. It is objective when it uses separate existence to manifest qualitative wholeness.

There is no lack of order in this understanding of objectivity. It's just a different kind of order. Autistic rationalism is out. Self-critical insightfulness is in.

Chapter 12

TRANS-MODEL ARGUMENTS: Learning how to learn from nature

The line between us and nature cannot be clear or definite
and indeed must remain in (a state of) constant negotiation.
Harry Hunt

Measurements, ostensibly "ahead" in time, seemingly
determine retrospectively an earlier particle position.
B. Greene

The intentionality of all consciousness is always unfolding
ahead of itself, endlessly carrying forward
toward what is beyond itself.
F. Brentano

Openness toward nature's *own* manner of doing things is the only way of getting to know what makes nature up and how. When society loses its knack for doing this, as ours has, it must try to recapture the lost ability. Without a concerted effort to know how nature does things on its own terms, scientists are not able to fathom it beyond a certain level of abstraction. They remain trapped in fragmented perceptions, reductionist modes of enquiry and humanly irrelevant practices. They may get to understand how they perceive. They don't get to perceive how, or why, they understand.

This restricted acquaintance with nature is reflected in the denotative language employed for representing it. There is no doubt that nature avoids delineating itself too clearly. It would be profitable to ask why. Heisenberg's uncertainty principle and Zadeh's fuzzy logic point to the ultimate limitations of objectifying consciousness. They could become our advisers on this tricky path to knowledge, alongside Xenophanes, Heraclitus, Socrates, Heidegger, Merlau Ponty, Gödel, and Sperry.

One thing is certain: no longer can we take for granted the ability of objectifications to carry us beyond our linear ways of thinking. The finite cannot investigate the infinite, the concrete cannot make out the fluid, the thinking fails to fathom what cannot be thought out. Gilbert Adair argues the point while reviewing Bart Kosko's *Fuzzy Thinking: The New Science of Fuzzy Logic*. "The best defence of fuzzy logic," he writes, "is that it works . . . Its fundamental breakthrough is to have shown how it becomes possible to emancipate logical thought from the Procrustean bed of the mathematical or scientific models."[225]

Before embarking on a search into why nature is as fuzzy as it appears, certain conditions need to be met. To begin with, the seeker must penetrate to the ontological depths of the physical things, states, events or relationships he is studying. It doesn't mean that he will now view things, states, events or relationships as definable only in terms of their roots in wholeness. It means that he will view them also as not fully abstractable.

Words follow in the footsteps of creation. Creation doesn't follow in the footsteps of words, Luther's translation of the opening sentence of St. John's Gospel notwithstanding.[226] When describing how entities come into being, one has to take into account the relative specificity of nature's constituent parts. Here our un-tutored consciousness can play tricks on us. Bertrand Russell draws attention to this danger. "The Law of the Excluded Middle," he maintains, "is true when precise symbols are employed, but it is not true when symbols are vague, as in fact all symbols are."[227]

To see things clearly isn't only a question of avoiding the projection of our conditioned mindset onto them. It is a question of realizing that we can never see an entity in the fullness of its being. This is not due to some weakness of our conceptual apparatus, or failure of our mindset. It is due to the fact that, in order to exist at all, each entity must maintain a connectedness to both other entities and to the whole.

In other words, the reality of an entity implies both its separateness from the whole, thanks to which it has become what it is, and its continuing relationship with it, thanks to which the entity appears to be remaining separate. It is the web of this subtle relationship that we cannot penetrate with our senses. What we can do is to experience it. We can comprehend why pre-literate languages use words for pointing simultaneously toward and away from specific meaning.

Inspired by James and Dewey, Iain McGilchrist informs us on why this

---

[225] Quotation from Gilbert Adair's review of Bart Kosko's *Fuzzy Thinking: The New Science of Fuzzy Logic,* Flamingo, an Imprint of Harper Collins Publishers, London, 1994, p 1.

[226] Martin Luther translated the Greek term "logos" as "das Wort" (the word), in spite of the fact that "logos" had originally meant "relationship" and/or "collecting," an activity akin to "relating." Collectivity relates things to one another and whoever does this also arranges for the things to connect in logical ways—hence the derived sense of "reason," which the term eventually took on.

[227] Bertrand Russell, "Vagueness," *Australian Journal of Philosophy*, Vol. 1, 1923.

happens. "According to the left hemisphere," he writes, "understanding is built up from the parts; one starts from one certainty . . . and advances as if building a wall, from the bottom up . . . According to the right hemisphere, understanding is derived from the whole, since it is only in the light of the whole that one can truly understand the nature of the parts."[228]

This is the notion with which we will now attempt to grapple.

Beyond solipsism and objectivism

A precondition for getting a full grasp of this issue is for the individual to be willing (and able) to free his mind from current epistemological exigencies. He must go about this, however, without totally rejecting the exigencies. He needs, instead, to systematically de-linearize his mind.

Furthermore, he needs to do so in such a manner that he can use the appropriate conceptual approach for assessing the qualitative nature of what he is observing. When he is dealing with a situation requiring conventional thinking, he employs conventional terms. When he is dealing with a situation requiring trans-organizational thinking, he employs terms pointing to trans-organizational realities.

Werner Heisenberg explains why it is so important to find a language that doesn't impose on an object or state some conceptual framework from without its domain. Discussing the particles in the nucleus of atoms, he observes: "It is not surprising that our language should be incapable of describing the processes occurring within atoms. For it was invented to describe the experiences of daily life, and these consist only of processes involving exceedingly large numbers of atoms."[229]

Describing things through a language appropriate to them is like inviting them to tell us their story in their own words. Imagine that the "new scientist" has developed a *bi-hemispheric intelligence* and a *trans-rational logic*, which allow him to understand what's happening beyond the strictly definable concepts, categories and rationales of "normal" scientific thinking. The two greatest self-locking objectifications in the history of philosophy—solipsistic subjectivity (the view that the self is all that knows) and alienating objectivity (the view that things exist apart from our perception of them) have been abandoned. In their stead a third

[228] Iain McGilchrist, *The Master and his Emissary,* Yale University Press, New Haven and London, 2009, p 142.
[229] Werner Heisenberg, *The Physical Principles of the Quantum Theory,* University of Chicago Press, Chicago, 1930, p 33.

option comes to view. It is based on what is here called *trans-modal understanding*.

When under the spell of this third option, the new scientist is in a position to release his objectifications, whatever they may be. In this endeavor he can be guided by Iain McGilchrist's insight that it is possible to know something only from a "somewhere" not informed by a fixed epistemology.[230] Valid knowledge is that alone which a sufficient number of individuals have repeatedly observed and consider factually true. Solipsistic subjectivity and alienating objectivity give way to insights, which a large number of people have independently acknowledged to be true, but only after having fully freed their minds from pre-conceived ideas.

After exposing oneself to the repercussions of McGilchrist's insight, a freer look at physical reality becomes possible. It weaves the detailed knowledge of particulars into the qualitative experience of the whole informing them.

The individual is now in a position to distinguish the subtle differences in the objects he is observing. One of the first such differences is that between the physical things, states, events or relationships themselves and that which the observer thinks these entities actually are. Another difference is that between the logic currently accepted by the scientific community at large and the logic of the entities under scrutiny.[231]

To distinguish such differences, the individual must develop not only *bi-hemispheric intelligence*. He must develop *trans-modal understanding*. He needs them both if he is to identify the delicate shadings among the various things, states, events or relationships he is studying. Life has granted him a capacity which allows him to isolate altogether different aspects of reality to those he had been familiar with in the past.

There is an even more fundamental way for consciousness to act. On the one hand, it can build up growing pressure for more composite physical units not only in linear space/time, but across and beyond linear space/time altogether.

On the other hand, consciousness can develop a growing awareness of the interdependence among space, time and form. *The universe builds itself up so that it can empower consciousness to build up the universe. Consciousness stimulates the universe*

[230] Op. cit. p 141.

[231] The correspondence between human understanding and nature's processes or forms has been much discussed in ancient as well as in modern times. Plato and Goethe both say that there must be something sun-like in us for us to be able to perceive the sun. Fairly recently R. Arnheim writes: "Mental depth is not thinkable without an awareness of physical depth. Hence the figurative quality of all theoretical speech . . . Man can confidently rely on the senses to supply him with the perceptual equivalents of all theoretical notions because these notions derive from sensory experience in the first place." (R. Arnheim, *Visual Thinking*, University of California Press, Berkeley, 1969, p 76.)

to complexify, so that the universe can stimulate consciousness to complexify.[232] Each of the two processes invites conditions that will help reality become more of what it has already been.

Grasping what exceeds our grasp

Science has so far clung to the notion that conceptualization is a question of putting together various pieces of the perceptible in a coherent fashion. But it has not enquired too deeply into how the perceptible itself is formed. Today this is beginning to change. New research shows that what we perceive depends, to a large extent, on how we objectify, weigh and appreciate nature. That is, it depends on how we have conditioned our consciousness to actually work.[233]

This includes what neurophysiological dynamics and what subjective influences are in vogue at the moment of enquiry. Novelty doesn't depend just on uncovering new data along some path. It depends on discovering completely new paths and on introducing altogether new ways of appreciating the landscape surrounding them.

Yet another way in which consciousness forms and transforms reality is awareness of the circumstances and dynamics involved in ever more pronounced complexification. As the individual becomes increasingly aware of how his conditioning prevents him from understanding the trans-modal structure of nature, he lifts his consciousness out of the local/temporal frame of the block universe; as he gives it space in this way, he starts to become familiar with the trans-modal processes and functions of nature; as he becomes familiar with these processes and functions, he gets to understand them better; and as he begins to understand them better, he finally learns to handle them in their own light.

This perception of the transformative role of a consciousness that has gradually freed itself from its space/time shackles, is self-releasing. The individual senses something because it isn't present; he knows it because he doesn't define it. Mere

---

[232] H. Hunt elucidates this point when he writes: "An illustration of the direct correspondences between consciousness and physical reality would be the way in which the basic form constants of meanders, branching, bursts, spirals and lattices form and reform on multiple levels of physical reality (molecular, organic, galactic) and also spontaneously and precisely reappear as the 'hallucinatory form constants' of psychedelic drugs and deep meditation. Their further visionary elaboration as the geometric mandala patterns of Eastern Tantra, shamanic art and Christian and Islamic designs was of great interest to C. G. Jung and part of his understanding of the underlying unity between his psychic 'archetypes' and physical matter." (H. Hunt, "The Truth Value of Mystical Experience," *Journal of Consciousness Studies,* Vol 3, No 12, 2006, p 15.)

[233] See for abundant information on this type of research in Iain McGilchrist *The Master and His Emissary,* Yale University Press, New Haven and London, 2009.

information cannot dispel the ignorance of an individual unable to experience the trans-modal functioning of nature with its non-perceptible, non-rational and non-thinkable overtones.

It is because the block universe equally exists in and beyond linear space and time that a seemingly irrelevant question can bring forth a relevant answer. The world doesn't suddenly restrict its role to that of an interlocutor engaged in personal dialogue with the questioner. *All* of the universe responds to any particular question put to it at any time, place or circumstance with *all* its variability, complexity and trans-logical rationale.

The two conditions for that to happen are (a) the presence of a deep and justified intentionality on the part of the inquiring individuals; and (b) the timeliness of the question asked. People must be so certain of the response they need that it doesn't even appear to them as a need. It appears like a completely natural outcome of ordinary events. An ancient Chinese text puts it this way:

> The right moment becomes the wrong,
> before one can take a breath.
> One who acts too soon anticipates the opportunity
> And one who acts too late misses the boat.
> The sun revolves, the moon wheels its course
> And the right moment waits for no man.
> Thus the sage values an inch of time
> Over a foot of precious jade.
> He knows that the right moment
> Is hard to catch and easy to miss.[234]

Asking the question with the proper intention at the right moment collapses into objecthood previously unformulated trans-local and trans-temporal states. These manifest in ways dictated by the specific stage of the evolution the questioner has reached. The particular piece of advice that the questioner needs for advancing on the particular path he is following reflects back on him in the guise of the specific response he is receiving.

---

[234] D.C. Lau and Roger T. Ames, translators, *Yuan Dao: Tracing Dao to Its Source*, Ballantine Publishing Group, New York, 1998, p 39. (The English translation was here rendered in a slightly edited version by the author.)

The right answer to the wrong question

Seen from this angle, it doesn't really matter what any question put to nature *is*. It matters *why* the questioner is asking. Neither does it matter how the questioner describes the answer. It matters what the questioner is actually sensitive to, to what degree and for what reason. The extent and depth of the questioner's sensitivity determines the content and relevance of the answers he receives.

Indeed, the more mistaken thinking and irrelevant information is reflected in his question, the more right thinking and relevant information the block universe often offers back to him! His false, incomplete or misconceived premises evoke true, complete and well-conceived responses because of the purity and power of his intention. There develops an increasingly powerful instinct for understanding and handling issues, which seem irrelevant, random and strange. Irrelevance then gives way to relevance, randomness to determinism, strangeness to familiarity and desultory motion to directed progression.

The block universe (or trans-modal reality) triggers all this by helping the questioner unbind his mind and unlock hitherto unapparent information. The questioner doesn't analyze anything and he doesn't construct anything. He just opens up to what lies under his nose. He invites relevant and meaningful information to surface through what he has not been reasonable, habitual or hopeful about—and *because* he has not been. The quality of his intention to get to the bottom of it all is the moving force

The co-presence of opposites

One indisputable certainty about the block universe is that it affects all aspects of physical existence, including the seemingly anomalous modalities of non-locality, non-temporality, retro-causality and non-linearity. These states undermine any absolute Newtonian conception of locality, temporality, causality or linearity, which may have survived the appearance of quantum mechanics and general relativity in the early 20th century.

Robert Jahn and Brenda Dunne have a lot to say about such opposite conceptions and the possibility of bridging the gap between them through a coherent theory. Discussing the famous wave-particle duality, they write: "The wave and particle perspectives are not mutually exclusive; rather some mixture of both is necessary to represent them fully. Our interpretation of this irreducible complementarity . . . is that it is not the physical world per se that imposes such [a] dichotomy; it is our consciousness. More precisely, it is imposed . . . by a consciousness interacting with its physical environment . . . a consciousness that has conceived both particles and waves and found it necessary and useful to represent it."[235]

A trans-modal consciousness would not suffer from such a dichotomy. Still less would it need the dichotomy to act. Trans-modal consciousness would know that wave behavior is dictated by the temporal modality of existence, while particle behavior is dictated by the non-temporal modality.

In other words, trans-modal consciousness would know that wave behavior focuses on self-escaping movement, while particle behavior focuses on self-defining structure. In the words of Heraclitus: "People don't understand how a thing [can] agree with itself [while] being at variance with it, [thereby] creating a harmonious [relationship] like [that which occurs when using] a bow or lyre."[236] Elsewhere Heraclitus points out: "An unapparent connection is stronger than an apparent one."[237] "Nature loves to conceal itself."[238]

Jahn and Dunne attribute the irreconcilability of opposites in our culture to the paradigm we are following. So long as "the old paradigm is retained," they write, "effects like the remote influence on physical behavior or the remote acquisition of information observed in our experiments, must [be considered] inherently anomalous.[239] But if consciousness were to allow itself the same wave/particle duality that it has already conceded to numerous physical processes, these situations would become more tractable. In particular, a wave-like consciousness could employ a lot of inference, diffraction, penetration and remote influence effects to achieve normally most of the anomalies of the particulate paradigm."[240]

The important thing to realize here is that non-locality, non-temporality, retro-causality and non-linearity should not be viewed as exclusive modalities, or even ontologies. They should be viewed as interpenetrating with locality, temporality, causality and linearity. The one modality perfectly fits in with and informs its seeming opposite.

More exactly, the two modalities merely complement, enrich and determine one another. To paraphrase Lewis Carroll's *Alice in Wonderland*, the more you are in the presence of non-locality, non-temporality, retro-causality or

---

[235] Robert Jahn and Brenda Dunne, *Margins of Reality: The Role of Consciousness in the Physical World,* A Harvest Book, Harcourt, Inc., San Diego, 1987, p 211.

[236] Heraclitus, fragment 51.

[237] Heraclitus, fragment 54.

[238] Heraclitus, fragment 123.

[239] Robert Jahn and Brenda Dunne refer here to the fascinating experiments they conducted at the Princeton University School of Engineering for 28 years, until spring 2007.

[240] Robert Jahn and Brenda Dunne, *Margins of Reality: The Role of Consciousness in the Physical World,* A Harvest Book, Harcourt, Inc., San Diego, 1987, p 212.

non-linearity, the more clearly you perceive the function of locality, temporality, causality and linearity.[241] The one simply fuses with and enlightens the other.

It is thus interesting to notice the experimental results obtained by physicist Anton Zeilinger.[242] They show that non-locality applies not merely to subatomic processes. It applies equally to atomic and hence more composite units of physical existence. Since general relativity stipulates that space and time in effect constitute a single dimension, the broadening of non-locality's purview by Zeilinger indicates that one cannot relegate locality and fragmentation to mere illusions, as Einstein did. Quite the contrary: Zeilinger's work opens a whole range of possibilities on the action of locality and non-locality on one another—not to mention beyond one another.

A self-causing, self-organizing and self-adjusting universe

Nothing of this means that the future determines the past, or that the past determines the future. It is rather that, when momentarily freed from the shackles of self-locking space and time, consciousness senses what happens in the past or the future, without having created it. It is like seeing a film a second time over. You now know how the story unfolds, but you have had nothing to do with its creation.

Another area where the block universe (or trans-modal reality) plays a constructive role, is that it acts as a protective shield for the present. Only that unfolds into recognizable form which accords with its total dynamics. Here objectification merely points to biological and cultural filters of how things may have happened. In fact, the whole universe determines the mosquito buzzing around my ear at this moment. We cannot break its appearance into smaller sections to study them separately. The mosquito is not just the product of the egg it grew out of. Nor does it reflect just the fact that the window was left open earlier, or that evolution took the particular path it did by creating insects to begin with.

So an important point needs to be raised in conclusion. The block universe primarily is the rationale informing its total dynamics—its trans-modality or trans-rationality, if you prefer. Its wholeness cannot be illumined through either

---

[241] The actual words of this passage in *Alice*. . . is put in the mouth of the Red Queen who says: "It takes all the running you can do to keep in the same place." In *Through the Looking Glass,* Carroll puts the following sentence in the mouth of the distressed rabbit: "The faster I go, the behinder I get."

[242] Anton Zeilinger, "The Message of the Quantum," *Nature,* Vol.438/8, Dec. 2005.

observation or analysis. It can be illumined only through a trans-modally functioning mind that has taken into account powerful intuitions rather than merely accurate objectifications. At the back of every recognizable cause there is a succession of progressively less recognizable conditions.

Chapter 13

TRANS-MODAL ORGANISATION: Plumbing the opportunities offered by the block universe

The story of the stars, that of life, of human beings,
and of thought is one and the same.
Yves Coppens

Physical theory is less a statement of abstract reality than
of our ability to acquire information about reality.
Robert Jahn and Brenda Dunne

Definitions are worthless in and of themselves. Their entire
value consists in the road travelled to formulate them.
Rene Schaerer

There is something intriguing about how the universe has evolved. The forms of physical existence unleashed by the big bang are not identifiable only in terms of the consciousness they have been expressions of right from the start. Neither are they restricted only to the dual fundamental modalities mentioned in the previous chapter—that associated with locality etc. and that associated with non-locality, etc. The big bang also unleashed other seemingly contradictory modalities. But these cannot be easily isolated, however objective one believes oneself to be.

Contradictory modalities can be isolated only by individuals willing (and able) to develop three important mental habits. The first is to continuously recognize that their cultural, psychological, and educational conditioning determines what can be identified. The second is their willingness to draw conclusions from this realization. And the third is to change their way of thinking in accordance with the major discoveries of 20th century science, like non-locality, non-temporality, retro-causality and others.

S. J. Goerner quotes a passage from Thomas Gentry, which illustrates this point. It goes as follows: "Imagine that the year is 1543 and that you have just completed reading the newly published *On the Revolution of the Heavenly Spheres* which has attempted to convince you that the daily experience of a stationary Earth being illuminated periodically by the moving sun is an illusion. What do you think the chances are that you would have accepted the Copernican argument that violates your direct perceptions?"[243]

In our times, a discovery of lesser significance than Copernicus' heliocentricity, but still significant enough, is the duality of repulsive and attractive forces that has been discovered in the universe. Despite the ontological differences between these twin forces, they are not incompatible with one another.

Quite the contrary, the repulsive force acts on the attractive both as a whole and individually. The repulsive force directs its attractive counterpart and vice versa.[244] By pulling the universe apart the repulsive force brings it together. In the same way, by bringing it together the attractive force pulls the universe apart. Repulsion prevents contraction from becoming so dominant that a second big bang becomes necessary to tear it apart once again. The universe learnt its lesson before it needed to. The interconnectedness of all things and all modalities, particularly the interconnectedness of time and no-time, made this possible.

A self-adjusting universe

In the previous chapter we examined two areas where the block universe (or trans-modal reality) becomes apparent to the unconditioned mind. Now a third area will be examined, that which Jung and Pauli called "synchronicity." It not only disregards the limitations of the classical conceptions of space and time. It makes nonsense of linear causality. Synchronicity reflects how the block universe responds to human needs in the experienced world—whether there is awareness of these needs or not.[245]

A fourth area where the block universe activity makes itself felt is existential feedback. Self-adjustment occurs because trans-modal reality reflects primordial consciousness in action, an innate awareness of the various activities trans-modal in which reality engages. One such activity is self-locking objectification. Primordial consciousness, the consciousness that is transformative

---

[243] S. J. Goerner, *After the Clockwork Universe: The Emerging Science and Culture of Integral Society*, Floris Books, Edinburgh, 1999, p 373.

[244] "Attractive forces" here denote the visible universe, while "repulsive forces" indicate the so-called "dark matter" and "dark energy," which "push" in the opposite direction.

[245] Iain McGilchrist, *The Master and His Emissary: The Divided Brain and the Making of the Western World,* Yale University Press, New Haven and London, 2009, p 133.

creation itself in the process of gradual growth, puts the brakes on the smooth internal transformation of things and events which the block universe (or trans-modal reality) is all about.

A second possible operation of trans-modal reality is to affect the fragments existing within the block universe. Trans-modality pushes them to reverse their ontological status as fragments. The quality of wholeness is restored to them so that they become more effective (and "self-enhancing") as fragments.

Of course, the fragments still remain what, and as, they were before. But the innate "awareness" which the fragments have now developed makes them increasingly mindful of their own ontological status. They are as they are because of the whole permeating them. When manifest to its offspring, nature takes on this operation.

The secret here lies in maintaining contact with what can happen and what should not. We are definitely able to tune into changes in the block universe and adjust our ways accordingly. The ancient Greeks linked this ability for self-adjustment and trans-modal operation with their sense of "measure in all things." They used it for indicating what a sane and rewarding life should be like and how one should conduct himself in order to live it.

Iain McGilchrist touches on this from the angle of attention. He writes: "It is not just that what we find determines the nature of the attention we accord to it, but that the attention we accord to it determines what we find . . . A thing depends on who is attending to it and in what way." This explains the crucial role played by primordial consciousness in the creation of the universe. It developed in the way it did because primordial consciousness attended to it in the way it did.

A fifth operation where the block universe becomes evident is what Ilya Prigogine has called "dissipative structures." Through the dispersion of physical patterns, the block universe (or trans-modal reality) is in total dynamic action on itself. Its function is to recognize permanence and perfection not in immutable structures, but in creative patterns manifesting within the totality of existence. Permanence implies the continuous inherent drive for change. Totality implies the qualitative interpenetration of all things across ontological and conceptual categories.

Trans-conceptual neurophysiology

A sixth operation where the block universe becomes evident is the neurophysiological expressions that McGilchrist mentions with respect to human bonding, based on the work by Panksepp, Fehr, Fishbacher, Gaechter, Rilling, Gutman, Zeh, and others. McGilchrist sums up their findings in the following words: "It is mutuality, not reciprocity, fellow feeling, not calculation, which is both the motive and the reward for successful cooperation. And the outcome, in utilitarian terms, is not the important point: it is the process, the relationship, that matters. On the neurophysiological level, we know that in experimental situations . . . subjects achieving mutual cooperation with another human individual show activity in areas of the brain associated with pleasure."[246]

This "nurturant behavior," as Panksepp calls it in another quotation mentioned by McGilchrist, results from the trans-modal and trans-rational operation of the block universe and the non-local consciousness it thrives on. "Lower" animals are also open to such an underlying force. However, dominated as they are by their survival-related specialization, they are unable to sense anything unrelated to it. Man is more sensitive because he is not interested only in survival. He is also more intelligent because, being intimately involved in universal trans-modality, he always receives pertinent information about it at the right moment. His only problem is to keep his mind open to the flow of such information.

One last indication for trans-modal operations is the so-called placebo effect. It perhaps represents the most impressive example of man being able to secure access to useful quantities and qualities from the block universe to heal himself when sick. Placebo is based on one's innate ability to get in touch with the block universe and tune into its internal patterns and powers. For example, believing that a pill will do him good, the individual contacts those switches of his unconscious which connect him to the healing power of wholeness. The pill becomes a tool in the hands of the whole. It manifests equally through alignment with key universal norms; through plumbing conventional or non-conventional sources; and through recognizing the healing potential of seemingly unrelated powers. One way or another, health is restored—when health can be restored.

Senses limiting thought

A few additional manifestations of block universe action on local and temporal conditions are precognition, remote viewing, prophetic dreams, remote cognition, ancient oracles, intuition and helpful day-to-day insights. These mind-states don't, of course, yield absolutely clear or correct formulations. That doesn't happen because the block universe (or trans-modal reality) doesn't exercise the

[246] Op. cit. p 147.

proper influences at the right moment or in the right way. This happens because humans are mostly overwhelmed by their own conditioning, which beclouds, alters, and restricts their smooth communication with the block universe. They get garbled or distorted messages from it.

Relevant to block universe presence may also be the Princeton Engineering Anomalies Research experiments on direct mind-to-mind and mind-to-machine transmissions over long or short distances.

These experiments were carried out without the use of information-carrying systems like telephones, the Internet, radio waves, TV, human touch, etc. As is mentioned in the Laboratory's website,[247] the most substantial portion of the PEAR experimental program examined anomalies arising in human-machine interactions. Human operators attempt to bias the output of random mechanical, electronic, optical, acoustical or fluid devices so that it conforms to pre-stated (or even non-pre-stated) intentions, without recourse to any known physical medium.

When these sophisticated devices are left to function on their own, they produce strictly random data. But when they are attended by humans, they manifest statistically significant deviations from average behavior. These differences, while small, persist over many millions of experiments and are therefore indicative of some sort of non-local influences. The attending individuals don't touch the devices, or communicate with them in any physical way, they are just present, or mindful of them.

In some PEAR experiments it was demonstrated that non-physical human messages were sent not only in *no* time, but *retrocausally*. In other words, the pertinent information was received *before* it was sent, or even conceived before the human operator had his session with the random event generator or other device! This shatters any notions of time, location, linearity or causality—and with it all our present conceptual apparatus. It follows that by getting rid of this type of conditioning, or at least by becoming aware of it, one opens up to information derived not only from other modalities, but from the trans-modality underlying them all. It becomes the medium through which mind acts on and through physical mechanisms.

This was also reflected in a different PEAR-related project. The collective energy of human consciousness around the world was measured through random event generators scattered in several places around the globe. Sharp

---

[247] Locate current information via an Internet search engine with keywords "PEAR" and "Princeton Engineering Anomalies Research."

deviation from "normal" unattended "behavior" was recorded before and after both the funeral of Princess Diana in 1997 and the terrorist attacks on September 11, 2001.[248] These readings offer strong evidence that the human mind, through some special activity as yet unknown, is in a position to influence the performance of machines, and probably of other random physical objects as well.

Special relativity and trans-modal reality

Special relativity may be indirectly connected with this. Driven by the belief that the universe constitutes an indivisible self-informing whole, Einstein did two things. On the scientific level he conceived the physical and dimensional forces of the universe as inter-related, and therefore as inter-dependent. On the philosophical level (which was of course informed by the scientific), he expressed the conviction that man "seeks to experience the totality of existence as a unit full of significance."[249]

In one place Einstein even makes the point that "the scientist is possessed of a sense of universal causation."[250] Elsewhere he insists that "behind all the discernible laws and connections [of nature,] there remains something subtle, intangible and inexplicable."[251] It stands to reason that if one "experiences the totality of existence," he would also be in a position to become aware of the other entities making up this totality.

Of course, Einstein believed that this "subtle, intangible and inexplicable something" would one day be worked out within the framework of a "unified field theory"—what today is called "a theory of everything." But the important thing about his conviction isn't that such an all-inclusive theory is possible to begin with. The important thing is his conviction that such a theory can be worked out through the exclusively self-locking conceptual operations of the left hemisphere, that wholeness can be built up intellectually through highly abstract mathematics rather than through the on-going mathematization of evolving informed hunches concerning the subject.

It follows that, seen from this angle, Einstein's ultimate contribution to our understanding of the world is not relativity or quantum mechanics, important

[248] Roger Nelson, The Global Consciousness Project.
[249] Quoted from Swami Tathagatananda, *Glimpses of Great Lives,* The Vedanta Society, 1999, p 90.
[250] Banesh Hoffmann, *Albert Einstein: Creator and Rebel*, Viking, New York, 1972, p 101.
[251] Quoted from Swami Tathagatananda, *Glimpses of Great Lives,* The Vedanta Society, 1999, p 384–5.

though these were and are. It is his sense that underlying all the multiplicity of physical forms and ways of operation, there prevails an ontological unity. This fundamental intuition means (a) that everything in nature relates to everything else;[252] (b) that when one realizes this, the world appears like a single mutually interpenetrating block universe; (c) that science should be turned around to illustrate this; (d) that one discipline, neurophysiology, has found evidence for nature actually "wanting" us to keep the two super-modalities of holism and fragmentation indistinguishably interpenetrating one another;[253] (e) that consequently, all we need is to figure out how this interpenetration operates; and finally (f) that our hunches concerning the underlying unity can be expressed in mathematical terms.

We may have to invent some additional self-transforming symbols to illustrate this self-transforming mathematics. But assuming that our universities still produce ingenious and original mathematicians, this should pose no insurmountable problem. If mathematics can faithfully describe observed relationships among entities and forces, they can surely also describe self-generated changes in the dynamics of these relationships.

Separateness in simultaneity

Einstein was certainly sensitive to the thought that our view of the block universe is affected by consciousness. But he didn't consider consciousness to be the very mechanism that collapses the universe into existence. That was left to later physicists to struggle with. As McGilchrist puts it: "The fact that in the twentieth century philosophers, like physicists, increasingly arrived at conclusions . . . at variance with their own left-hemisphere methodology and suggest the primacy of the world as the right hemisphere would deliver it, tells something important."[254]

---

[252] This includes time, space, the speed of light, the strong and weak nuclear forces and mass.

[253] Iain McGilchrist quotes H. Hecaen (in p 148 of his *The Master and his Emissary)* to the effect that "there is an inability to carry out an action" by patients who have suffered lesions in the right hemisphere. As has been pointed out repeatedly, the right hemisphere is the one which connects us to wholeness. Nature seems to find the interpenetration of the two hemispheres a necessary condition for the proper execution of specific jobs. Wholeness thus informs all long-term actions. Being in touch with it constitutes an organic need and universal imperative—key to our effective operation as human beings. *No practical task—physical, exploratory, medical, theoretical or economic—can be executed properly without reference to it.* This reference may not be explicit. But it must be there, in the depth of our unconscious, personal as well as collective.

[254] Iain McGilchrist, *The Master and his Emissary: The Divided Brain and the Making of the Western World,* Yale University Press, New Haven and London, 2009, p 161.

Two things follow. The first is that if classical deterministic science is pursued systematically and with intellectual honesty, it reduces to wholeness rather than to an as yet undiscovered single type of small units. The second thing following is that we should be grateful to Einstein for conceiving the notion of the block universe to begin with. One of the clearest non-mathematical formulations he came up with in this respect is the following:

"Two events that appear simultaneous to one observer will not appear simultaneous to another, who is moving more rapidly."[255] This formulation implies that the reverse also holds: events which do not appear simultaneous to one observer will appear simultaneous to another, who happens to be moving more slowly. Curved space/time is just one of the ways the block universe appears to a person steeped in classical deterministic thinking, as Einstein was.

The important thing to realize here is that events in the physical world articulate themselves both simultaneously and separately, however contradictory this may appear to the eyes of the pre-epistemologically naive observer. On the one hand, height, depth and width express a single objective dimension: space/time. Its main function is to promote the dynamic inter-relationship of physical forces. On the other hand, human perception and conception express a second subjective dimension: mind/matter. Its function is to maintain the inter-penetration of all physical states with our capacity for conceiving them through the senses, or computing them with the help of mathematics.[256]

Things or states support one another across space/time and mind/matter because they are part of the same self-determining packet of existence. Objectification, speed, angle, location and conception all depend on one another. Anyone attempting to define them separately ends up weaving tautologies.

Plato, and the Egyptian priests before him, gave substance to this understanding through their theory of forms (or ideas.) In particular, Plato's forms are a description in space/time of a function that takes place in no-space/time. "Forms in the mind of God," as he called them, are necessary for forms in space/time to organize coherently the loose particles into which physical reality broke up after the big bang. If one sees this formation process from within space/time,

---

[255] Walter Isaacson, *Einstein: His Life and Universe,* Simon and Schuster, New York, 2007, p 387.

[256] For all his faith in the extension of mathematical verities, Einstein was not convinced that they could describe nature faithfully—not at least as they were practised in his time. This reservation comes out in an often quoted saying of his: "As far as the laws of mathematics refer to reality, they are not certain. As far as they *are* certain, they do not refer to reality." String theorists should bear this in mind.

one has evolution. If one sees it from without space/time, he gets the "eternal forms." With its capacity for acting *through* states and entities, trans-modal reality constitutes the principal expression of this.

In Plato's time-bound understanding, this implies what he viewed as static "perfection." From our standpoint, the perfect form is two things. First, it is that which has exhausted, through evolution, its inherent potential. Second, it is that which has utilized all the chances and opportunities arising from its mutual interaction with the environment. It represents a process that has run its course and now exists free from space/time considerations—immutable because no further mutations of it are possible.

This is why trans-modal consciousness and bi-hemispheric intelligence enable us to "pull out" of the block universe whatever information or energy we need for coping effectively with present circumstances. Our mind allows us to participate in two worlds: that of space/time and that of no-space/time. Early man knew how to handle this instinctively. He used his ability to exact guidance from the universe in order to deal with events and developments of significance to him *now*. Trans-modal nature demands abandonment to and trust in the process of unpremeditated communion with itself. It offers better understanding of what needs to be done at each moment than the objective programming offered by the fragmented (and fragmenting) approach of today's science.

Fragments suggestive of the whole

Here an opportunity arises for those who are unable to translate what they perceive into how they perceive. It allows us to use the block universe in advantageous ways. In the words of Chris Clarke, from within its own depths, human intuition "directly contacts the creative process within nature, realizes that process within itself and brings nature's reality to conscious expression."[257]

How can the block universe be addressed through a language that has been formed for elucidating involvement only with local, partial, temporal or rational circumstances? The answer is that what looks like a shortcoming in how we use language when dealing with the block universe, isn't really. As has been suggested throughout this book, things naturally point to the general picture of which they are part manifestations. But the attention we pay to these manifestations overshadows their indirect function. Thus, we don't actually need a different language

[257] Chris Clarke, "The Re-invention of Religion," *The Network Review*, No 100, Summer 2009, p 55.

to deal with the block universe. We only need to broaden (and deepen) the way we use existing language.

In other words, we only need to re-invent poly-semantics. Just as for the experienced archaeologist one potsherd suggests the shape of the pot it is a fragment of, and a handle points to the missing blade, so the same words, grammar and syntax point to a fuller understanding of reality once we have become aware of the nature and the function of trans-modal consciousness and the trans-modal reality it helps to organize.

From bi-hemispheric intelligence to the co-present universe and back

Let us explore the block universe a little further. Since it is impossible to develop bi-hemispherical intelligence without first familiarizing ourselves with the notion and possibilities of trans-modal reality, we will deal with these two manifestations as though bi-hemispheric intelligence and trans-modal reality are actually one.

Bi-hemispheric intelligence brings about one effect in order to catalyze another on a different level of physical organization. We do this each time an action on our part brings about a reaction where none was expected, or we just anticipated one of a predetermined nature. In most cases this normally unforeseeable outcome ends up having the opposite effect than what was expected from it.

Thus, a setback in one area may forestall a calamity in another; a negative act may catalyze a positive outcome; action may be initiated that brings about seemingly unrelated changes; or it becomes possible to "borrow energy" from events, experiences or pieces of knowledge rooted in different time frames, situations or places in order to meet immediate needs and exhaust the dynamics of dangerous developments.

Nothing of this happens because some hidden potentiality in the universe brings it about. It happens because non-locality, non-temporality, retro-causality and the other modalities in existence are intrinsic parts of the over-all creative mechanism of the universe and act on specific circumstances in space and time.

Chapter 14

SUB-ATOMIC PHYSICS AND THE BRAIN: Conclusions from chapters 12 & 13

When researching nature, instead
of looking for and finding certain quantities,
"man encounters his own self."
Werner Heisenberg, as quoted by Hannah Arendt

There is a oneness between the
physical and the psychological spheres—
between the quantitative and the qualitative
aspects of reality.
Marie Louise von Franz

What conclusions can be drawn from the two previous chapters on trans-conceptual understanding and trans-modal reality? What links that which happens in subatomic physics to that which happens in the brain when we perceive or feel something? Seeing clearly is a prerequisite for sensing what exists beyond "things." It requires the application of a special kind of logic that is not informed either by the senses, or by the clear-cut contours that the senses assign to physical objects.

There is an ongoing debate today in physics and neuroscience about which approach is best for comprehending what occurs on their deeper levels of organization. This debate is not always conducted along uncompromising lines. Indeed, some physicists encourage self-investigation as a means for acquiring a better understanding of nature. Wolfgang Pauli was one of them. He believed that our examination of "external objects" should go hand-in-hand with an investigation of the "inner origins" of scientific concepts.[258]

In this way the debate in physics and neuroscience brings to the foreground the oneness of ultimate physical and mental processes. The established approach

[258] Wolfgang Pauli, as quoted by Marie Louise von Franz from *Naturerklaerung und Psyche, l.c.*, Zuerich, 1952, p 163.

in science has it that only object-mediated thinking is able to make out what happens on these deeper levels of physical organization since they too are made up of objects. Distinct units build up into larger groupings prompted by their inherent possibilities.

The minority approach in the above debate adheres to a more whole-making attitude. Distinct physical units act as local manifestations of the whole. But the latter is so open-ended and deep that it includes even its conceptual opposites. The most important of these is fragmentation.

Four consequences follow. Their common point is that established order eventually calls for a reaction to itself because of its inherent incompleteness. The inclusion of a reaction in the conditions being reacted to reflects an ontological imperative.

The four consequences are: First, the rational necessitates the non-rational. It calls for a broader, deeper and more graded conception of what is "appropriate." Something may be rational, but just up to a point. Or something may be rational only in relation to a particular function. Fuzzy logic describes these eventualities. Its account applies not only to the particular things under investigation. It applies to the very concept of logic, including its insistence on neat outcomes.

Second, inconsistency becomes part of the prevailing consistency. The incompleteness of nature itself calls for such an inclusion. Eventually inconsistency becomes so relevant to what is or is not happening, that it generates a deeper form of consistency. In this way inconsistency invites more and more inconsistencies. Reality is enriched because of its very incompleteness and imperfection. Ontological variability depends on ontological insufficiency.

Third, continuous continuity eventually breeds discontinuity. Stagnation sets in where nothing changes. The gaps introduced in a seemingly continuous flow allow for possible changes of direction. These in turn allow for qualitative unity to articulate itself in new disguises. A continuity of directions transmogrifies into a continuity of qualities.

Fourth, fragmentation eventually plays a role in the operation of wholeness. It may establish itself as a new arrangement for the inner balances of nature, thereby giving rise to a new type of fragmentation and a new type of interaction. In this sense, fragmentation strengthens the ability of wholeness to actually do things, in addition to just being things.

The above four examples of incompleteness in action are rendered possible not because nature offers so much, but because it offers it so haphazardly. Perennial incompleteness transforms into a perennial pursuit for "more" close-knit order. It allows nature to continue existing in some form of organized existence or other—often not obvious to investigators who rely too heavily on object-mediated thinking.

Total awareness of what is being played out and why, plus openness to change with parallel acceptance of partial changelessness, are the only means for bridging the gap between complete and incomplete existence. Order and chaos finally amalgamate in a complex interaction that can be expressed through something here called The Law of Perennial Rebalancing.

Everything is as it is because it is not as it appears to be to the undiscerning eye. Absence realized creates presence. Automatic reaction establishes intelligent choice. Thanks to the need for perennial rebalancing, all come to be what they were not in the beginning. Man himself is what he is in virtue of not being what he can be.

In the two previous chapters the suggestion was made that the difference between the two basic theories on how to understand subatomic physics and brain science are not, strictly speaking, scientific or philosophical. They are, according to Heisenberg, a question of the language used (and by extension) a question of the mind using the language. This difference concerns quite literally how mind operates with and beyond objects, without doing injustice to either.

It all depends on the as yet unchartered waters of pre-science and pre-philosophy. The question is how we objectify the world to begin with, how we build up our perceptions of it into conceptions, and how we act in the light of these conceptions. The question furthermore is how we select our objectifications and use them for building up the theoretical foundations needed for our research and the interpretation of its results.

But if the two basic theories on how to understand subatomic physics and brain science are not, strictly speaking, scientific or philosophical, neither are they epistemological. They are pre-epistemological. The question of validity, in the usual sense, doesn't come into it. *The question is all about how and why we objectify reality in the particular way we do.* Our inclinations color what we understand. Research in the subatomic world and in neuroscience clearly shows the importance not only of how we select what we perceive, but of how we perceive to begin with so as to be in a position to make selections at all.

If we are dominated by object-mediated thinking (i.e. if we think about everything in terms of clearly definable units) we conceive the subatomic world in terms of particles and their interactions. Being impressed by clearly outlined forms, such as are available on the level of physical organization on which humans operate, we then tend to see everything in terms of the logic informing that level.

This happened to Niels Bohr, who in the early 1920s conceived nuclei and the electrons going around them as mini-solar systems. He held onto this metaphor until Pauli and Schrödinger—each in their different way—pointed out its inappropriateness for subatomic physics. Electrons and nuclei just don't behave like planets and suns.

On the other hand, if we are informed by wholeness (i.e., if we think about the world in terms of ontological qualities and indefinable connections), we conceive the same subatomic world in the much more inclusive sense of de Broglie's "waves" and Schrödinger's "wave mechanics." Science historian Arthur I. Miller points out that "something more than mathematics is involved in wave equations."[259] Physicist Vasileios Basios explains that waves point in the direction of wholes because there is no beginning or end to them. They come out of nowhere and merge back into nowhere.

Basios also believes that the moment has come to apply Einstein's understanding that theory leads to facts and not facts to theory. For example, the data on which Bohr based his understanding that electrons circulate around a nucleus in the same way as planets circulate around the sun, are quite correct. But Basios also points out that Bohr's object-mediated approach at the time didn't allow the latter to see that a wave-like interpretation fits the facts much more appropriately than his solar-system interpretation.

If we are aware of the extent to which our thinking dominates science (which many scientists are unable to do in the light of their present belief in object-mediated thinking), we conceive the subatomic world in both exclusive and inclusive terms *simultaneously*. We freely alternate between the one mode and its seeming opposite according to the specific problems we are dealing with in science or in philosophy.

This makes for increased complication, as Heisenberg realized when he tried to bridge the gap between particle and wave mechanics. Bohr eventually realized that no general rules could be applied here. Electrons can be either here or there, they may disappear entirely or change trajectories—indeed, they needn't be either particles or waves. They can be something in between, virtual subatomic entities or a whirlwind of chaotic energy—something that takes form only when specific circumstances require it do so.

Erwin Schrödinger's work shows that an inclusive approach to subatomic physics offers a more dynamic and comprehensive view of physical reality. But this

---

[259] Arthur I. Miller, *137: Jung, Pauli and the Pursuit of a Scientific Obsession,* W.W. Norton and Co, New York, London, 2008, p 105.

doesn't diminish the usefulness of the exclusive, object-mediated, approach. To the contrary, it bridges the gap between the two seemingly different conceptions of reality. The only problem is that the wholeness mechanics end up being a lot more complicated when they come to bridge the gap between wholeness itself and object-mediated understanding—or between inclusive and exclusive thinking.

According to the principle outlined in the above paragraphs, qualitative inclusive thinking embraces its exclusive counterpart. By the same token, qualitative exclusive thinking excludes rejection of the inclusion principle. It just doesn't deal with inclusive thinking when engaged in exclusive research or vice versa.

There is a close resemblance of the above conceptual "duality" with that existing between the right and left hemisphere of the brain. Just as the two hemispheres work best when in organic balance with one another, so the wave/particle "duality" works best when there prevails in the two hemispheres a spirit of mutual understanding, cooperation and service. This spirit enables the one hemisphere to do a better job thanks to the qualities, sensibilities and support of the other.

In the light of the conclusions presented above, is there any room left for what is usually called "objective proof"? Must we give in to the idea that everything is—and will always be—uncertain, in the Heisenbergian sense? Are we in a position to measure only one aspect of reality at a time and are we therefore unable to get a fuller picture of it?

Six points need to be taken into account before beginning to look for an answer.

First, the classical way of checking a theoretical principle against reality needs to stop being considered an absolute rule. What has been discussed in the preceding material makes that clear. The reductionist principle cannot be applied across the board, as Descartes thought it could. Today there are far too many disciplines around for that to be possible, or even desirable.

Second, the key role in objective demonstration always lay in the notion of absolute correspondence between reality and its mathematical description. This notion may now be applied only in limited and fairly simple cases.

Third, objective proof for broad subjects, physical or philosophical, will now appear counterproductive. Such proof, however, when the subject is specific, will still be useful. The more specific a subject is, the more provable it becomes.

Fourth, until the 1920s, classical proof was pretty much a mechanistic exercise in self-reference. It implied that things can be faithfully accounted for only through symbols and relationships predetermined by the investigators. This meant that unforeseen components that may appear during an investigation may be written off just because they don't fit the investigators' choice of symbols. Few ask themselves whether the particular symbols chosen, or the particular manner they tie into one another, reflect the only way to understand the phenomena being investigated.

Fifth, the discovery of fuzzy logic and of chaos theory changes the pursuit of object-mediated proof. Clear definability of objects must now be abandoned as a prerequisite for investigating the world in a scientific sense—or even to prove its actual existence.

Sixth, truth isn't a synonym for proof. Gödel points that out in his mathematical demonstration for the existence of God. According to him, proof depends only on the consistency with which the reasoning mechanism is being used. It has nothing to do with the subject the mechanism is being used for. Something true may not be provable. Something provable may not be true. That is the price for using mathematics to describe nature. Its accuracy reflects how it is being used. It doesn't reflect how the world actually *is*.

What reality turns out to be turns out to depend entirely on how free from the classical notion of practicing physics and neurophysiology we are. In epitomizing the new trans-conceptual ways of thinking in this area, Marie Louise von Franz observes: "Scientists can no longer hope to describe any aspect or quality of external objects in a completely independent, 'objective,' manner." A little further down the same page, echoing the views of Carl G. Jung, she writes: "The total psychological condition of the observer (both conscious and unconscious) might play a role as well."[260]

In this book the notion is upheld that the "total psychological condition of the observer (both conscious and unconscious) not only *might* play a role as well." It *does* play a role as well. Indeed, it plays *the principal role*. We see as we are. Seeing and being are one and the same. By broadening the base of our being we broaden our viewpoint and by broadening our viewpoint we are obliged to look at the world from a deeper standpoint, a deeper level of organization.

The more we sink into our being the more liable we are to find the right answer—and think in its light.

[260] Marie Louise von Franz, "Science and the Unconscious," in Carl G. Jung, *Man and his Symbols,* Picador, Pan Books, London, 1978, p 382.

Chapter 15

RE-WHOLIFYING LANGUAGE: Pre-literate sensibilities in the service of modern science

Things...are whole and not whole; they are brought together
and taken apart; they are in tune and out of tune. Out of all things
comes a unity and out of unity come all things.
Heraclitus

If our nervous system evolved in the hunter-gatherer phase before
literacy and logic, why such neural complexity? Language and social
organization are usually considered responsible. But perhaps "primitive man"
fed our nervous system with wider sensory inputs. Rather
than seeking something new [in our times], revisiting old
ways of knowing could [prove] profitable.
John F. Caddy

[In microphysics,] the objective probabilities of future outcomes
are contained as co-present dispositional factors,
which incline or pre-dispose the future
to occur in certain specific ways.
A. Dobbs

What was mentioned in the previous chapter naturally leads to the following important question: Can the intimations about trans-modality (or the block universe) affect the conceptual practices of modern science? They can—*if* we change the way we understand and treat our objectifications. A return is needed to the way of using language to reflect and convey states like non-locality, entanglement, non-temporality, retrocausality and others. In pre-literate cultures language functioned in such ways. This ability must be re-evoked, without losing any of the practices and properties language may have developed since.

One of the most serious complaints against the mentality informing science today is that it has locked too much into its objectifications and concerned itself too little with the contexts informing them. One path out of this situation would be to change the existing grammatical and syntactical rules. Another would be to replace the accepted language of science with a new one that is more related to the picture provided by 20th-century physics.

But a third solution is also possible: no linguistic practice will be pursued that alienates the reader or listener from the writer or speaker. Nobody should be pushed to ask "what nonsense is this?" Existing grammatical and syntactical forms of speech and writing must be retained, and respected.

There are practical as well as ontological reasons for following the latter path. Language must rediscover its original function, as Lao Tse suggested 2,500 years ago. It must relearn to use words not merely for denoting things, relationships, actions or states, but for what escapes their definitions. Such a usage of language would not merely describe the explicit. It would hint at the implicit. We would use it to transcend, or at least minimize, our current conceptual limitations.

Such a usage would also help us rediscover the ability to *awaken* information in the individual, not merely to *impart* it. People will employ linguistic communication in ways that will prevent them from getting attached to their own formulations, or those of others. What they know will thus not become a barrier to what they ignore, and what they understand will not overshadow what they don't. Meaning for them will not be restricted to content, nor will silence indicate only the unutterable.

Indeed, expressing the function of dynamic wholeness, language will operate as that modality which best enriches its users. It will provide intimations of relevant reality, not objectified images of it. It will bring up the ability to extract from the block universe whatever we require to become what we can.[261] It will quietly make us aware of the whole as—and *when*—we carve it up.

Tapping into universal resources

There is nothing particularly new about such an approach to language. Plotinus made a strong case for it when he wrote: "Someone may claim that in knowledge

[261] Up until the death of Plato, ancient Greek was such a language—more or less. Its huge vocabulary and relative ambiguity testifies to its roots in the tradition of non-literate languages, which are based very much on daily existence. This explains the qualitative difference between Greek and Latin. The latter is concept-orientated; hence it became the language of law. The former is experience-orientated; hence it became the vehicle for poetry and philosophy. Martin Heidegger makes this point in several of his writings.

the part is not the whole. Now, that express knowledge, which has been brought into readiness because there is a requirement for it, constitutes an actualized part of the whole. Thus, it is placed in front. The other parts follow as unnoticed possibilities, so that all are co-present in the original part."[262] In the Plotinean sense, knowledge is a hologram—"a whole in many places," as he describes it.[263]

Plotinus shows that there is a need to go much deeper into the question of verbal and written communication than we have done since his time. Maria Theodoropoulos writes about this: "Meaning has its origins in pre-conceptual structures, which arise out of direct sensorimotor experiences, body physiology and the neuronal structure of the brain."[264] McGilchrist uses the expressions "pre-consciously" and "pre-attentional" to illustrate the same point.[265] Anthropologist Jacobo Grinberg coined the term "pre-space" to describe his experiments on the passing of information from person to person in a non-local and non-temporal manner.[266]

As already suggested in previous chapters, the block universe consists of an organic interpenetration of the space/time super-modality with the non-space/time super-modality. The distinction between the two systems is purely man made. When our collective or individual consciousness feels the need for some specific information or quality from the block universe, it raises this particular information or quality from its spaceless and timeless super-modality into its space-ridden and time-informed counterpart.

This happens in accordance with our biological, conceptual, cultural, educational and psychological conditioning. Both the similarities and the differences among the various insights arising from the interpenetration of the two super-modalities can be explained in this way. Without any warning, there is what Plato called a sudden illumination about a particular subject.[267] It happens only when the individual doesn't identify with anything in particular, least of all with his own self.

---

[262] Plotinus' original Greek doesn't read as smoothly as the English rendition here represented. If one wanted to produce an absolutely faithful rendition in English, one would have to include numerous brackets around some words. These brackets have been here omitted to make the text more accessible.

[263] Plotinus, *Ennead* IV. 7 ("On the Immortality of the Soul").

[264] Maria Theodoropoulou, "Vioma, Synaesthema ke Metaphora" ["Experience, Emotion and Metaphor"], *Ek ton Hysteron,* No 11, July 2004.

[265] Iain McGilchrist, *The Master and his Emissary: The Divided Brain and the Making of the Western World,* Yale University Press, New Haven and London, 2009, p 162.

[266] Grinberg presented his ideas on "pre-space" communication during a conference on science and consciousness in Merida, Mexico, May 1992.

[267] Plato, *Seventh Letter.*

The Japanese call this state of breaking through to wholeness-imbued specificity "satori;" in science or philosophy it is called "sudden insight;" in art it is called "inspiration." When the illumination is about illumination itself, or about the mechanics of conditioning, the event is called enlightenment. One sign of its genuineness is that it cannot become an object of attachment, even when it articulates itself in the form of an all-explaining truth. Enlightenment is not the end-product of some highly sophisticated spiritual technology. It is what occurs when spiritual technology is left aside and one abandons himself to trans-modal reality. One doesn't only change his outlook. One becomes an altogether different person—a changed human being.

Early man used language in the light of the first three experiences described above. Words allowed him to develop his innate ability to grasp and handle challenging situations on their own terms.[268] For these early humans, trans-modality signaled abandonment to helpful insight. The trans-modal mind offered them a far better understanding of what needed to be done than their own individual consciousness could.

Early man and the block universe

In particular, their equivalent of what we today call the trans-modal mind pushed early man in three specific directions. The first was to cut through those of his assumptions that beclouded his judgement. The second was to coax his intuition back into life. The third was to develop active receptivity, the art of paying attention to the slightest changes and micro-events in his physical and mental environment. Seemingly insignificant circumstances would then bring into focus significant realities. By pushing in these three directions, the trans-modal mind empowered early man to deal with the challenges of life effectively.

Skill acquisition by the young, healing, technology, securing sufficient food, developing wisdom, human quality testing, survival techniques, behavioral codes and many other situations were dealt with (at least in part) in such a trans-modal fashion by early man. It reflected a tendency in him to know what he needed when he needed it, without consciously working it out. His requirements dictated what he should seek and how he should act.

[268] This is also how medical homeopathy obtains results. By administering a preparation that exacerbates the patient's condition, homeopathic medication pushes him into a situation in which his self-healing potential becomes active. The autoimmune system and the placebo effect embody aspects of the same self-healing mechanism.

The only condition for an individual to acquire such guidance was for him to remain in close communion with nature. This would allow him to be *spontaneous* under all circumstances. It wasn't a question of pressing the button that would produce desired results. It was a question of preparing the conditions for the results to occur. Among these, the most important was what the Taoist sages called "chen ren"—the ability to become an "authentic person."

The ancient Chinese knew that before man learns anything, he already knows it. Indeed, they believed that he is able to learn something only because he already knows it—plus all else with which this something interpenetrates. Thus, the authentic person, the chen ren, is one "who does not pretend to not know what he in fact knows." Pretense of ignorance is the by-product of an inflated self. It removes the individual from total immersion in the block universe, where the absence of space/time allows him to be in instantaneous communion with everything that matters.[269]

The knower, as it were, experiences the no-self in the heart of the self. When the individual claims that he doesn't know, all he does is to stop identifying with the whole. He is left merely with his detached and limited self who, of course, "doesn't know."

Trans-modality reflects the unquestioned trust of early man who was in touch, that nature cannot but provide. All he had to do was to guard against his tendency for locking into the objectifications he makes in the course of his daily activities. Remaining alert to this danger permitted him to retain a clear picture of what is happening. His trans-modal mind made use of what lay hidden from his senses, either in the senses themselves, or beyond them.

The power of penetration

This may explain why trans-modality (and its offshoot inter-conceptuality) occasionally appear absurd or irrelevant to people with a conventional bend of mind. Trans-modality indeed breaks the social norms of thought under which we labor. The person is led to discern the significant in the jumbled, the authentic in the derived. Early man had this problem far less than we have. His social conventions strictly concerned survival. For the rest, the individual was free to feel and think.

---

[269] This was explained to the author by *I Ching* researcher Tew Bunnag in a conversation in early July 2010.

Some may believe that because of this seeming unconventionality, trans-modal consciousness and its bi-hemispheric intelligence are incompatible with science or scholarship. Such reservations arise from a misunderstanding.

Trans-modality applies only to the way mind works in an environment dominated by object-mediated and self-locking thinking. The inconsistencies appearing in the inter-conceptual descriptions of reality are due to the essential difference between the two super-modalities: the local/linear and the non-local/non-linear. The world itself can be studied equally by a science that takes these conceptual differences into account, treating them with the same inquisitiveness it treats the realities the conceptual differences are about.

Inter-conceptual language enables us to hint at the objective world of which we are part, so that we can then pick our way through it more easily. Inter-conceptual language also enables us to know why we move in the particular direction we do. Bringing to the foreground these two capabilities is the reason why the specific understanding triggered by inter-conceptual language cannot be transmitted, registered or recalled like a bit of computer information. Development of the individual is impeded each time he slides into self-locked thinking.

As Bika Reed points out, inspired by her work on ancient Egyptian thinking: "Man is both the product and the creator of the stages in the evolution of his intelligence."[270] It is a question of deciding whether one wants to be puppet or puppet maker. As Reed adds: "Man seeks such relationships and situations as will provoke his own transformation." With this short sentence, Reed puts in a nutshell the essential function of trans-modal reality and the inter-conceptual language serving it. This language articulates itself through humans who are made conscious of both their blockages and their openness.

Inter-conceptual language works because inter-conceptual thinking represents an age-old practice allowing one to jump start his broken relationship with nature. Inter-conceptual language puts one into a frame of mind that guides him in accordance with both his present needs and his long-term goals. If indeed everything is everywhere at all times, as A. N. Whitehead claims, it is also true that *all knowledge is available to all individuals at all times and in all circumstances.*

---

[270] *The Revelation of the Soul of Shu,* translated by Bika Reed from an ancient Egyptian text in the coffin of Gwa, a physician of the 12th dynasty, now in the British Museum. Bika Reed presents her translation and comments in *The Field of Transformations: A quest for the Immortal Essence of Human Awareness,* Inner Traditions International, Ltd., Rochester, Vermont, 1987, pp 121-122.

The only difference is that this last piece of knowledge points to both objective information and to the ultimate emptiness out of which objective information develops. The fact that one no longer locks into his objectifications allows this to happen. One knows because he senses the fullness of being; and one senses the fullness of being because he identifies with it. Information is formulated to articulate knowledge and to make it more explicit, while language is employed for bringing one in touch with what really matters. The more in touch one is, the less need does he have for detailed explanation.

Four different ways of inter-conceptual expression

We can now see why inter-conceptual language may invite penetration into the deeper levels of organization of an entity in spite of there being no conscious intention to do so. For example, you may be reading a text about how to handle a particular practical problem. Suddenly you realize not just how to tackle that problem; you remember how to secure answers to an array of complex mathematical questions! The right response used the wrong event to surface, simply because the right moment had arrived for it to do so.

Inter-conceptual language may even invite an awareness of opposite states or conditions in both the physical and the mental world. You become conscious of them merely because you have experienced the dynamic physical world as it comes into contact with you. Each thought or event touches off an opposite or different thought or event. Each function relates with other functions on a different level of organization and abstraction.

Inter-conceptual language may also invite awareness of complementary states, quite often in ways entirely unforeseen (or unforeseeable). For example, the word "love" may evoke in you the notion of "knowledge"— a (seemingly) unusual association. Trans-modality has made you aware that you can only know what you love, just as you can only love what you know, as Petros Lezos put it.[271]

A further example concerns the verb "to organise." It can evoke in one the need for openness. But trans-modality "reveals" that if one organizes things too closely he will miss out on change; and if one changes too quickly, he will render organization impossible.

It follows that regardless of what the subject discussed points toward or away from, inter-conceptual language catalyzes deeper insights into other subjects altogether, exactly as trans-modal reality itself does. But the individual must

[271] Petros Lezos in personal communication with the author, March 1982.

not intend this to happen, or expect that it will. It just does, *if* the necessities of the moment call for it.[272]

The trans-modal mind triggers insights of this kind continuously. But one tends to ignore them. The ordinary mind overwhelms one with its obsessions over what one "thinks" he needs, not to count the self-locking objectifications it has made of these needs.

When all is said and done, the trans-modal mind makes use of where the individual now stands within the whole, so that he may grow in awareness of his present needs and available options. The individual will come to know what difficulties he is now facing; he will grow conscious of the deep sensibilities and feelings he is capable of; he will discover the level at which he inter-relates with other individuals or states; and finally, he will penetrate to his own deep and unique connection with things and states beyond space or time—and beyond even that beyond.

Removing the layers

Let us return to the ancient Egyptian sensitivity toward trans-modality touched upon by Bika Reed. But let us also extend our interest to the equivalent sensitivity of the Greeks, which the Egyptians stimulated. Emphasis on the Greek experience is particularly interesting here, because the Greeks consciously rejected the use of writing for many centuries after it appeared in other eastern Mediterranean cultures. They felt that writing restricted the breadth, depth and poly-semantics of the oral tradition, and so should be avoided.

The result was that when in the end the Greeks did endorse writing for practical reasons, they incorporated in their texts as much as they could of their pre-literate sensibilities. Ancient Greek thus became a window on the trans-modal mindset, from which we today can learn so much about the sensibilities and sensitivities of inter-conceptual language.

But we cannot go about this task without careful preparation. To learn something from the way the Egyptians and the Greeks worked with trans-modality, we must first remove from the world of myth the successive layers of philosophy, philology, psychology, history and sociology placed on it by Western scholarship.

---

[272] For example, one may be reading an archaeological tract on excavations in southern Mexico. Suddenly one gets an insight into dark energy physics, Mediterranean gardening or goldfish breeding habits. There is no obvious connection between what one is reading and what one is suddenly having an insight into. The words read just touch off an awareness of seemingly unrelated subjects or ideas. They trigger insights beyond their current denotative potential.

This will help us perceive things far from the fragmenting and theoretical practices these layers reflect. If it is true that we cannot analyze chemical compounds without knowing about how chemistry works, or we cannot date ancient artefacts without a background in archaeology, it is equally true that we cannot understand the human predicament without knowing something about the specific consciousness that has engineered it.

The ancient Greeks in particular are very helpful in this sense. They were particularly aware of the ultimate challenge that consciousness poses to man. Xenophanes remarks in the 6th century BC: "No man knows, or ever will know, the truth about the gods or about the other things I speak of; for even if one chanced to say the complete truth, yet he knows it not. Seeming is wrought over all things."[273]

Xenophanes' contemporary, Heraclitus, also has some important things to say about consciousness: "Eyes and ears are evil witnesses for men when they have souls lacking in comprehension of the language of eyes and ears."[274] Elsewhere Heraclitus touches on the question of how deep consciousness goes. He says: "You cannot find the boundaries of soul, even if you travel along every single path. Such deep measure does it have."[275]

But the Egyptians were the first in the Eastern Mediterranean to realize how the consciousness problem arose and what can be done about it. That indeed seems to have been the ultimate purpose of their religion, which they partly bequeathed to the Greeks. One of their texts says:

> I am Shu . . . dweller within the one million beings. From them I gain awareness. I disseminate to his own generations the word of the one who creates himself from himself . . . The generations will identify me . . . with the great mystical ship steered by him who liberates his being from his own self . . . For I have seen the abyss becoming "I." He knew not the place in which I became, nor did he see me becoming his own face. I forge my soul on the Lake of Fire . . . My becoming is the force of the entire creation, as it flows forth from the word of the great Lord of "This."[276]

---

[273] Xenophanes, *Fragment* 189.
[274] Heraclitus, *Fragment* 107.
[275] Heraclitus, *Fragment 45*.
[276] *The Revelation of the Soul of Shu,* translated by Bika Reed from an ancient Egyptian text in the coffin of Gwa, a physician of the 12th dynasty, now in the British Museum. Bika Reed presents her translation and comments in *The Field of Transformations: A Quest for the Immortal Essence of Human Awareness,* Inner Traditions International, Ltd., Rochester, Vermont, 1987, pp 145–146.

The Revelation of the Soul of Shu also makes it clear, however, that man enters what the Egyptians considered to be "god" completely lacking in understanding. He gains it only through exposure to, and direct personal experience of the divine.

On the face of it, this appears contradictory. In the just quoted text, god receives awareness from his creature. In other sections of the same text, the creature receives awareness from its creator. Ultimately, there is no discrepancy. More importantly, there is no distinction. On the one hand "god" creates the world by creating his own self. On the other hand, man is presented as totally at one with god. The vehicle for this identity is consciousness itself.

Religion in ancient Egypt and Greece was born out of a sound comprehension of what happens to the mind when it superimposes self-locking objectification on self-releasing reality, or even on no-objectification whatever. So long as man lives with self-releasing objectifications, he doesn't need religion. He begins to need it only when he slips into self-locking objectification. Religion[277] then helps him to re-immerse himself in, or to reconnect with, the lost experience of oneness he enjoyed when his consciousness still worked by engaging in no objectifications, or at least by releasing those he did engage in after he was done with them.

Dis-objectifying objectification

How did ancient Egyptian and Greek religion achieve this? What conceptual tools did their followers use and how did they convey the sense that there is in the world something beyond phenomena? It is here that the subtle role, the wisdom, and the efficacy of the trans-modal mind becomes apparent.

Both the Egyptian and the Greek collective unconscious had a strongly practical bend. It realized that once the cat was out of the bag, it could not be put back into it again. The collective unconscious of the two ancient peoples saw that once self-locking objectification became the tool whereby they apprehended reality, it could not, and should not, be stopped.

There were many reasons for this. One of the most significant was the realization that object-mediated thinking had benefits. As pointed out in an earlier section of this book, this type of thinking allowed humans to realize two goals. The first was to become specifically aware of what exists under their noses. The second was to utilize that material as best they could. Thus, what the collective

[277] The term "religio" in Latin means "linking up."

unconscious of the two peoples did was to use the process of objectification to undo the negative effects of self-locking objectification, while retaining the positive ones.

This was achieved through both ritual and myth, which later developed into drama and philosophy. Words, images, objects, and sounds, all now conceived both for what they convey and for what they don't, were employed to cultivate the sense of a fathomless background out of which arises a fathomable presence.[278] Fathomless background and fathomable presence were not just conceived as the two different aspects of getting to know and to handle reality. They were simultaneously isolated and integrated, beheld and intuited, understood and experienced. It was impossible for the individual to be shown the one without him automatically sensing the other. He couldn't be specific without also being general, or general without also being specific.

Suggestive rather than straight language

Why was indirect or suggestive language used so extensively not only by the Egyptians and the Greeks, but by all mythic cultures? Why not employ straightforward explanations of the type we use today when facing conceptual difficulties?

Two main reasons made the Egyptians and early Greeks avoid explications of this kind. The first applies more to the Greeks than the Egyptians. The former were extremely sensitive to the dangers of doctrine. Abhorring fixations of any kind, they feared that straight teachings, which transformed language into object-mediated expressions, would lead people to understand religions in terms of prescriptive doctrines, exactly as happened later in all three of the monotheistic religions.

The early Greeks had a profound respect for the uniqueness of each person, his freedom of choice and the particularities of his unique understanding. They felt that language informed by object-mediated thinking had a levelling effect. A sentence can mean only one thing to all people. But the Greeks wanted language to be all things to each person. In this way the individual would become aware of what is pertinent to each level of abstraction, each circumstance, each moment and each mode of thinking. He was shown the gates of wholeness but had to cross them by himself.

---

[278] David Bohm's "implicate order" is the closest concept in physics to this fathomless background. Of lesser meaningfulness are the terms "quantum vacuum" and "zero-point energy."

The second and more important reason why the mythic mind preferred to use the suggestive medium of myth to formulate its messages, reflects the way this mind understood what happens to consciousness when it manifests as object-mediated thinking. The same reason also explains the particular trans-modal approach used by Egypt and early Greece to affect a link between self-locking objectification and trans-modal consciousness.

Mythic consciousness is fully aware of what man needs to stay out of. The beginning of it all being the "word,"[279] mythic man wanted to use it in ways that circumvent the shortcomings of language. This is how (and why) symbol began to be used in mythic religions. A straight call about the need to revert to something like trans-modal consciousness seemed counterproductive to the Egyptians and early Greeks.

The solution for them was symbolic language, which could best be secured by myth. That is why even Aristotle, father of formal logic, considered myth as "something of a philosopher." [280] Throughout antiquity mythology was perceived as catalyzing a level of understanding that was deep and rich. Without fixing anything, myth is able to point to intuitions, hidden variables and non-abstractable realities in a way that "formal" linguistic expressions cannot.

To reverse the fragmenting effect of object-mediated language, the mythic mind uses objectified personages to point to what remains after their removal from the mythic narrative by serious worshippers. Thus, myth-informed drama drew the worshipper into its embrace in such a manner that he became aware of two things. The first was the deeper causes of the drama he was witnessing or remembering. These invariably pointed to ignorance, greed, dull-wittedness, egotism and other human weaknesses and failings, linked to self-locking objectification. The second thing was the state of wholeness, from which these weaknesses remove one. The cathartic influence mythic drama is reputed to have had on people is due to this reversal of the fragmenting effect of self-locking objectification.

---

[279] "Word," in Greek, "logos," originally implied "relationship." This indicates that the ancient Greeks knew what modern physics has discovered. Creation applies more to the relationship of particles to one another than to the particles themselves. This relationship was called by the Greeks "cosmos," i.e., "jewel" or "applied beauty." The second law of thermodynamics makes this clear, as does quantum mechanics.

[280] Aristotle, *Metaphysics,* XII, 7

Teaching trans-modal understanding

One last question remains to be tackled. Can one learn about trans-modal reality, inter-conceptual language and bi-hemispheric intelligence? Can one be instructed to use them to one's advantage? Indeed, are trans-modal reality, inter-conceptual language and bi-hemispheric intelligence teachable like chemistry, sociology or German? Ray Monk offers a part answer in his book on Wittgenstein. In discussing the latter's views on psychology and experience, he writes something that applies also to the understanding and handling of trans-modal reality, inter-conceptual language and bi-hemispheric intelligence.

Monk epitomizes Wittgenstein's thinking as follows:

> Yes, some [people] can [learn.] Not however by taking a course, but through experience.—Can someone else be a man's teacher in this? Certainly. From time to time he gives him the right tip.—This is what "learning" and "teaching" are like here. What one acquires is not a technique; one learns correct judgement. There are also rules, but they do not form a system, and only experienced people can apply them properly—unlike calculating rules. This is not because the science is undeveloped, but because the methods it employs are inappropriate to its task.[281]

There is a reality that runs through all realities. There is a concept that underlies all concepts. There is an intelligence that informs all intelligences. Being made aware of these makes life more meaningful and transparent. If one recognizes their actuality, that will in itself illumine him.

Having an illumined understanding is far more important than what one's understanding actually illumines. In the same way, having the ability to access knowledge is far more important than the knowledge one accesses. All the understanding and all the knowledge in the world are useless to him who has locked himself into them. The certainty of knowledge comes from an awareness of its conditioned nature and its limited applicability.

Trans-modal comprehension isn't a closed circuit. It is an inter-conceptual, poly-rational, trans-attitudinal, bi-hemispheric and cross-explanatory exercise.

---

[281] Ray Monk, *Ludwig Wittgenstein, The Duty of Genius,* Penguin Books, New York, 1990, p 549.

Chapter 16

WHERE (AND HOW) DO WE GO FROM HERE?: Theoretical and practical considerations

Major refinements of our information processing tools are forcing us to re-invite the subjective aspects of information into the workshop of science, and thereby to recover the baby we threw out with the bath water more than three centuries ago.
Robert Jahn and Brenda Dunne

Never before has the need for qualitative change in science been so apparent and pressing. The importance of complexity studies lies in that it has made such a radical change not just possible, but imperative. It can only directly inform and inspire the struggle for introducing self-reflection into the practice—and the understanding—of science.
Vasileios Basios

The problems with studying [anomalous] phenomena are based not on their inability to be broached through scientific inquiry, but rather in the kinds of basic assumptions that many scientists, make about the nature of the world around them when constructing hypotheses and interpreting data.
John Valentino

Reading this book leads to an inescapable conclusion: If we want science to enlighten us more in the future than it does presently, we must change its attitude toward both physical reality and its own self. The strictly object-mediated approach, which has been accepted since Newton, Descartes and Laplace, needs urgent revision. As has been hopefully shown in *Science, Objectivity, and Consciousness*, this applies particularly to the way nature's numerous inter-relationships are perceived and investigated. As currently applied, the logic of that investigation is derived from units conceived as hard objects. It is not informed by their inter-relationship. We treat as one, phenomena that are qualitatively different.

Dynamic patterns simply cannot be studied in the same way as distinct units. Seeing the patterns emerging from interacting units, i.e. seeing the patterns as self-organizing systems, depends on an ability to sense what is going on in between and beyond the inter-relating units. On the other hand, apprehending the inter-relating units as mere "objects" depends on using the senses not only to observe reality, but to think about it and to handle it.

One of the important things modern science has revealed is that when we objectify things, there is a price to pay. *Objectifications always end up with something less than the real thing itself.* They lead to a conceptual crystallization of entities which in fact have acquired only temporary form and structure. So we cannot know with absolute certainty what will and what will not change in them. The origins of strange attractors in the non-detectable initial circumstances of chaos theory, plus Gödel's incompleteness theorem and Heisenberg's uncertainty principle, render any sweeping generalization about patterns, transformations, methods or outcomes unreliable.

The implication is that if we eventually want to draw a clear line between the investigation of "things" and the investigation of the changing patterns of their interaction, we should encourage a thorough, sustained and widespread program of mental de-conditioning and conceptual re-education. Without such a dual program we will not manage to restrict Newton, Descartes and Laplace to the levels of description where their thinking actually applies.[282]

In the words of John Valentino: "Scientists start out with hypotheses that are predicated on a particular model of the physical universe." However, Valentino continues, "in modern physics there are massive, well-established bodies of data and theories that bring into question the assumption that all interactions . . . are inherently causal and exist in the kind of time-linear fashion that most of us take for granted via our 'common sense.'"

"Simply put," Valentino concludes, "empirical facts and observations in everything from relativity to quantum mechanics show that the universe is more fundamentally complex than it appears to be on the surface."[283]

---

[282] The real problem about the work of the three sages lies in that it was generalised much beyond its level of description. This ignored two important points about physical reality. The first is that physical reality doesn't exist on one level of organisation. The second is that even if there was some awareness of the above, there was no comprehension of the fact that different sensibilities and laws apply to different levels of description.

[283] John Valentino, "You'll Never Get There from Here: REG Experiments and Conventional Assumptions about Reality," in *Filters and Reflections: Perspectives on Reality,* edited by Zachary Jones, Brenda Dunne, Elissa Hoeger and Robert Jahn, ICRL Press, Princeton, New Jersey, 2009, pp 251–269.

At the very least, then, we should stop inviting researchers and scholars to continue pursuing their present mechanistic analyses. Analysis constitutes synthesis in reverse. The assumption of mainstream science that nature represents an objectively ascertainable structure made of ever smaller autonomous units, which obey a consistent rationale, is encouraged by our culture.

This encouragement is ill advised. Nature's creativity is always top down. But top-down causation expresses itself either directly or indirectly. In direct expression, the top arranges the bottom according to its own formal needs. In indirect expression, the fragments build themselves up through dictates from the top by means of reverse causation. Existing already here among us and inside of us, the future acts like a magnet on the present and the past. It makes them "behave" in the way they do so that the future becomes essentially inevitable. If a mistake is made during the exercise, it will be corrected retroactively so that things will in the end actually happen as they already have!

This doesn't mean that the top dictates how the bottom grows. Neither does it mean that the bottom dictates how the top should be conceived. It means only that top and bottom are in fact one, but we, in our ignorance, conceive them as two polar opposites in a single process of creation.

Non-linear interactions are possible only because the wholeness provided by the block universe assures us of the prevalence of ontological over mechanistic requirements. Here time and space are not determined by sequentially successive stages. They are determined by structural (or formal) exigencies, as these appear in the ever self-adjusting conditions of the block universe. In such a frame, entities just "grab" what they need ontologically from past or future and from here or there, using this "stuff" as their particular formal and developmental needs require. Their non-linear, non-local and non-temporal action can be named "ontic linearity," "ontic locality," and "ontic time."

Therefore, in the end there exists some linearity, locality and temporality in the world after all. But it differs substantially from what we humans comprehend as linearity, locality and temporality. We experience relationships, space and time in linear terms. Our biological, cultural and educational make-up requires it. But the block universe has no priorities or discriminations. It thus has no need for structural patterns either. It just pursues its eternal balancing act by constantly fine-tuning its processes.

That explains how the fundamental opposites of the type "locality and non-locality," "temporality and non-temporality," "linearity and non-linearity" can actually be co-present and complementary to one another in the block universe. That is also from where the block universe draws its explanatory power for all phenomena observed by man through the millennia—both ordinary and anomalous. To benefit from this great explanatory power, one just needs to look upon reality as a *composite super-entity* integrating all observable, computable and intuitable situations.

It should not be thought that the block universe blots out choice, evolution, uncertainty, creativity or open-endedness. The block universe just represents the framework within which all this takes place in a manner guaranteeing that primordial wholeness is eventually restored in and through its fragmentation after the big bang.

As chaos theory suggests, strange attractors don't actually specify how X unit interacts with Y unit to produce Z end product. The top doesn't force the bottom into specific patterns of behavior or relationship. Rather the top and the bottom co-manifest, without the one preceding or following the other. When we are focused on the bottom expression of creation, we take bottom considerations into account. When we are focused on the top expression, we take top considerations into account.

That is, at any rate, the picture currently suggested by the non-temporal aspects of non-locality, general relativity and reverse causation. To discover more about them we need to bring in a systematic concern for consciousness. A *self-reflective interdisciplinary science of consciousness* will mandate this. In turn a deeper understanding of consciousness will mandate a *science toward the limits.*

In the words of Vasileios Basios: "We are fast approaching the point where we need to concern ourselves not only with the study of nature, but with the nature of that study."[284]

From external to internal patterns

At this point some readers may consider putting forward the following conjecture. Thanks to the introduction of consciousness studies in the past thirty years, we have achieved a mutually beneficial solution. We can improve our understanding of both science and consciousness simply by making them interact.

What a delusion! Using a closed science to investigate a restricted consciousness will not help us use consciousness to open up that closed science. It is only by approaching consciousness more *deeply* that we can broaden the purview of science, as it is only by *broadening* the purview of science more qualitatively that we can approach consciousness more deeply.

---

[284] Vasileios Basios, 'Complexity, Interdependence and Objectification,' in op. cit., pp 187–206.

To bring about such a conceptual change we need to get serious about the notion of *in-depth understanding*. Specifically, we need to introduce depth as an indispensable principle into the validation kit of science, alongside evidence, objectivity and consistency. Surface reality has turned out deceptive for us because the surface understanding we use to investigate it has made it so.

Significance isn't just what can be proven to be factually so. Significance is what penetrates appearances, obvious relationships, and projections from observed appearances and relationships. We sensitize ourselves to the patterns active in the processes we study—and then we sensitize ourselves to the patterns behind or through these patterns. In isolating them we become aware that our minds also generate not just patterns, but patterns of patterns, patterns through patterns, and patterns beyond patterns.

Relationships among entities represent the one ontological component of existence. Layered existence represents the other. We see patterns all around us because we are able to perceive how things relate to one another, and we are able to perceive how things relate to one another because we are a bundle of complex relationships ourselves.

The same goes for the relationship between patterns of, through or beyond patterns in nature, and patterns of, through and beyond patterns in our minds. What happens on the one level of abstraction also happens when the levels are many, either in parallel or in vertical arrangement.

We don't become aware of all this by applying the same logic to the investigation of patterns as we apply to the investigation of things. Seeing the things themselves depends on using the senses. Seeing the patterns tying them together depends on just sensing their energetic and ontological interactions. The senses and their logic are much more explicit than the patterns and their rationale, and can, when awareness is lacking, completely overshadow the latter.

This brings up a series of important questions. Where do the physical patterns begin and the mind patterns end? Are patterns physical and what does it mean that something is physical to begin with? Aren't things just patterns rendered accessible to the senses by way of having "congealed" into specific—and therefore recognizable—forms?

Here we gravitate toward deep ontology. In research, as currently performed, the scientist chooses and (ideally) exhausts all there is to be objectively known about his subject. In pattern-investigation, the scientist pursues at least two additional courses. First, he develops a feeling for why he chooses a particular research subject to begin with. Secondly, he senses how this feeling illumines two further questions. The first concerns other units or states to which the initial research subject possibly relates. The second question concerns the extent to which such relations catapult the other units or states into existence.

Scientific research normally focuses specifically on objectified entities. Pattern research focuses on the complex interactions among them. The subject of the particular research reflects an ability of mind (1) to become aware of its potentialities; (2) to not exclude what lies beyond its (seeming) grasp; and (3) to not equate the deepest information it is capable of grasping with ultimate reality. When mind succeeds in developing this threefold cognitive ability, the individual discovers that specific knowledge arises in him effortlessly each time (and so long as) he needs it.

He knows what he knows because he has become who he is. He hasn't become who he is because he knows what he knows.

How to apply the new insights

How do we start tackling all this seriously? The suggestion put forward here is that some initiative be undertaken for gradually creating a consciousness-informed science. For such an enterprise to succeed, it must be carried out in the light of the major scientific breakthroughs of the 20th century. They contain precious clues about how object-mediated thinking dominates, and thereby distorts, all understanding. What still remains to be done is to integrate all these breakthroughs into a single self-explanatory whole that takes into account both the physics involved and the implications of physics for consciousness.

To benefit conceptually from the major scientific breakthroughs of the 20th century, we will have to go into epistemology and what, in this book, has been called pre-epistemology. Normally epistemology calls for some general criteria about what constitutes “safe” knowledge. The recent history of science, however, has shown that the assumptions behind such criteria cannot be taken as applying to all situations at all times everywhere.

That is where (and why) pre-epistemology comes in. It needs to be established in order to help us formulate a new kind of basic assumptions that are informed by an improved understanding of two fundamental functions. The first is how the mind objectifies reality. The second is how the mind extends its objectifications beyond their initial purview. Once we have obtained this overview, we can easily detect what the logic of our senses fails to let through. We can thus learn how to learn, judge how to judge, and think how to think. More importantly, we can become more thorough in how we choose research subjects, interpret their findings, and become more effective in making use of them.

This will allow us to make better sense of the great insights gained by 20th-century physics; to perceive the reasons for the confusing directions of 20th-century biology; and most important of all, to comprehend why mathematics is unable to provide ultimate answers or complete solutions.

In other words, we get a bird's-eye view of the actual unity lying behind the various disjointed parts of the world modern science has investigated—on the conceptual, the theoretical and the practical level.

For example, the discovery of non-locality in physical reality elicits two types of expectations. The first is for the translation of physical non-locality into conceptual non-locality. The second expectation is for a realistic explanation of the seeming contradiction between locality and non-locality. What are the fundamental ontological needs served by locality and non-locality? Do the two interpenetrate? Are locality and non-locality intertwined, and if so, how and to what extent? How does non-locality affect time and linearity?

One way to answer such questions is for the proposed new self-aware science to push for an in-depth transformation of all major 20th-century advances into qualities of actual thinking. For example, since non-linearity is a fact on a deep level of physical organization, it must also be reflected in the way our consciousness operates. Since the uncertainty principle applies to our perception of particle movement and location, it must also be reflected in the way we carve up reality. Since mathematics is incomplete in itself, as Gödel and Chaitin have demonstrated, incompleteness must also apply to our understanding of the objectifiable world and the laws of objectivity laid down by it.

The other major breakthroughs of 20th-century science beg for similar theoretical transformations into ways and qualities of thinking. Among them can be counted general relativity, quantum mechanics, reverse causation, non-linearity, fuzzy logic, complexity theory, and others. In many areas conflicting results are waiting to be bridged by taking them to a deeper and more fundamental level of organization.

That is in accordance with Einstein's famous dictum that we should not attempt to solve a problem on the level of its iteration. The practice of recent decades has shown that when we don't follow Einstein's advice, we end up with long-winded and extremely complicated answers. Occam's razor calls for the simplest possible solutions—which also happen to be the deepest.

Immediate tasks for creating a self-aware science

But let us become more specific about what needs to be done for *a science toward the limits* to become a reality.

Science, Objectivity, and Consciousness has been all about the need for a kind of science that will be informed by a *self-reflective interdisciplinary science of consciousness*. Individuals interested in such a project could form a volunteer group, for example "A Consciousness Initiative Group," that will push for developing *a science toward the limits*.

The Consciousness Initiative Group would have many initial tasks. Five stand out. The first is to create an open-ended theoretical framework for the proposed new science, with its underpinnings in consciousness theory and research. The particular question here would be the extent to which the new science will differ from the old. Getting the input of practicing scientists on this would be invaluable. Theoreticians or philosophers, though extremely helpful, would not be enough.

The second task would be to catalogue and correlate information about which aspects of consciousness are currently being researched by which discipline in which university or lab, and which aspects of this research influence the disciplines in return. Among the specific sciences to focus on here are physics, neurophysiology, psychology, mathematics, anthropology, fuzzy logic, psycho-immunology, information science, linguistics, philosophy, history of art and ideas, epistemology, comparative religion, biology, and the meditative traditions. The research outcomes in these areas should ideally be stored in a consciousness data bank, to which scientists and scholars will have free access.

Parallel to the above could be an investigation of the antiquity, awareness and influence of consciousness in the development of major civilizations. This could be coupled with an effort to pick up John Brockman's challenge concerning a "third culture" beyond the two of C.P. Snow, science and the humanities.

Again, the Consciousness Initiative Group could encourage comparative studies of the non-technical work of the great scientists and scholars since the 1850s, whose writings bear directly or indirectly on the issue of consciousness—and "who . . . are taking the place of the traditional intellectual in rendering visible the deeper meanings of our lives, redefining who and what we are," as John Brockman puts it.[285] Among the luminaries whose work could thus be studied, compared and learnt from should be Maxwell, Faraday, Einstein, Eddington, Jung, Jeans, Heisenberg, Gödel, Quine, Schröedinger,

[285] John Brockman, *The Third Culture: Beyond the Scientific Revolution,* Simon & Schuster, 1995, p 4.

Medawar, Tarski, Chaitin, Goodwin, Varela, Penrose, Gell-Man, Heidegger and Prigogine, among others.

The third major task for the Consciousness Initiative Group could be to oversee the preparation of some initial publicity material that will illustrate the overall idea of a *science toward the limits* and its profound implications for society at large. Definitely included here could be explicit references to the actual applications of the proposed new outlook in science guided by results of a *self-reflective interdisciplinary science of consciousness.*

For this purpose, attractive brochures, email newsletters, and interactive media should be prepared. They will be distributed among scientists, professionals, business people, academics, artists, intellectuals, doctors, cultural institutions, select young people and private foundations —particularly the Howard Hughes Medical Institute, Janelia Research Campus, and the Center for Consciousness Studies at the University of Arizona in Tucson. To the extent that sufficient intellectual support and funding interest were expressed among the recipients of such initial material, an institute could eventually be established that will take further the idea of a new, self-aware science.

The fourth task could be to coordinate the introduction of a *self-reflective interdisciplinary science of consciousness* in universities as a first step in the direction of the new self-aware science. This task, slow and copious, will entail special presentations to and private meetings with faculty members and students. In such sessions special care must be taken to stress that the consciousness studies proposed will differ from those being currently carried out in universities. The difference lies in that the here proposed investigations are premised on an awareness of the basic assumptions informing consciousness research. Consciousness cannot be investigated without asking serious questions about how it is conceived by the investigator, and to what extent the latter is willing (and able) to ask himself why he is conceiving consciousness in the particular way he does.

The fifth task could be to make the educated public aware of the pressing need to incorporate the consciousness component into major decision making on questions of social import. This task would entail articles, videos, documentaries, and round table discussions.

The magic of interpersonal dialogue

Right from the beginning of this last chapter it became evident that both the proposed a *science toward the limits* and the group that will possibly act as its midwife must operate on the deepest possible conceptual level. The present practice of treating consciousness as a "function" mechanically produced by, or at least existing in, the brain, needs to be revised. We must ask ourselves: what should be the premises of consciousness research in the light of what sensitive and intelligent workers in the field have discovered?

By the same token, we must avoid introducing into our thinking on consciousness images and notions from different domains of human interest and activity, such as, for example, information theory, engineering, computer technology, and Boolean symbolic logic, etc. Cognitive science is particularly prone to introducing and working from such models. They have been useful in studying what happens to the injured brain. They have not explained where the healthy brain gets its cues from or how.[286]

Researchers and philosophers must be encouraged to examine their own personal understanding of how consciousness works and what are the conditions necessary for science to explore it. To secure the effectiveness of such questioning, the Consciousness Initiative Group (and hopefully, the faculty members of *self-reflective interdisciplinary science of consciousness* departments in universities) should consider their task, assess their findings, and grow organically in the light of *inter-personal dialogue*.

Inter-personal dialogue is a technique practiced by pre-literate societies throughout the globe before the advent of individualism, what Steve Taylor calls "the ego explosion."[287] Aiming at getting collectively to the bottom of any important issue to the tribe, inter-personal dialogue works by creating a common conceptual ground among discussants. How a conclusion is reached matters as much (if not more) as what the conclusion itself stipulates. That is the point on which all one-man decision making fails. Inter-personal dialogue enables participants to tap into the particular knowledge field in which both their topic and its potential implications are rooted.

Results in inter-personal dialogue are secured by way of utilizing the interest of interlocutors in obtaining the truest possible answer. That is achieved by encouraging interlocutors to mobilize a number of innate qualities and abilities. Among them are: freely expressing insights into the subject under discussion;

---

[286] This has become a very important issue now that consciousness research at the University of Arizona and elsewhere has discovered "brain default networks," or "dark brain energy"—i.e., "neuronal activity in the absence of sensory inputs," as it is described in technical jargon. (See the September 21, 2009, email announcement for the ninth biennial Tucson conference Toward a Science of Consciousness, organised by The Center for Consciousness Studies, The University of Arizona.)

[287] Steve Taylor, *The Fall,* O Books, an imprint of The Bothy, John Hunt Publishing Ltd, Winchester. UK, p 104.

bringing to the foreground a love of reality as it is without projecting onto it preconceived notions; touching off the need for mutual self-respect; manifesting a willingness (and ability) to keep ego, career preoccupations, and unquestioned beliefs out of the exchanges; and, above all, recapturing our now-lost talent for experiencing the present, thereby drawing information from the non-local, non-temporal and non-linear aspects of the universe.

Interpersonal dialogue touches off these qualities and abilities even among discussants who have very high opinions of themselves! The system just enables such individuals to recognize and respect the collective wisdom arising from the exchanges in which they participate. They actually perceive this collective wisdom to be of greater value than their own isolated (and therefore incomplete) understanding.

Inter-personal dialogue (now adapted for modern use by physicist David Bohm) isn't only capable of accessing hitherto unformulated insights, pieces of information or sensibilities. It is capable of maintaining high standards in assessing these formulations; in masterminding their application to practical needs; and in determining their possible implications for other areas of interest.[288]

Reversing harmful attitudes

The burden on the shoulders of the Consciousness Initiative Group will be heavy. There will be lots of failures, frustrations and seemingly insurmountable difficulties. Above all, there will be mountains of work to be done as members try to translate the insights obtained through interpersonal dialogue into concrete and wise action. But even modest successes of the Consciousness Initiative Group will signal an important departure from scientific and social practices which have only a very limited scope. Thus, a beginning can be made for reversing many current unsatisfactory scientific and social attitudes. Some of the specific changes anticipated are:

1. *Re-scientification.* As things stand today, very little can be done to protect science against erosion from business interests, political agendas, circular thinking, institutional prejudice, career considerations, paradigmatic bias, trivialization, conceptual stagnation, funding pressures and subconscious conditioning. One way to cope with this situation is increased awareness. First, we need to understand more about how consciousness works. And second, we need to

---

[288] The Dialogue Project at MIT has collected impressive evidence for this.

understand how we can best bring our deeper understanding of consciousness to bear on the workings of science as a whole, on both the theoretical level and the practical.

After such a stage has been reached, the Consciousness Initiative Group could concentrate on organizing a well-thought-out conference about the validation issue in science. Gaining some clarity here will allow the scientific community to serve both knowledge and scholarship better than it does at present. It will become obvious to all open-minded individuals that whatever reduces the scientific-ness of science or the scholarship of scholars also reduces the humanity of humans.

2. *Self-criticism.* Undoubtedly there is today a lot of criticism among scientists about the work and the interpretations of other scientists. But this criticism doesn't affect the basic premises underlying the way science actually works and argues. When a *self-reflective interdisciplinary science of consciousness* becomes an integral part of the overall scientific enterprise, they should devote some of their energy to the drafting of suggestions not only about a new epistemology and pre-epistemology, but about a social framework that could be informed by them.

All social and environmental issues originate in (and from) the mind. Thus, we don't just need to understand how our attitudes, our thinking and our behaviors arise, or why. We need to act on what we discover when they do arise. If properly pursued, the new *science of consciousness* will enhance our ability to do just that. It will help us deal more effectively with environmental and social issues, plus prevent the fossilization of provisional insights. In science, as in society, there never are, and never should be, final answers.

3. *De-artificializing intelligence.* Since the 1960s a lot has been made of the claim of some scientists that intelligence is reproducible in or by computers. Research since that time has shown three things. First, the brain is not a computer or even wetware. Second, though indeed capable of computing, the brain doesn't reach its conclusions by so doing. Its computations come mainly *after* insight has occurred and simply justify it in the light of reason. Third, understanding is, in fact, a product of the whole brain working in unison through direct, non-local, non-linear and non-temporal insight. The mechanical, linear, localized and temporal processes through which computers function, make that impossible.

The Consciousness Initiative Group will need to clarify, expand and deepen the above notions. Artificial intelligence could claim the name only if its advocates were in a position to create machines capable of unmediated direct insight, in exact imitation of how the natural brain operates. The best one can say about neural networks and robots today is that they have shown themselves to be clever at working practical needs out and handling them efficiently. But by no means can this be considered as a sign of intelligence. Intelligence is not a question of finding out what to do with what and how. It is a question of finding out if doing so represents the right thing under the circumstances, and why.

4. *Re-wholification.* The multi-levelled, trans-qualitative, cross-functional and inter-dimensional understanding of reality, which has resulted from the significant 20th-century breakthroughs in science, demand from us a wholifying attitude. Because of its involvement with sensitive conceptual issues, our dynamic new picture of reality doesn't depend only on abstractable observations. It depends equally on the observer as a qualifying agent. How can we avoid projecting onto our observations ideas informed by elements outside of them? How can we secure a truthful account of what in fact we do observe? How can we study our subjectivity objectively when we seem so biased in our approach to objectivity?

We can approach the above in two ways. The first, and easy one, is to cultivate self-awareness, to study consciousness in depth, and to be scrupulously honest in our descriptions (and assessments) of reality. The second way is to be constantly open to the non-quantifiable and non-objectifiable ultimate wholeness at the ontological roots of every particular entity, idea or combination thereof. Religion, philosophy, scientific belief and social philosophy are as "good" as we are. There can be no effective or balanced comprehension without conscious reference to such an intuitive sense of wholeness at the heart of everything, and our willingness to let it be without explaining it, leave alone explaining it away. Unless we understand how we understand, we cannot understand what we understand. Still less can we understand why we should avoid getting trapped in what we do in fact understand, or how we can remain conceptually open to what as yet we don't.

5. *Re-contextualisation.* A typical example of what has happened to our way of thinking is the current inability to contextualize what we observe, think or do. What relates appears more important to us than how it relates, why it relates or even the relationship itself. Yet recent science shows that how relationship is achieved counts more than what relates as such. Our senses may transmit and our brains may think according to what our biology dictates and invites. Yet what is received and conceptualized remains our own responsibility. Perhaps nature has given us the power to see where things belong so that we can become its eyes.

6. *Self-examination.* We have lost the ability to see why we need to bridge the gap between subject and object—and more importantly, how to go about actually building the bridge.

Almost by definition, consciousness cannot become an object of research without the investigator also asking himself what informs his own consciousness as he kicks off his research. If consciousness studies are to become a source of guidance for both a *science toward the limits* and for society at large, they must start from a consciousness of their own assumptions, quality and methods. The scientific claim to objectivity demands it.

7. *Re-inventing objectification.* There is little doubt that objectification represents the No. 1 survival tool for animals and humans. But for us today it has become a liability. By gradually developing the habit of locking into our objectifications and then conceptualizing all else in their image and logic, we have estranged ourselves from four important aspects of nature. The first is its variety, the second its complexity, the third our own deeper qualities and potentialities and the fourth is the wholeness informing all these.

So self-locking objectification needs to be shelved. But the possibility for object-mediated thinking needs to be retained—on two special conditions. The first is to purge this thinking from our tendency to use it exclusively. The second is to stop extending object-based logic beyond its immediate practical applications. To achieve that a special education program needs to be established that will make people aware of how and why objectification has become a problem in our times. Such a program will then help people achieve two significant goals. The first is to learn how to release objectifications once their usefulness has passed. The second is to learn how to integrate object-mediated thinking with reliable intuition and direct personal experience of nature. Both these will prove essential for building a sane society.

8. *Rehumanising technology.* Our sense of measure with respect to technology has more or less disappeared today. Developing a new way of investigating consciousness will allow us once again to conceive mechanical constructs as mere extensions of natural human handling abilities, not as autonomous systems. This will not only demand greater familiarity with our defining traits as human beings. It will demand an in-depth knowledge of the particular quality permeating these traits.

It will also demand protection against the ever-present danger of identifying with mechanical constructs and thus abstracting their use on the strength of human criteria. Unwitting identification with the ways in which technology works and the principles underpinning it, is the main instigator of many of the problems currently experienced by society. The more we develop our technology, the more must we develop our humanity. Technology itself demands it. Without humanity it becomes less effective itself, and more dangerous for others.

9. *Redeveloping development.* One of the most important projects facing mankind today is handling more effectively the sensitive, complicated and difficult issues of human welfare. Most important among these projects is achieving a kind of development that can be shown to be not only economically viable, but environmentally sustainable and humanly enriching. The notion of development itself needs development if its many current negative aspects are to diminish.

Short-term planning, which glosses over social, environmental or individual long-term well-being, is no longer acceptable. The same applies to exclusively specialized knowledge, which ignores overarching human concerns. "Development toward what?" and "knowledge in relationship to what?" have become not only legitimate, but pressing, questions for our times. Just as a type of progress that doesn't free us to actualize our potentialities is not worth the name, so a type of knowledge that doesn't point to broader (and therefore deeper) frameworks, is not worth having.

10. *Re-personalising society.* If there is a common sentence on the lips of practically all people today, it is that things are not going well. A golden opportunity therefore arises today to discover the consciousness component inherent in this negative state of affairs. It will help us advance a number of socially relevant tasks. Among them are:

a. To develop a non-ideological but environmentally friendly economic development code based on self-adjusting dynamic principles.

b. To develop a natural way of increasing serotonin presence in the brain without using antidepressants, perhaps along the lines of psycho-immunology.

c. To create a new validation system for science, free from linear and object-mediated dictates.

d. To help create a fuzzy computer capable of assisting the individual scientist sift through huge quantities of information and arrive at an understanding relevant to both his personal intuitions and to objectivity.

e. To try and determine whether science has limitations and see in which area or level these exist.

f. To define what may be considered as physical reality.

g. To address the question of what is quality in life and how this can best be pursued.

h. To come up with reliable advice on how to handle stress rather than avoid it, in the light of a less mechanical conception of consciousness.

With these ten proposals (out of more than one hundred in the author's files) on how a consciousness-informed acquisition of knowledge could affect science and society, this book comes to an end. The need for consciousness to be investigated by a science finely tuned is matched only by the need for science to be informed by a consciousness fully alert. How consciousness treats science and society tomorrow will depend on how science and society treat consciousness today. A life not consciously mediated is unworthy of a species that prides itself on being not only conscious, but self-conscious.

ACKNOWLEDGMENTS

Many thanks to those great many men and women who have toiled through the centuries so that we may stand at the precipice of a new era in the discovery of nature in—and through—ourselves.

There is a rather large group of people who must be personally acknowledged as having a powerful impact on *Science, Objectivity, and Consciousness.* So as not to torture the reader with a never-ending list of names, I will attempt brevity. If in the process I should omit anyone deserving attention here, please accept my sincere apologies.

Thank you, Tew Bunnag, David Lorimer, Peter Fenwick, Ian McGilchrist, Max Velmans, and Danah Zohar for your tireless efforts to reach the truth behind our many communications on subjects of consciousness, science and philosophy.

All my dear friends of "Tuesdays meetings" at Grenta Zeppos', and also Yiannis Lamprianidis, Philip Noelbaker, Eddie and Mary Bridges, Vishnunarayanan Namboothiri, and Fotini Apostolopoulou, thank you.

Thank you, Sir Roger Penrose, Ilya Prigogine, Patrick Bateson, Karl E. Gustafson, E.C. George Sudarshan, Ramesh Kumar, Ian Marshall, Massimo Mercati, Max Payne, Bruno D' Udine, Charles Whitehead, Basil Hiley, Yukio-Pegio Gunji, John S. Nicolis, Antonio Giuditta, Theodosios P. Tassios, Manos Danezis, Stratos Theodossiou, Anne Baring, Fritjof Capra, Rupert Sheldrake, Ravi Ravindra, Beverly Rubik, and so many others who have helped to confirm the insights that led to the production of this book.

For supporting my projects in so many different ways, Jeremy Naydler and Louanne Richards, William Anderson, Lady Maureen Allen, Countess Angelika Cawdor, Sylvia and Jonathan Stadall, James Witchalls, Chris Clarke, Metod Saniga, Rosolino Buccheri, Philip Franses, and Martin Redfern, thank you.

Special thanks to my adoring wife, Ruth Mary James Bouratinos, for all that she endured while the work was moving forward, and to my children, Ilaira and Emily, whose faith and love kept me warm during late night sessions on the computer. And of course, my grandchildren—Kostis, Daphne, and Emilios—for providing the exuberance needed for this ambitious project. And Ilaira's husband, Richard Grant, for his brilliant work as chief editor and for his patience and skill in weaving together my work in such a concise and consistent whole. And, of course, I must also thank Vasileios Basios for his efforts and vision of the promise of the book even before it was clear what that was.

And finally, thanks to the many members of the Princeton Engineering Anomalies Research PEARtree discussion group, ICRL Press, and in particular, Brenda Dunne, without whose faith and support this book would not have seen the light of day.

Lightning Source UK Ltd.
Milton Keynes UK
UKHW011336121118
332199UK00003B/590/P